PEARSON

Barry Render • Ralph M. Stair, Jr.
Michael E. Hanna • Trevor S. Hale

Quantitative Analysis for Management

Third Custom Edition for San Jose State University

Taken from:
Quantitative Analysis for Management, Twelfth Edition
by Barry Render, Ralph M. Stair, Jr., Michael E. Hanna, and Trevor S. Hale

Cover Art: Courtesy of Pearson Learning Solutions.

Taken from:

Quantitative Analysis for Management, Twelfth Edition
by Barry Render, Ralph M. Stair, Jr., Michael E. Hanna, and Trevor S. Hale
Copyright © 2015, 2012, 2009 by Pearson Education, Inc.
Upper Saddle River, New Jersey 07458

This special edition published in cooperation with Pearson Learning Solutions.

Pearson Learning Solutions, 501 Boylston Street, Suite 900, Boston, MA 02116
A Pearson Education Company
www.pearsoned.com

Printed in the United States of America

1 2 3 4 5 6 7 8 9 10 V092 17 16 15 14

000200010271949024

LB

PEARSON   ISBN 10: 1-323-05315-8
ISBN 13: 978-1-323-05315-7

Barry Render is Professor Emeritus, the Charles Harwood Distinguished Professor of Operations Management, Crummer Graduate School of Business, Rollins College, Winter Park, Florida. He received his B.S. in Mathematics and Physics at Roosevelt University and his M.S. in Operations Research and his Ph.D. in Quantitative Analysis at the University of Cincinnati. He previously taught at George Washington University, the University of New Orleans, Boston University, and George Mason University, where he held the Mason Foundation Professorship in Decision Sciences and was Chair of the Decision Science Department. Dr. Render has also worked in the aerospace industry for General Electric, McDonnell Douglas, and NASA.

Dr. Render has coauthored 10 textbooks published by Pearson, including *Managerial Decision Modeling with Spreadsheets, Operations Management, Principles of Operations Management, Service Management, Introduction to Management Science*, and *Cases and Readings in Management Science*. More than 100 articles of Dr. Render on a variety of management topics have appeared in *Decision Sciences, Production and Operations Management, Interfaces, Information and Management, Journal of Management Information Systems, Socio-Economic Planning Sciences, IIE Solutions,* and *Operations Management Review*, among others.

Dr. Render has been honored as an AACSB Fellow and was named twice as a Senior Fulbright Scholar. He was Vice President of the Decision Science Institute Southeast Region and served as software review editor for *Decision Line* for six years and as Editor of the *New York Times* Operations Management special issues for five years. From 1984 to 1993, Dr. Render was President of Management Service Associates of Virginia, Inc., whose technology clients included the FBI, the U.S. Navy, Fairfax County, Virginia, and C&P Telephone. He is currently Consulting Editor to *Financial Times Press*.

Dr. Render has taught operations management courses at Rollins College for MBA and Executive MBA programs. He has received that school's Welsh Award as leading professor and was selected by Roosevelt University as the 1996 recipient of the St. Claire Drake Award for Outstanding Scholarship. In 2005, Dr. Render received the Rollins College MBA Student Award for Best Overall Course, and in 2009 was named Professor of the Year by full-time MBA students.

Ralph Stair is Professor Emeritus at Florida State University. He earned a B.S. in chemical engineering from Purdue University and an M.B.A. from Tulane University. Under the guidance of Ken Ramsing and Alan Eliason, he received a Ph.D. in operations management from the University of Oregon. He has taught at the University of Oregon, the University of Washington, the University of New Orleans, and Florida State University.

He has taught twice in Florida State University's Study Abroad Program in London. Over the years, his teaching has been concentrated in the areas of information systems, operations research, and operations management.

Dr. Stair is a member of several academic organizations, including the Decision Sciences Institute and INFORMS, and he regularly participates in national meetings. He has published numerous articles and books, including *Managerial Decision Modeling with Spreadsheets, Introduction to Management Science, Cases and Readings in Management Science, Production and Operations Management: A Self-Correction Approach, Fundamentals of Information Systems, Principles of Information Systems, Introduction to Information Systems, Computers in Today's World, Principles of Data Processing, Learning to Live with Computers, Programming in BASIC, Essentials of BASIC Programming, Essentials of FORTRAN Programming,* and *Essentials of COBOL Programming.* Dr. Stair divides his time between Florida and Colorado. He enjoys skiing, biking, kayaking, and other outdoor activities.

Michael E. Hanna is Professor of Decision Sciences at the University of Houston–Clear Lake (UHCL). He holds a B.A. in Economics, an M.S. in Mathematics, and a Ph.D. in Operations Research from Texas Tech University. For more than 25 years, he has been teaching courses in statistics, management science, forecasting, and other quantitative methods. His dedication to teaching has been recognized with the Beta Alpha Psi teaching award in 1995 and the Outstanding Educator Award in 2006 from the Southwest Decision Sciences Institute (SWDSI).

Dr. Hanna has authored textbooks in management science and quantitative methods, has published numerous articles and professional papers, and has served on the Editorial Advisory Board of *Computers and Operations Research.* In 1996, the UHCL Chapter of Beta Gamma Sigma presented him with the Outstanding Scholar Award.

Dr. Hanna is very active in the Decision Sciences Institute, having served on the Innovative Education Committee, the Regional Advisory Committee, and the Nominating Committee. He has served on the board of directors of the Decision Sciences Institute (DSI) for two terms and also as regionally elected vice president of DSI. For SWDSI, he has held several positions, including president, and he received the SWDSI Distinguished Service Award in 1997. For overall service to the profession and to the university, he received the UHCL President's Distinguished Service Award in 2001.

Trevor S. Hale is Associate Professor of Management Science at the University of Houston–Downtown (UHD). He received a B.S. in Industrial Engineering from Penn State University, an M.S. in Engineering Management from Northeastern University, and a Ph.D. in Operations Research from Texas A&M University. He was previously on the faculty of both Ohio University–Athens, and Colorado State University–Pueblo.

Dr. Hale was honored three times as an Office of Naval Research Senior Faculty Fellow. He spent the summers of 2009, 2011, and 2013 performing energy security/cyber security research for the U.S. Navy at Naval Base Ventura County in Port Hueneme, California.

Dr. Hale has published dozens of articles in the areas of operations research and quantitative analysis in journals such as the *International Journal of Production Research*, the *European Journal of Operational Research*, *Annals of Operations Research*, the *Journal of the Operational Research Society,* and the *International Journal of Physical Distribution and Logistics Management* among several others. He teaches quantitative analysis courses in the University of Houston–Downtown MBA program and Masters of Security Management for Executives program. He is a senior member of both the Decision Sciences Institute and INFORMS.

BRIEF CONTENTS

CHAPTER 2   Probability Concepts
and Applications 23

CHAPTER 3   Decision Analysis 65

CHAPTER 7   Linear Programming Models: Graphical
and Computer Methods 239

CHAPTER 8   Linear Programming Applications 291

CHAPTER 9   Transportation, Assignment, and Network
Models 323

CHAPTER 11   Project Management 395

CONTENTS

PREFACE ix

CHAPTER 2 **Probability Concepts and Applications 23**

2.1 *Introduction 24*

2.2 *Fundamental Concepts 24*

Two Basic Rules of Probability 24

Types of Probability 25

Mutually Exclusive and Collectively
  Exhaustive Events 26

Unions and Intersections of Events 27

Probability Rules for Unions, Intersections,
  and Conditional Probabilities 28

2.3 *Revising Probabilities with Bayes' Theorem 29*

General Form of Bayes' Theorem 31

2.4 *Further Probability Revisions 31*

2.5 *Random Variables 32*

2.6 *Probability Distributions 34*

Probability Distribution of a Discrete
  Random Variable 34

Expected Value of a Discrete Probability
  Distribution 34

Variance of a Discrete Probability Distribution 35

Probability Distribution of a Continuous
  Random Variable 36

2.7 *The Binomial Distribution 37*

Solving Problems with the Binomial Formula 38

Solving Problems with Binomial Tables 39

2.8 *The Normal Distribution 40*

Area Under the Normal Curve 42

Using the Standard Normal Table 42

Haynes Construction Company Example 43

The Empirical Rule 46

2.9 *The F Distribution 46*

2.10 *The Exponential Distribution 48*

Arnold's Muffler Example 49

2.11 *The Poisson Distribution 50*

*Summary 52   Glossary 52   Key
Equations 53   Solved Problems 54   Self-Test 56
Discussion Questions and Problems 57
Case Study: WTVX 63   Bibliography 63*

Appendix 2.1:   *Derivation of Bayes' Theorem 63*

CHAPTER 3 **Decision Analysis 65**

3.1 *Introduction 66*

3.2 *The Six Steps in Decision Making 66*

3.3 *Types of Decision-Making Environments 67*

3.4 *Decision Making Under Uncertainty 68*

Optimistic 68

Pessimistic 69

Criterion of Realism (Hurwicz Criterion) 69

Equally Likely (Laplace) 70

Minimax Regret 70

3.5 *Decision Making Under Risk 71*

Expected Monetary Value 71

Expected Value of Perfect Information 72

Expected Opportunity Loss 74

Sensitivity Analysis 74

3.6 *A Minimization Example 75*

3.7 *Using Software for Payoff Table Problems 77*

QM for Windows 77

Excel QM 78

3.8 *Decision Trees 79*

Efficiency of Sample Information 84

Sensitivity Analysis 84

3.9 *How Probability Values Are Estimated
by Bayesian Analysis 85*

Calculating Revised Probabilities 85

Potential Problem in Using Survey Results 87

3.10 *Utility Theory 88*

Measuring Utility and Constructing
  a Utility Curve 89

Utility as a Decision-Making Criterion 92

*Summary 94   Glossary 94
Key Equations 95   Solved Problems 95
Self-Test 100   Discussion Questions and
Problems 101   Case Study: Starting Right
Corporation 109   Case Study: Blake
Electronics 110   Bibliography 112*

CHAPTER 7   **Linear Programming Models: Graphical and Computer Methods   239**

7.1   *Introduction   240*

7.2   *Requirements of a Linear Programming Problem   240*

7.3   *Formulating LP Problems   241*
Flair Furniture Company   241

7.4   *Graphical Solution to an LP Problem   243*
Graphical Representation of Constraints   243
Isoprofit Line Solution Method   247
Corner Point Solution Method   250
Slack and Surplus   252

7.5   *Solving Flair Furniture's LP Problem Using QM for Windows, Excel 2013, and Excel QM   253*
Using QM for Windows   253
Using Excel's Solver Command to Solve LP Problems   254
Using Excel QM   257

7.6   *Solving Minimization Problems   259*
Holiday Meal Turkey Ranch   259

7.7   *Four Special Cases in LP   263*
No Feasible Solution   263
Unboundedness   263
Redundancy   264
Alternate Optimal Solutions   265

7.8   *Sensitivity Analysis   266*
High Note Sound Company   267
Changes in the Objective Function Coefficient   268
QM for Windows and Changes in Objective Function Coefficients   268
Excel Solver and Changes in Objective Function Coefficients   269
Changes in the Technological Coefficients   270
Changes in the Resources or Right-Hand-Side Values   271
QM for Windows and Changes in Right-Hand-Side Values   272
Excel Solver and Changes in Right-Hand-Side Values   272
Summary   274   Glossary   274
Solved Problems   275   Self-Test   279
Discussion Questions and Problems   280
Case Study: Mexicana Wire Works   288
Bibliography   290

CHAPTER 8   **Linear Programming Applications   291**

8.1   *Introduction   292*

8.2   *Marketing Applications   292*
Media Selection   292
Marketing Research   293

8.3   *Manufacturing Applications   296*
Production Mix   296
Production Scheduling   297

8.4   *Employee Scheduling Applications   301*
Labor Planning   301

8.5   *Financial Applications   303*
Portfolio Selection   303
Truck Loading Problem   306

8.6   *Ingredient Blending Applications   308*
Diet Problems   308
Ingredient Mix and Blending Problems   309

8.7   *Other Linear Programming Applications   311*
Summary   313   Self-Test   313
Problems   314   Case Study: Cable & Moore   321   Bibliography   322

CHAPTER 9   **Transportation, Assignment, and Network Models   323**

9.1   *Introduction   324*

9.2   *The Transportation Problem   325*
Linear Program for the Transportation Example   325
Solving Transportation Problems Using Computer Software   325
A General LP Model for Transportation Problems   326
Facility Location Analysis   327

9.3   *The Assignment Problem   330*
Linear Program for Assignment Example   330

9.4   *The Transshipment Problem   332*
Linear Program for Transshipment Example   332

9.5   *Maximal-Flow Problem   335*
Example   335

9.6   *Shortest-Route Problem   337*

9.7   *Minimal-Spanning Tree Problem   338*
Summary   342   Glossary   343
Solved Problems   343   Self-Test   345
Discussion Questions and Problems   346
Case Study: Andrew–Carter, Inc.   357
Case Study: Northeastern Airlines   358
Case Study: Southwestern University Traffic Problems   359   Bibliography   360

Appendix 9.1:   *Using QM for Windows   360*

CHAPTER 11   **Project Management   395**

11.1   *Introduction   396*

11.2   *PERT/CPM   397*
General Foundry Example of PERT/CPM   397
Drawing the PERT/CPM Network   399
Activity Times   399
How to Find the Critical Path   400
Probability of Project Completion   405
What PERT Was Able to Provide   406
Using Excel QM for the General Foundry Example   406
Sensitivity Analysis and Project Management   407

11.3   *PERT/Cost 409*

Planning and Scheduling Project Costs:
  Budgeting Process 409

Monitoring and Controlling Project Costs 412

11.4   *Project Crashing 414*

General Foundary Example 415

Project Crashing with Linear Programming 416

11.5   *Other Topics in Project Management 419*

Subprojects 419

Milestones 419

Resource Leveling 419

Software 419

*Summary 419   Glossary 420
Key Equations 420   Solved Problems 421
Self-Test 423   Discussion Questions and
Problems 424   Case Study: Southwestern
University Stadium Construction 429
Case Study: Family Planning Research Center of
Nigeria 430   Bibliography 432*

Appendix 11.1:   *Project Management with QM
for Windows   432*

INDEX 579

PREFACE

OVERVIEW

Welcome to the twelfth edition of *Quantitative Analysis for Management*. Our goal is to provide undergraduate and graduate students with a genuine foundation in business analytics, quantitative methods, and management science. In doing so, we owe thanks to the hundreds of users and scores of reviewers who have provided invaluable counsel and pedagogical insight for more than 30 years.

To help students connect how the techniques presented in this book apply in the real world, computer-based applications and examples are a major focus of this edition. Mathematical models, with all the necessary assumptions, are presented in a clear and "plain-English" manner. The ensuing solution procedures are then applied to example problems alongside step-by-step "how-to" instructions. We have found this method of presentation to be very effective and students are very appreciative of this approach. In places where the mathematical computations are intricate, the details are presented in such a manner that the instructor can omit these sections without interrupting the flow of material. The use of computer software enables the instructor to focus on the managerial problem and spend less time on the details of the algorithms. Computer output is provided for many examples throughout the book.

The only mathematical prerequisite for this textbook is algebra. One chapter on probability and another on regression analysis provide introductory coverage on these topics. We employ standard notation, terminology, and equations throughout the book. Careful explanation is provided for the mathematical notation and equations that are used.

NEW TO THIS EDITION

- An introduction to business analytics is provided.
- Excel 2013 is incorporated throughout the chapters.
- The transportation, assignment, and network models have been combined into one chapter focused on modeling with linear programming.
- Specialized algorithms for the transportation, assignment, and network methods have been combined into Online Module 8.
- New examples, over 25 problems, 8 QA in Action applications, 4 Modeling in the Real World features, and 3 new Case Studies have been added throughout the textbook. Other problems and Case Studies have been updated.

SPECIAL FEATURES

Many features have been popular in previous editions of this textbook, and they have been updated and expanded in this edition. They include the following:

- *Modeling in the Real World* boxes demonstrate the application of the quantitative analysis approach to every technique discussed in the book. Four new ones have been added.

- *Procedure* boxes summarize the more complex quantitative techniques, presenting them as a series of easily understandable steps.

- *Margin notes* highlight the important topics in the text.

- *History* boxes provide interesting asides related to the development of techniques and the people who originated them.

- *QA in Action* boxes illustrate how real organizations have used quantitative analysis to solve problems. Several new QA in Action boxes have been added.

- *Solved Problems*, included at the end of each chapter, serve as models for students in solving their own homework problems.

- *Discussion Questions* are presented at the end of each chapter to test the student's understanding of the concepts covered and definitions provided in the chapter.

- *Problems* included in every chapter are applications oriented and test the student's ability to solve exam-type problems. They are graded by level of difficulty: introductory (one bullet), moderate (two bullets), and challenging (three bullets). More than 40 new problems have been added.

- *Internet Homework Problems* provide additional problems for students to work. They are available on the Companion Website.

- *Self-Tests* allow students to test their knowledge of important terms and concepts in preparation for quizzes and examinations.

- *Case Studies*, at the end of each chapter, provide additional challenging managerial applications.

- *Glossaries*, at the end of each chapter, define important terms.

- *Key Equations*, provided at the end of each chapter, list the equations presented in that chapter.

- *End-of-chapter bibliographies* provide a current selection of more advanced books and articles.

- *The software POM-QM for Windows* uses the full capabilities of Windows to solve quantitative analysis problems.

- *Excel QM* and *Excel 2013* are used to solve problems throughout the book.

- Data files with Excel spreadsheets and POM-QM for Windows files containing all the examples in the textbook are available for students to download from the Companion Website. Instructors can download these plus additional files containing computer solutions to the relevant end-of-chapter problems from the Instructor Resource Center Web site.

- *Online modules* provide additional coverage of topics in quantitative analysis.

- The Companion Website, at www.pearsonhighered.com/render, provides the online modules, additional problems, cases, and other material for almost every chapter.

SIGNIFICANT CHANGES TO THE TWELFTH EDITION

In the twelfth edition, we have introduced Excel 2013 in all of the chapters. Screenshots are integrated in the appropriate sections so that students can easily learn how to use Excel for the calculations. The Excel QM add-in is used with Excel 2013 allowing students with limited Excel experience to easily perform the necessary calculations. This also allows students to improve their Excel skills as they see the formulas automatically written in Excel QM.

From the Companion Website, students can access files for all of the examples used in the textbook in Excel 2013, QM for Windows, and Excel QM. Other files with all of the end-of-chapter problems involving these software tools are available to the instructors.

Business analytics, one of the hottest topics in the business world, makes extensive use of the models in this book. A discussion of the business analytics categories is provided, and the relevant management science techniques are placed into the appropriate category.

The transportation, transshipment, assignment, and network models have been combined into one chapter focused on modeling with linear programming. The specialized algorithms for these models have been combined into a new online module.

Examples and problems have been updated, and many new ones have been added. New screen-shots are provided for almost all of the examples in the book. A brief summary of the other changes in each chapter are presented here.

Chapter 1 *Introduction to Quantitative Analysis.* A section on business analytics has been added, the self-test has been modified, and two new problems were added.

Chapter 2 *Probability Concepts and Applications.* The presentation of the fundamental concepts of probability has been significantly modified and reorganized. Two new problems have been added.

Chapter 3 *Decision Analysis.* A more thorough discussion of minimization problems with payoff tables has been provided in a new section. The presentation of software usage with payoff tables was expanded. Two new problems were added.

Chapter 4 *Regression Models.* The use of different software packages for regression analysis has been moved to the body of the textbook instead of the appendix. Five new problems and one new QA in Action item have been added.

Chapter 5 *Forecasting.* The presentation of time-series forecasting models was significantly revised to bring the focus on identifying the appropriate technique to use based on which time-series components are present in the data. Five new problems were added, and the cases have been updated.

Chapter 6 *Inventory Control Models.* The four steps of the Kanban production process have been updated and clarified. Two new QA in Action boxes, four new problems, and one new Modeling in the Real World have been added.

Chapter 7 *Linear Programming Models: Graphical and Computer Methods.* More discussion of Solver is presented. A new Modeling in the Real World item was added, and the solved problems have been revised.

Chapter 8 *Linear Programming Applications.* The transportation model was moved to Chapter 9, and a new section describing other models has been added. The self-test questions were modified; one new problem, one new QA in Action summary, and a new case study have been added.

Chapter 9 *Transportation, Assignment, and Network Models.* This new chapter presents all of the distribution, assignment, and network models that were previously in two separate chapters. The modeling approach is emphasized, while the special-purpose algorithms were moved to a new online module. A new case study, Northeastern Airlines, has also been added.

Chapter 10 *Integer Programming, Goal Programming, and Nonlinear Programming.* The use of Excel 2013 and the new screen shots were the only changes to this chapter.

Chapter 11 *Project Management.* Two new end-of-chapter problems and three new QA in Action boxes have been added.

Chapter 12 *Waiting Lines and Queuing Theory Models.* Two new end-of-chapter problems were added.

Chapter 13 *Simulation Modeling.* One new Modeling in the Real World vignette, one new QA in Action box, and a new case study have been added.

Chapter 14 *Markov Analysis*. One new QA in Action box and two new end-of-chapter problems have been added.

Chapter 15 *Statistical Quality Control*. One new Modeling in the Real World vignette, one new QA in Action box, and two new end-of-chapter problems have been added.

Modules 1–8 The only significant change to the modules is the addition of Module 8: *Transportation, Assignment, and Network Algorithms*. This includes the special-purpose algorithms for the transportation, assignment, and network models.

ONLINE MODULES

To streamline the book, eight topics are contained in modules available on the Companion Website for the book.

1. Analytic Hierarchy Process
2. Dynamic Programming
3. Decision Theory and the Normal Distribution
4. Game Theory
5. Mathematical Tools: Determinants and Matrices
6. Calculus-Based Optimization
7. Linear Programming: The Simplex Method
8. Transportation, Assignment, and Network Algorithms

SOFTWARE

Excel 2013 Instructions and screen captures are provided for, using Excel 2013, throughout the book. Instructions for activating the Solver and Analysis ToolPak add-ins in Excel 2013 are provided in an appendix. The use of Excel is more prevalent in this edition of the book than in previous editions.

Excel QM Using the Excel QM add-in that is available on the Companion Website makes the use of Excel even easier. Students with limited Excel experience can use this and learn from the formulas that are automatically provided by Excel QM. This is used in many of the chapters.

POM-QM for Windows This software, developed by Professor Howard Weiss, is available to students at the Companion Website. This is very user-friendly and has proven to be a very popular software tool for users of this textbook. Modules are available for every major problem type presented in the textbook.

COMPANION WEBSITE

The Companion Website, located at www.pearsonhighered.com/render, contains a variety of materials to help students master the material in this course. These include the following:

Modules There are eight modules containing additional material that the instructor may choose to include in the course. Students can download these from the Companion Website.

Files for Examples in Excel, Excel QM, and POM-QM for Windows Students can download the files that were used for examples throughout the book. This helps them become familiar with the software, and it helps them understand the input and formulas necessary for working the examples.

Internet Homework Problems In addition to the end-of-chapter problems in the textbook, there are additional problems that instructors may assign. These are available for download at the Companion Website.

Internet Case Studies Additional case studies are available for most chapters.

POM-QM for Windows Developed by Howard Weiss, this very user-friendly software can be used to solve most of the homework problems in the text.

Excel QM This Excel add-in will automatically create worksheets for solving problems. This is very helpful for instructors who choose to use Excel in their classes but who may have students with limited Excel experience. Students can learn by examining the formulas that have been created, and by seeing the inputs that are automatically generated for using the Solver add-in for linear programming.

INSTRUCTOR RESOURCES

- *Instructor Resource Center:* The Instructor Resource Center contains the electronic files for the test bank, PowerPoint slides, the Solutions Manual, and data files for both Excel and POM-QM for Windows for all relevant examples and end-of-chapter problems. (www.pearsonhighered.com/render).
- *Register, Redeem, Login:* At www.pearsonhighered.com/irc, instructors can access a variety of print, media, and presentation resources that are available with this text in downloadable, digital format. For most texts, resources are also available for course management platforms such as Blackboard, WebCT, and Course Compass.
- *Need help?* Our dedicated technical support team is ready to assist instructors with questions about the media supplements that accompany this text. Visit http://247pearsoned.custhelp.com/ for answers to frequently asked questions and toll-free user support phone numbers. The supplements are available to adopting instructors. Detailed descriptions are provided on the Instructor Resource Center.

Instructor's Solutions Manual The Instructor's Solutions Manual, updated by the authors, is available for download from the Instructor Resource Center. Solutions to all Internet Homework Problems and Internet Case Studies are also included in the manual.

PowerPoint Presentation An extensive set of PowerPoint slides is available for download from the Instructor Resource Center.

Test Bank The updated test bank is available for download from the Instructor Resource Center.

TestGen The computerized TestGen package allows instructors to customize, save, and generate classroom tests. The test program permits instructors to edit, add, or delete questions from the test bank; edit existing graphics and create new graphics; analyze test results; and organize a database of test and student results. This software allows the instructors to benefit from the extensive flexibility and ease of use. It provides many options for organizing and displaying tests, along with search and sort features. The software and the test banks can be downloaded at www.pearsonhighered.com/render.

ACKNOWLEDGMENTS

We gratefully thank the users of previous editions and the reviewers who provided valuable suggestions and ideas for this edition. Your feedback is valuable in our efforts for continuous improvement. The continued success of *Quantitative Analysis for Management* is a direct result of instructor and student feedback, which is truly appreciated.

The authors are indebted to many people who have made important contributions to this project. Special thanks go to Professors Faizul Huq, F. Bruce Simmons III, Khala Chand Seal, Victor E. Sower, Michael Ballot, Curtis P. McLaughlin, and Zbigniew H. Przanyski for their contributions to the excellent cases included in this edition.

We thank Howard Weiss for providing Excel QM and POM-QM for Windows, two of the most outstanding packages in the field of quantitative methods. We would also like to thank the reviewers who have helped to make this textbook the most widely used one in the field of quantitative analysis:

Stephen Achtenhagen, *San Jose University*

M. Jill Austin, *Middle Tennessee State University*

Raju Balakrishnan, *Clemson University*

Hooshang Beheshti, *Radford University*

Jason Bergner, *University of Central Missouri*

Bruce K. Blaylock, *Radford University*

Rodney L. Carlson, *Tennessee Technological University*

Edward Chu, *California State University, Dominguez Hills*

John Cozzolino, *Pace University–Pleasantville*

Ozgun C. Demirag, *Penn State–Erie*

Shad Dowlatshahi, *University of Wisconsin, Platteville*

Ike Ehie, *Southeast Missouri State University*

Richard Ehrhardt, *University of North Carolina–Greensboro*

Sean Eom, *Southeast Missouri State University*

Ephrem Eyob, *Virginia State University*

Mira Ezvan, *Lindenwood University*

Wade Ferguson, *Western Kentucky University*

Robert Fiore, *Springfield College*

Frank G. Forst, *Loyola University of Chicago*

Ed Gillenwater, *University of Mississippi*

Stephen H. Goodman, *University of Central Florida*

Irwin Greenberg, *George Mason University*

Nicholas G. Hall, *Ohio State University*

Robert R. Hill, *University of Houston–Clear Lake*

Gordon Jacox, *Weber State University*

Bharat Jain, *Towson University*

Vassilios Karavas, *University of Massachusetts Amherst*

Darlene R. Lanier, *Louisiana State University*

Kenneth D. Lawrence, *New Jersey Institute of Technology*

Jooh Lee, *Rowan College*

Richard D. Legault, *University of Massachusetts–Dartmouth*

Douglas Lonnstrom, *Siena College*

Daniel McNamara, *University of St. Thomas*

Peter Miller, *University of Windsor*

Ralph Miller, *California State Polytechnic University*

Shahriar Mostashari, *Campbell University*

David Murphy, *Boston College*

Robert C. Myers, *University of Louisville*

Barin Nag, *Towson State University*

Nizam S. Najd, *Oklahoma State University*

Harvey Nye, *Central State University*

Alan D. Olinsky, *Bryant College*

Savas Ozatalay, *Widener University*

Young Park, *California University of Pennsylvania*

Cy Peebles, *Eastern Kentucky University*

Yusheng Peng, *Brooklyn College*

Dane K. Peterson, *Southwest Missouri State University*

Sanjeev Phukan, *Bemidji State University*

Ranga Ramasesh, *Texas Christian University*

William Rife, *West Virginia University*

Bonnie Robeson, *Johns Hopkins University*

Grover Rodich, *Portland State University*

Vijay Shah, *West Virginia University–Parkersburg*

L. Wayne Shell, *Nicholls State University*

Thomas Sloan, *University of Massachusetts–Lowell*

Richard Slovacek, *North Central College*

Alan D. Smith, *Robert Morris University*

John Swearingen, *Bryant College*

F. S. Tanaka, *Slippery Rock State University*

Jack Taylor, *Portland State University*

Madeline Thimmes, *Utah State University*

M. Keith Thomas, *Olivet College*

Andrew Tiger, *Southeastern Oklahoma State University*

Chris Vertullo, *Marist College*

James Vigen, *California State University, Bakersfield*

William Webster, *University of Texas at San Antonio*

Larry Weinstein, *Eastern Kentucky University*

Fred E. Williams, *University of Michigan–Flint*

Mela Wyeth, *Charleston Southern University*

Oliver Yu, *San Jose State University*

We are very grateful to all the people at Pearson who worked so hard to make this book a success. These include Donna Battista, editor in chief; Mary Kate Murray, senior project manager; and Kathryn Dinovo, senior production project manager. We are also grateful to Tracy Duff, our project manager at PreMediaGlobal. We are extremely thankful to Annie Puciloski for her tireless work in error checking the textbook. Thank you all!

Barry Render
brender@rollins.edu

Ralph Stair

Michael Hanna
hanna@uhcl.edu

Trevor S. Hale
halet@uhd.edu

CHAPTER 2

Probability Concepts and Applications

LEARNING OBJECTIVES

After completing this chapter, students will be able to:

1. Understand the basic foundations of probability analysis.
2. Describe statistically dependent and independent events.
3. Use Bayes' theorem to establish posterior probabilities.

4. Describe and provide examples of both discrete and continuous random variables.
5. Explain the difference between discrete and continuous probability distributions.
6. Calculate expected values and variances and use the normal table.

CHAPTER OUTLINE

2.1 Introduction
2.2 Fundamental Concepts
2.3 Revising Probabilities with Bayes' Theorem
2.4 Further Probability Revisions
2.5 Random Variables
2.6 Probability Distributions

2.7 The Binomial Distribution
2.8 The Normal Distribution
2.9 The *F* Distribution
2.10 The Exponential Distribution
2.11 The Poisson Distribution

Summary • Glossary • Key Equations • Solved Problems • Self-Test • Discussion Questions and Problems • Internet Homework Problems • Case Study: WTVX • Bibliography
Appendix 2.1:   Derivation of Bayes' Theorem

2.1   Introduction

Life would be simpler if we knew without doubt what was going to happen in the future. The outcome of any decision would depend only on how logical and rational the decision was. If you lost money in the stock market, it would be because you failed to consider all the information or to make a logical decision. If you got caught in the rain, it would be because you simply forgot your umbrella. You could always avoid building a plant that was too large, investing in a company that would lose money, running out of supplies, or losing crops because of bad weather. There would be no such thing as a risky investment. Life would be simpler, but boring.

It wasn't until the sixteenth century that people started to quantify risks and to apply this concept to everyday situations. Today, the idea of risk or probability is a part of our lives. "There is a 40% chance of rain in Omaha today." "The Florida State University Seminoles are favored 2 to 1 over the Louisiana State University Tigers this Saturday." "There is a 50–50 chance that the stock market will reach an all-time high next month."

A probability is a numerical statement about the chance that an event will occur.

A **probability** *is a numerical statement about the likelihood that an event will occur.* In this chapter, we examine the basic concepts, terms, and relationships of probability and probability distributions that are useful in solving many quantitative analysis problems. Table 2.1 lists some of the topics covered in this book that rely on probability theory. You can see that the study of quantitative analysis and business analytics would be quite difficult without it.

2.2   Fundamental Concepts

There are several rules, definitions, and concepts associated with probability that are very important in understanding the use of probability in decision making. These will be briefly presented with some examples to help clarify them.

Two Basic Rules of Probability

There are two basic rules regarding the mathematics of probability:

People often misuse the two basic rules of probabilities when they use statements such as, "I'm 110% sure we're going to win the big game."

1. The probability, P, of any event or state of nature occurring is greater than or equal to 0 and less than or equal to 1. That is,

$$0 \leq P(\text{event}) \leq 1 \tag{2-1}$$

A probability of 0 indicates that an event is never expected to occur. A probability of 1 means that an event is always expected to occur.

2. The sum of the simple probabilities for all possible outcomes of an activity must equal 1. Regardless of how probabilities are determined, they must adhere to these two rules.

TABLE 2.1

Chapters in This Book That Use Probability

CHAPTER	TITLE
3	Decision Analysis
4	Regression Models
5	Forecasting
6	Inventory Control Models
11	Project Management
12	Waiting Lines and Queuing Theory Models
13	Simulation Modeling
14	Markov Analysis
15	Statistical Quality Control
Module 3	Decision Theory and the Normal Distribution
Module 4	Game Theory

TABLE 2.2

Relative Frequency Approach to Probability for Paint Sales

QUANTITY DEMANDED (GALLONS)	NUMBER OF DAYS	PROBABILITY
0	40	0.20 (= 40/200)
1	80	0.40 (= 80/200)
2	50	0.25 (= 50/200)
3	20	0.10 (= 20/200)
4	10	0.05 (= 10/200)
	Total 200	1.00 (= 200/200)

Types of Probability

There are two different ways to determine probability: the **objective approach** and the **subjective approach**.

The **relative frequency approach** is an objective probability assessment. The probability assigned to an event is the relative frequency of that occurrence. In general,

$$P(\text{event}) = \frac{\text{Number of occurrences of the event}}{\text{Total number of trials or outcomes}}$$

Here is an example. Demand for white latex paint at Diversey Paint and Supply has always been 0, 1, 2, 3, or 4 gallons per day. (There are no other possible outcomes and when one occurs, no other can.) Over the past 200 working days, the owner notes the frequencies of demand as shown in Table 2.2. If this past distribution is a good indicator of future sales, we can find the probability of each possible outcome occurring in the future by converting the data into percentages.

Thus, the probability that sales are 2 gallons of paint on any given day is $P(2 \text{ gallons}) = 0.25 = 25\%$. The probability of any level of sales must be greater than or equal to 0 and less than or equal to 1. Since 0, 1, 2, 3, and 4 gallons exhaust all possible events or outcomes, the sum of their probability values must equal 1.

Objective probability can also be set using what is called the **classical** or **logical method**. Without performing a series of trials, we can often logically determine what the probabilities of various events should be. For example, the probability of tossing a fair coin once and getting a head is

$$P(\text{head}) = \frac{1 \longleftarrow \textit{Number of ways of getting a head}}{2 \longleftarrow \textit{Number of possible outcomes (head or tail)}}$$

Similarly, the probability of drawing a spade out of a deck of 52 playing cards can be logically set as

$$P(\text{spade}) = \frac{13 \longleftarrow \textit{Number of chances of drawing a spade}}{52 \longleftarrow \textit{Number of possible outcomes}}$$
$$= \frac{1}{4} = 0.25 = 25\%$$

When logic and past history are not available or appropriate, probability values can be assessed *subjectively*. The accuracy of subjective probabilities depends on the experience and judgment of the person making the estimates. A number of probability values cannot be determined unless the subjective approach is used. What is the probability that the price of gasoline will be more than $4 in the next few years? What is the probability that our economy will be in a severe depression in 2020? What is the probability that you will be president of a major corporation within 20 years?

There are several methods for making subjective probability assessments. Opinion polls can be used to help in determining subjective probabilities for possible election returns and potential political candidates. In some cases, experience and judgment must be used in making subjective assessments of probability values. A production manager, for example, might believe that the probability of manufacturing a new product without a single defect is 0.85. In the Delphi method, a panel of experts is assembled to make their predictions of the future. This approach is discussed in Chapter 5.

Where do probabilities come from? Sometimes they are subjective and based on personal experiences. Other times they are objectively based on logical observations such as the roll of a die. Often, probabilities are derived from historical data.

Mutually Exclusive and Collectively Exhaustive Events

Events are said to be **mutually exclusive** if only one of the events can occur on any one trial. They are called **collectively exhaustive** if the list of outcomes includes every possible outcome. Many common experiences involve events that have both of these properties.

In tossing a coin, the possible outcomes are a head or a tail. Since both of them cannot occur on any one toss, the outcomes head and tail are mutually exclusive. Since obtaining a head and obtaining a tail represent every possible outcome, they are also collectively exhaustive.

Figure 2.1 provides a Venn diagram representation of mutually exclusive events. Let A be the event that a head is tossed, and let B be the event that a tail is tossed. The circles representing these events do not overlap, so the events are mutually exclusive.

The following situation provides an example of events that are not mutually exclusive. You are asked to draw one card from a standard deck of 52 playing cards. The following events are defined:

$$A = \text{event that a 7 is drawn}$$
$$B = \text{event that a heart is drawn}$$

FIGURE 2.1

Venn Diagram for Events That Are Mutually Exclusive

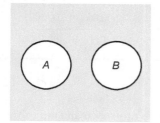

MODELING IN THE REAL WORLD

Liver Transplants in the United States

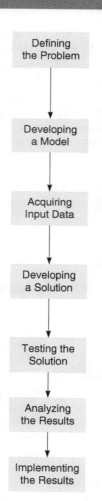

Defining the Problem → Developing a Model → Acquiring Input Data → Developing a Solution → Testing the Solution → Analyzing the Results → Implementing the Results

Defining the Problem

The scarcity of liver organs for transplants has reached critical levels in the United States; 1,131 individuals died in 1997 while waiting for a transplant. With only 4,000 liver donations per year, there are 10,000 patients on the waiting list, with 8,000 being added each year. There is a need to develop a model to evaluate policies for allocating livers to terminally ill patients who need them.

Developing a Model

Doctors, engineers, researchers, and scientists worked together with Pritsker Corp. consultants in the process of creating the liver allocation model, called ULAM. One of the model's jobs would be to evaluate whether to list potential recipients on a national basis or regionally.

Acquiring Input Data

Historical information was available from the United Network for Organ Sharing (UNOS), from 1990 to 1995. The data were then stored in ULAM. "Poisson" probability processes described the arrivals of donors at 63 organ procurement centers and arrival of patients at 106 liver transplant centers.

Developing a Solution

ULAM provides probabilities of accepting an offered liver, where the probability is a function of the patient's medical status, the transplant center, and the quality of the offered liver. ULAM also models the daily probability of a patient changing from one status of criticality to another.

Testing the Solution

Testing involved a comparison of the model output to actual results over the 1992–1994 time period. Model results were close enough to actual results that ULAM was declared valid.

Analyzing the Results

ULAM was used to compare more than 100 liver allocation policies and was then updated in 1998, with more recent data, for presentation to Congress.

Implementing the Results

Based on the projected results, the UNOS committee voted 18–0 to implement an allocation policy based on regional, not national, waiting lists. This decision is expected to save 2,414 lives over an 8-year period.

Source: Based on A. A. B. Pritsker. "Life and Death Decisions," *OR/MS Today* (August 1998): 22–28.

FIGURE 2.2

Venn Diagram for Events That Are Not Mutually Exclusive

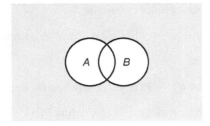

The probabilities can be assigned to these using the relative frequency approach. There are four 7s in the deck and thirteen hearts in the deck. Thus, we have

$$P(\text{a 7 is drawn}) = P(A) = {}^{4}\!/_{52}$$
$$P(\text{a heart is drawn}) = P(B) = {}^{13}\!/_{52}$$

These events are not mutually exclusive as the 7 of hearts is common to both event A and event B. Figure 2.2 provides a Venn diagram representing this situation. Notice that the two circles intersect, and this intersection is whatever is in common to both. In this example, the intersection would be the 7 of hearts.

Unions and Intersections of Events

The **intersection** of two events is the set of all outcomes that are common to both events. The word *and* is commonly associated with the intersection, as is the symbol ∩. There are several notations for the intersection of two events:

$$\text{Intersection of event } A \text{ and event } B = A \text{ and } B$$
$$= A \cap B$$
$$= AB$$

The notation for the probability would be

$$P(\text{Intersection of event } A \text{ and event } B) = P(A \text{ and } B)$$
$$= P(A \cap B)$$
$$= P(AB)$$

The probability of the intersection is sometimes called a **joint probability**, which implies that both events are occurring at the same time or jointly.

The **union** of two events is the set of all outcomes that are contained in either of these two events. Thus, any outcome that is in event A is in the union of the two events, and any outcome that is in event B is also in the union of the two events. The word *or* is commonly associated with the union, as is the symbol ∪. Typical notation for the union of two events would be

$$\text{Union of event } A \text{ and event } B = (A \text{ or } B)$$

The notation for the probability of the union of events would be

$$P(\text{Union of event } A \text{ and event } B) = P(A \text{ or } B)$$
$$= P(A \cup B)$$

In the previous example, the intersection of event A and event B would be

$$(A \text{ and } B) = \text{the 7 of hearts is drawn}$$

The notation for the probability would be

$$P(A \text{ and } B) = P(7 \text{ of hearts is drawn}) = {}^{1}\!/_{52}$$

Also, the union of event A and event B would be

$$(A \text{ or } B) = (\text{either a 7 is drawn or a heart is drawn})$$

and the probability would be

$$P(A \text{ or } B) = P(\text{any 7 or any heart is drawn}) = {}^{16}/_{52}$$

To see why $P(A \text{ or } B) = {}^{16}/_{52}$ and not ${}^{17}/_{52}$ (which is $P(A) + P(B)$), count all of the cards that are in the union, and you will see there are 16. This will help you understand the general rule for the probability of the union of two events that is presented next.

Probability Rules for Unions, Intersections, and Conditional Probabilities

The general rule for the probability of the union of two events (sometimes called the additive rule) is the following:

$$P(A \text{ or } B) = P(A) + P(B) - P(A \text{ and } B) \qquad (2\text{-}2)$$

To illustrate this with the example we have been using, to find the probability of the union of the two events (a 7 or a heart is drawn), we have

$$
\begin{aligned}
P(A \text{ or } B) &= P(A) + P(B) - P(A \text{ and } B) \\
&= {}^{4}/_{52} + {}^{13}/_{52} - {}^{1}/_{52} \\
&= {}^{16}/_{52}
\end{aligned}
$$

One of the most important probability concepts in decision making is the concept of a conditional probability. A **conditional probability** is the probability of an event occurring given that another event has already happened. The probability of event A given that event B has occurred is written as $P(A|B)$. When businesses make decisions, they often use market research of some type to help determine the likelihood of success. Given a good result from the market research, the probability of success would increase.

The probability that A will occur given that event B has occurred can be found by dividing the probability of the intersection of the two events (A and B) by the probability of the event that has occurred (B):

$$P(A|B) = \frac{P(AB)}{P(B)} \qquad (2\text{-}3)$$

From this, the formula for the intersection of two events can be easily derived and written as

$$P(AB) = P(A|B)P(B) \qquad (2\text{-}4)$$

In the card example, what is the probability that a 7 is drawn (event A) given that we know that the card drawn is a heart (event B)? With what we already know, and given the formula for conditional probability, we have

$$P(A|B) = \frac{P(AB)}{P(B)} = \frac{{}^{1}/_{52}}{{}^{13}/_{52}} = {}^{1}/_{13}$$

With this card example, it might be possible to determine this probability without using the formula. Given that a heart was drawn and there are 13 hearts with only one of these being a 7, we can determine that the probability is $^{1}/_{13}$. In business, however, we sometimes do not have this complete information and the formula is absolutely essential.

Two events are said to be **independent** if the occurrence of one has no impact on the occurrence of the other. Otherwise, the events are dependent.

For example, suppose a card is drawn from a deck of cards and it is then returned to the deck and a second drawing occurs. The probability of drawing a seven on the second draw is $^{4}/_{52}$ regardless of what was drawn on the first draw because the deck is exactly the same as it was on the first draw. Now contrast to a similar situation with two draws from a deck of cards, but the first card is not returned to the deck. Now there are only 51 cards left in the deck, and there are either three or four 7s in the deck depending on what the first card drawn happens to be.

A more precise definition of statistical independence would be the following: Event A and event B are independent if

$$P(A \mid B) = P(A)$$

Independence is a very important condition in probability as many calculations are simplified. One of these is the formula for the intersection of two events. If A and B are independent, then the probability of the intersection is

$$P(A \text{ and } B) = P(A)P(B)$$

Suppose a fair coin is tossed twice. The events are defined as:

A = event that a head is the result of the first toss

B = event that a head is the result of the second toss

These events are independent because the probability of a head on the second toss will be the same regardless of the result on the first toss. Because it is a fair coin, we know there are two equally likely outcomes on each toss (head or tail), so

$$P(A) = 0.5$$

and

$$P(B) = 0.5$$

Because A and B are independent,

$$P(AB) = P(A)P(B) = 0.5(0.5) = 0.25$$

Thus, there is a 0.25 probability that two tosses of a coin will result in two heads.

If events are not independent, then finding probabilities may be a bit more difficult. However, the results may be very valuable to a decision maker. A market research study about opening a new store in a particular location may have a positive outcome, and this would cause a revision of our probability assessment that the new store would be successful. The next section provides a means of revising probabilities based on new information.

2.3   Revising Probabilities with Bayes' Theorem

Bayes' theorem is used to incorporate additional information as it is made available and help create revised or *posterior probabilities* from the original or *prior probabilities*. This means that we can take new or recent data and then revise and improve upon our old probability estimates for an event (see Figure 2.3). Let us consider the following example.

A cup contains two dice identical in appearance. One, however, is fair (unbiased) and the other is loaded (biased). The probability of rolling a 3 on the fair die is $\frac{1}{6}$, or 0.166. The probability of tossing the same number on the loaded die is 0.60.

We have no idea which die is which, but select one by chance and toss it. The result is a 3. Given this additional piece of information, can we find the (revised) probability that the die rolled was fair? Can we determine the probability that it was the loaded die that was rolled?

FIGURE 2.3
Using Bayes' Process

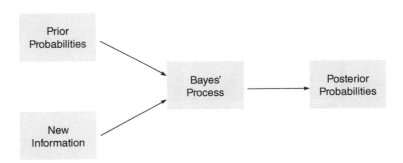

The answer to these questions is yes, and we do so by using the formula for joint probability under statistical dependence and Bayes' theorem. First, we take stock of the information and probabilities available. We know, for example, that since we randomly selected the die to roll, the probability of it being fair or loaded is 0.50:

$$P(\text{fair}) = 0.50 \quad P(\text{loaded}) = 0.50$$

We also know that

$$P(3|\text{fair}) = 0.166 \quad P(3|\text{loaded}) = 0.60$$

Next, we compute joint probabilities $P(3 \text{ and fair})$ and $P(3 \text{ and loaded})$ using the formula $P(AB) = P(A|B) \times P(B)$:

$$P(3 \text{ and fair}) = P(3|\text{fair}) \times P(\text{fair})$$
$$= (0.166)(0.50) = 0.083$$
$$P(3 \text{ and loaded}) = P(3|\text{loaded}) \times P(\text{loaded})$$
$$= (0.60)(0.50) = 0.300$$

A 3 can occur in combination with the state "fair die" or in combination with the state "loaded die." The sum of their probabilities gives the unconditional or marginal probability of a 3 on the toss, namely, $P(3) = 0.083 + 0.300 = 0.383$.

If a 3 does occur, and if we do not know which die it came from, the probability that the die rolled was the fair one is

$$P(\text{fair}|3) = \frac{P(\text{fair and 3})}{P(3)} = \frac{0.083}{0.383} = 0.22$$

The probability that the die rolled was loaded is

$$P(\text{loaded}|3) = \frac{P(\text{loaded and 3})}{P(3)} = \frac{0.300}{0.383} = 0.78$$

These two conditional probabilities are called the **revised** or **posterior probabilities** for the next roll of the die.

Before the die was rolled in the preceding example, the best we could say was that there was a 50–50 chance that it was fair (0.50 probability) and a 50–50 chance that it was loaded. After one roll of the die, however, we are able to revise our **prior probability** estimates. The new posterior estimate is that there is a 0.78 probability that the die rolled was loaded and only a 0.22 probability that it was not.

Using a table is often helpful in performing the calculations associated with Bayes' theorem. Table 2.3 provides the general layout for this, and Table 2.4 provides this specific example.

TABLE 2.3

Tabular Form of Bayes' Calculations Given That Event B Has Occurred

STATE OF NATURE	P(B| STATE OF NATURE)	PRIOR PROBABILITY	JOINT PROBABILITY	POSTERIOR PROBABILITY
A	$P(B|A)$	$\times P(A)$	$= P(B \text{ and } A)$	$P(B \text{ and } A)/P(B) = P(A|B)$
A'	$P(B|A')$	$\times P(A')$	$= P(B \text{ and } A')$	$P(B \text{ and } A')/P(B) = P(A'|B)$
			$P(B)$	

TABLE 2.4

Bayes' Calculations Given That a 3 Is Rolled in Example 7

STATE OF NATURE	P(3| STATE OF NATURE)	PRIOR PROBABILITY	JOINT PROBABILITY	POSTERIOR PROBABILITY
Fair die	0.166	$\times 0.5$	$= 0.083$	$0.083/0.383 = 0.22$
Loaded die	0.600	$\times 0.5$	$= 0.300$	$0.300/0.383 = 0.78$
			$P(3) = 0.383$	

General Form of Bayes' Theorem

Another way to compute revised probabilities is with Bayes' theorem.

Revised probabilities can also be computed in a more direct way using a general form for **Bayes' theorem**:

$$P(A|B) = \frac{P(B|A)P(A)}{P(B|A)P(A) + P(B|A')P(A')} \tag{2-5}$$

where

A' = the complement of the event A;
for example, if A is the event "fair die," then A' is "loaded die"

We originally saw in Equation 2-3 the conditional probability of event A, given event B, is

$$P(A|B) = \frac{P(AB)}{P(B)}$$

A Presbyterian minister, Thomas Bayes (1702–1761), did the work leading to this theorem.

Thomas Bayes derived his theorem from this. Appendix 2.1 shows the mathematical steps leading to Equation 2-5. Now let's return to the example.

Although it may not be obvious to you at first glance, we used this basic equation to compute the revised probabilities. For example, if we want the probability that the fair die was rolled given the first toss was a 3, namely, P(fair die | 3 rolled), we can let

event "fair die" replace A in Equation 2-5

event "loaded die" replace A' in Equation 2-5

event "3 rolled" replace B in Equation 2-5

We can then rewrite Equation 2-5 and solve as follows:

$$P(\text{fair die} | 3 \text{ rolled})$$

$$= \frac{P(3|\text{fair})P(\text{fair})}{P(3|\text{fair})P(\text{fair}) + P(3|\text{loaded})P(\text{loaded})}$$

$$= \frac{(0.166)(0.50)}{(0.166)(0.50) + (0.60)(0.50)}$$

$$= \frac{0.083}{0.383} = 0.22$$

This is the same answer that we computed earlier. Can you use this alternative approach to show that P(loaded die | 3 rolled) = 0.78? Either method is perfectly acceptable, but when we deal with probability revisions again in Chapter 3, we may find that Equation 2-5 or the tabular approach is easier to apply.

2.4 Further Probability Revisions

Although one revision of prior probabilities can provide useful posterior probability estimates, additional information can be gained from performing the experiment a second time. If it is financially worthwhile, a decision maker may even decide to make several more revisions.

Returning to the previous example, we now attempt to obtain further information about the posterior probabilities as to whether the die just rolled is fair or loaded. To do so, let us toss the die a second time. Again, we roll a 3. What are the further revised probabilities?

To answer this question, we proceed as before, with only one exception. The probabilities $P(\text{fair}) = 0.50$ and $P(\text{loaded}) = 0.50$ remain the same, but now we must compute $P(3, 3 | \text{fair}) = (0.166)(0.166) = 0.027$ and $P(3, 3 | \text{loaded}) = (0.6)(0.6) = 0.36$. With these joint probabilities of two 3s on successive rolls, given the two types of dice, we may revise the probabilities:

$$P(3, 3 \text{ and fair}) = P(3, 3 | \text{fair}) \times P(\text{fair})$$

$$= (0.027)(0.5) = 0.013$$

$$P(3, 3 \text{ and loaded}) = P(3, 3 | \text{loaded}) \times P(\text{loaded})$$

$$= (0.36)(0.5) = 0.18$$

IN ACTION   Flight Safety and Probability Analysis

With the horrific events of September 11, 2001, and the use of airplanes as weapons of mass destruction, airline safety has become an even more important international issue. How can we reduce the impact of terrorism on air safety? What can be done to make air travel safer overall? One answer is to evaluate various air safety programs and to use probability theory in the analysis of the costs of these programs.

Determining airline safety is a matter of applying the concepts of objective probability analysis. The chance of getting killed in a scheduled domestic flight is about 1 in 5 million. This is probability of about .0000002. Another measure is the number of deaths per passenger mile flown. The number is about 1 passenger per billion passenger miles flown, or a probability of about .000000001. Without question, flying is safer than many other forms of transportation, including driving. For a typical weekend, more people are killed in car accidents than a typical air disaster.

Analyzing new airline safety measures involves costs and the subjective probability that lives will be saved. One airline expert proposed a number of new airline safety measures. When the costs involved and probability of saving lives were taken into account, the result was about a $1 billion cost for every life saved on average. Using probability analysis will help determine which safety programs will result in the greatest benefit, and these programs can be expanded.

In addition, some proposed safety issues are not completely certain. For example, a Thermal Neutron Analysis device to detect explosives at airports had a probability of .15 of giving a false alarm, resulting in a high cost of inspection and long flight delays. This would indicate that money should be spent on developing more reliable equipment for detecting explosives. The result would be safer air travel with fewer unnecessary delays.

Without question, the use of probability analysis to determine and improve flight safety is indispensable. Many transportation experts hope that the same rigorous probability models used in the airline industry will some day be applied to the much more deadly system of highways and the drivers who use them.

Sources: Based on Robert Machol. "Flying Scared," *OR/MS Today* (October 1997): 32–37; and Arnold Barnett. "The Worst Day Ever," *OR/MS Today* (December 2001): 28–31.

Thus, the probability of rolling two 3s, a marginal probability, is $0.013 + 0.18 = 0.193$, the sum of the two joint probabilities:

$$P(\text{fair} \mid 3, 3) = \frac{P(3, 3 \text{ and fair})}{P(3, 3)}$$

$$= \frac{0.013}{0.193} = 0.067$$

$$P(\text{loaded} \mid 3, 3) = \frac{P(3, 3 \text{ and loaded})}{P(3, 3)}$$

$$= \frac{0.18}{0.193} = 0.933$$

What has this second roll accomplished? Before we rolled the die the first time, we knew only that there was a 0.50 probability that it was either fair or loaded. When the first die was rolled in the previous example, we were able to revise these probabilities:

probability the die is fair $= 0.22$

probability the die is loaded $= 0.78$

Now, after the second roll in this example, our refined revisions tell us that

probability the die is fair $= 0.067$

probability the die is loaded $= 0.933$

This type of information can be extremely valuable in business decision making.

2.5   Random Variables

We have just discussed various ways of assigning probability values to the outcomes of an experiment. Let us now use this probability information to compute the expected outcome, variance, and standard deviation of the experiment. This can help select the best decision among a number of alternatives.

TABLE 2.5   Examples of Random Variables

EXPERIMENT	OUTCOME	RANDOM VARIABLES	RANGE OF RANDOM VARIABLES
Stock 50 Christmas trees	Number of Christmas trees sold	X = number of Christmas trees sold	0, 1, 2, . . . , 50
Inspect 600 items	Number of acceptable items	Y = number of acceptable items	0, 1, 2, . . . , 600
Send out 5,000 sales letters	Number of people responding to the letters	Z = number of people responding to the letters	0, 1, 2, . . . , 5,000
Build an apartment building	Percent of building completed after 4 months	R = percent of building completed after 4 months	$0 \leq R \leq 100$
Test the lifetime of a lightbulb (minutes)	Length of time the bulb lasts up to 80,000 minutes	S = time the bulb burns	$0 \leq S \leq 80,000$

A **random variable** assigns a real number to every possible outcome or event in an experiment. It is normally represented by a letter such as X or Y. When the outcome itself is numerical or quantitative, the outcome numbers can be the random variable. For example, consider refrigerator sales at an appliance store. The number of refrigerators sold during a given day can be the random variable. Using X to represent this random variable, we can express this relationship as follows:

$$X = \text{number of refrigerators sold during the day}$$

In general, whenever the experiment has quantifiable outcomes, it is beneficial to define these quantitative outcomes as the random variable. Examples are given in Table 2.5.

When the outcome itself is not numerical or quantitative, it is necessary to define a random variable that associates each outcome with a unique real number. Several examples are given in Table 2.6.

There are two types of random variables: *discrete random variables* and *continuous random variables*. Developing probability distributions and making computations based on these distributions depends on the type of random variable.

A random variable is a **discrete random variable** if it can assume only a finite or limited set of values. Which of the random variables in Table 2.5 are discrete random variables? Looking at Table 2.5, we can see that the variables associated with stocking 50 Christmas trees, inspecting 600 items, and sending out 5,000 letters are all examples of discrete random variables. Each of these random variables can assume only a finite or limited set of values. The number of Christmas trees sold, for example, can only be integer numbers from 0 to 50. There are 51 values that the random variable X can assume in this example.

A **continuous random variable** is a random variable that has an infinite or an unlimited set of values. Are there any examples of continuous random variables in Table 2.5 or 2.6? Looking

Try to develop a few more examples of discrete random variables to be sure you understand this concept.

TABLE 2.6

Random Variables for Outcomes That Are Not Numbers

EXPERIMENT	OUTCOME	RANDOM VARIABLES	RANGE OF RANDOM VARIABLES
Students respond to a questionnaire	Strongly agree (SA) Agree (A) Neutral (N) Disagree (D) Strongly disagree (SD)	$X = \begin{cases} 5 \text{ if SA} \\ 4 \text{ if A} \\ 3 \text{ if N} \\ 2 \text{ if D} \\ 1 \text{ if SD} \end{cases}$	1, 2, 3, 4, 5
One machine is inspected	Defective Not defective	$Y = \begin{cases} 0 \text{ if defective} \\ 1 \text{ if not defective} \end{cases}$	0, 1
Consumers respond to how they like a product	Good Average Poor	$Z = \begin{cases} 3 \text{ if good} \\ 2 \text{ if average} \\ 1 \text{ if poor} \end{cases}$	1, 2, 3

at Table 2.5, we can see that testing the lifetime of a lightbulb is an experiment whose results can be described with a continuous random variable. In this case, the random variable, S, is the time the bulb burns. It can last for 3,206 minutes, 6,500.7 minutes, 251.726 minutes, or any other value between 0 and 80,000 minutes. In most cases, the range of a continuous random variable is stated as: lower value $\leq S \leq$ upper value, such as $0 \leq S \leq 80,000$. The random variable R in Table 2.5 is also continuous. Can you explain why?

2.6   Probability Distributions

Earlier we discussed the probability values of an event. We now explore the properties of **probability distributions**. We see how popular distributions, such as the normal, Poisson, binomial, and exponential probability distributions, can save us time and effort. Since a random variable may be *discrete* or *continuous*, we consider **discrete probability distributions** and **continuous probability distributions** seperately.

Probability Distribution of a Discrete Random Variable

When we have a *discrete random variable*, there is a probability value assigned to each event. These values must be between 0 and 1, and they must sum to 1. Let's look at an example.

The 100 students in Pat Shannon's statistics class have just completed a math quiz that he gives on the first day of class. The quiz consists of five very difficult algebra problems. The grade on the quiz is the number of correct answers, so the grades theoretically could range from 0 to 5. However, no one in this class received a score of 0, so the grades ranged from 1 to 5. The random variable X is defined to be the grade on this quiz, and the grades are summarized in Table 2.7. This discrete probability distribution was developed using the relative frequency approach presented earlier.

The distribution follows the three rules required of all probability distributions: (1) the events are mutually exclusive and collectively exhaustive, (2) the individual probability values are between 0 and 1 inclusive, and (3) the total of the probability values sum to 1.

Although listing the probability distribution as we did in Table 2.7 is adequate, it can be difficult to get an idea about characteristics of the distribution. To overcome this problem, the probability values are often presented in graph form. The graph of the distribution in Table 2.7 is shown in Figure 2.4.

The graph of this probability distribution gives us a picture of its shape. It helps us identify the central tendency of the distribution, called the mean or **expected value**, and the amount of variability or spread of the distribution, called the **variance**.

Expected Value of a Discrete Probability Distribution

The expected value of a discrete distribution is a weighted average of the values of the random variable.

Once we have established a probability distribution, the first characteristic that is usually of interest is the *central tendency* of the distribution. The expected value, a measure of central tendency, is computed as the weighted average of the values of the random variable:

$$E(X) = \sum_{i=1}^{n} X_i P(X_i)$$
$$= X_1 P(X_1) + X_2 P(X_2) + \cdots + X_n P(X_n) \tag{2-6}$$

TABLE 2.7
Probability Distribution for Quiz Scores

RANDOM VARIABLE (X)-SCORE	NUMBER	PROBABILITY $P(X)$
5	10	0.1 = 10/100
4	20	0.2 = 20/100
3	30	0.3 = 30/100
2	30	0.3 = 30/100
1	10	0.1 = 10/100
	Total 100	1.0 = 100/100

FIGURE 2.4
Probability Distribution for Dr. Shannon's Class

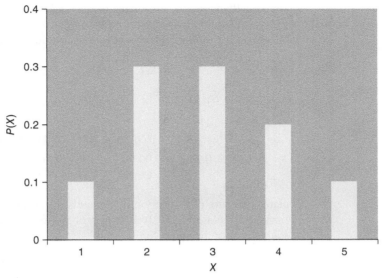

where

X_i = random variable's possible values

$P(X_i)$ = probability of each of the random variable's possible values

$\sum_{i=1}^{n}$ = summation sign indicating we are adding all n possible values

$E(X)$ = expected value or mean of the random variable

The expected value or mean of any discrete probability distribution can be computed by multiplying each possible value of the random variable, X_i, times the probability, $P(X_i)$, that outcome will occur and summing the results, $\sum$. Here is how the expected value can be computed for the quiz scores:

$$E(X) = \sum_{i=1}^{5} X_i P(X_i)$$
$$= X_1 P(X_1) + X_2 P(X_2) + X_3 P(X_3) + X_4 P(X_4) + X_5 P(X_5)$$
$$= (5)(0.1) + (4)(0.2) + (3)(0.3) + (2)(0.3) + (1)(0.1)$$
$$= 2.9$$

The expected value of 2.9 is the mean score on the quiz.

Variance of a Discrete Probability Distribution

In addition to the central tendency of a probability distribution, most people are interested in the variability or the spread of the distribution. If the variability is low, it is much more likely that the outcome of an experiment will be close to the average or expected value. On the other hand, if the variability of the distribution is high, which means that the probability is spread out over the various random variable values, there is less chance that the outcome of an experiment will be close to the expected value.

The *variance* of a probability distribution is a number that reveals the overall spread or dispersion of the distribution. For a discrete probability distribution, it can be computed using the following equation:

A probability distribution is often described by its mean and variance. Even if most of the men in class (or the United States) have heights between 5 feet 6 inches and 6 feet 2 inches, there is still some small probability of outliers.

$$\sigma^2 = \text{Variance} = \sum_{i=1}^{n} [X_i - E(X)]^2 P(X_i) \qquad (2\text{-}7)$$

where

X_i = random variable's possible values

$E(X)$ = expected value of the random variable

$[X_i - E(X)]$ = difference between each value of the random variable and the expected value

$P(X_i)$ = probability of each possible value of the random variable

To compute the variance, each value of the random variable is subtracted from the expected value, squared, and multiplied times the probability of occurrence of that value. The results are then summed to obtain the variance. Here is how this procedure is done for Dr. Shannon's quiz scores:

$$\text{Variance} = \sum_{i=1}^{5}[X_i - E(X)]^2 P(X_i)$$

$$\text{Variance} = (5 - 2.9)^2(0.1) + (4 - 2.9)^2(0.2) + (3 - 2.9)^2(0.3) + (2 - 2.9)^2(0.3)$$
$$+ (1 - 2.9)^2(0.1)$$
$$= (2.1)^2(0.1) + (1.1)^2(0.2) + (0.1)^2(0.3) + (-0.9)^2(0.3) + (-1.9)^2(0.1)$$
$$= 0.441 + 0.242 + 0.003 + 0.243 + 0.361$$
$$= 1.29$$

A related measure of dispersion or spread is the **standard deviation**. This quantity is also used in many computations involved with probability distributions. The standard deviation is just the square root of the variance:

$$\sigma = \sqrt{\text{Variance}} = \sqrt{\sigma^2} \qquad (2\text{-}8)$$

where

$$\sqrt{} = \text{square root}$$
$$\sigma = \text{standard deviation}$$

The standard deviation for the random variable X in the example is

$$\sigma = \sqrt{\text{Variance}}$$
$$= \sqrt{1.29} = 1.14$$

These calculations are easily performed in Excel. Program 2.1A provides the output for this example. Program 2.1B shows the inputs and formulas in Excel for calculating the mean, variance, and standard deviation in this example.

Probability Distribution of a Continuous Random Variable

There are many examples of *continuous random variables*. The time it takes to finish a project, the number of ounces in a barrel of butter, the high temperature during a given day, the exact length of a given type of lumber, and the weight of a railroad car of coal are all examples of continuous random variables. Since random variables can take on an infinite number of values, the fundamental probability rules for continuous random variables must be modified.

As with discrete probability distributions, the sum of the probability values must equal 1. Because there are an infinite number of values of the random variables, however, the probability of each value of the random variable must be 0. If the probability values for the random variable values were greater than 0, the sum would be infinitely large.

PROGRAM 2.1A

Excel 2013 Output for the Dr. Shannon Example

	A	B	C	D
1	X	P(X)	XP(X)	(X - E(X))²P(X)
2	5	0.1	0.5	0.441
3	4	0.2	0.8	0.242
4	3	0.3	0.9	0.003
5	2	0.3	0.6	0.243
6	1	0.1	0.1	0.361
7		E(X) = ΣXP(X) =	2.9	1.290
8				1.136

PROGRAM 2.1B

Formulas in an Excel Spreadsheet for the Dr. Shannon Example

	C	D
2	=A2*B2	=(A2-$C$7)^2*B2
3	=A3*B3	=(A3-$C$7)^2*B3
4	=A4*B4	=(A4-$C$7)^2*B4
5	=A5*B5	=(A5-$C$7)^2*B5
6	=A6*B6	=(A6-$C$7)^2*B6
7	=SUM(C2:C6)	=SUM(D2:D6)
8		=SQRT(D7)

FIGURE 2.5

Graph of Sample Density Function

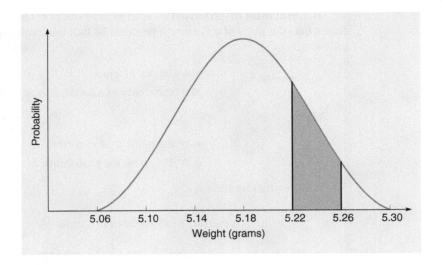

A probability density function, f(X), is a mathematical way of describing the probability distribution.

With a continuous probability distribution, there is a continuous mathematical function that describes the probability distribution. This function is called the **probability density function** or simply the **probability function**. It is usually represented by $f(X)$. When working with continuous probability distributions, the probability function can be graphed, and the area underneath the curve represents probability. Thus, to find any probability, we simply find the area under the curve associated with the range of interest.

We now look at the sketch of a sample density function in Figure 2.5. This curve represents the probability density function for the weight of a particular machined part. The weight could vary from 5.06 to 5.30 grams, with weights around 5.18 grams being the most likely. The shaded area represents the probability the weight is between 5.22 and 5.26 grams.

If we wanted to know the probability of a part weighing exactly 5.1300000 grams, for example, we would have to compute the area of a line of width 0. Of course, this would be 0. This result may seem strange, but if we insist on enough decimal places of accuracy, we are bound to find that the weight differs from 5.1300000 grams *exactly*, be the difference ever so slight.

This is important because it means that, for any continuous distribution, the probability does not change if a single point is added to the range of values that is being considered. In Figure 2.5, this means the following probabilities are all exactly the same:

$$P(5.22 < X < 5.26) = P(5.22 < X \leq 5.26) = P(5.22 \leq X < 5.26)$$
$$= P(5.22 \leq X \leq 5.26)$$

The inclusion or exclusion of either endpoint (5.22 or 5.26) has no impact on the probability.

In this section, we have investigated the fundamental characteristics and properties of probability distributions in general. In the next three sections, we introduce three important continuous distributions—the normal distribution, the F distribution, and the exponential distribution—and two discrete distributions—the Poisson distribution and the binomial distribution.

2.7 The Binomial Distribution

Many business experiments can be characterized by the **Bernoulli process**. The probability of obtaining specific outcomes in a Bernoulli process is described by the binomial probability distribution. In order to be a Bernoulli process, an experiment must have the following characteristics:

1. Each trial in a Bernoulli process has only two possible outcomes. These are typically called a success and a failure, although examples might be yes or no, heads or tails, pass or fail, defective or good, and so on.
2. The probability stays the same from one trial to the next.
3. The trials are statistically independent.
4. The number of trials is a positive integer.

A common example of this process is tossing a coin.

The **binomial distribution** is used to find the probability of a specific number of successes out of n trials of a Bernoulli process. To find this probability, it is necessary to know the following:

$$n = \text{the number of trials}$$
$$p = \text{the probability of a success on any single trial}$$

We let

$$r = \text{the number of successes}$$
$$q = 1 - p = \text{the probability of a failure}$$

The binomial formula is

$$\text{Probability of } r \text{ successes in } n \text{ trials} = \frac{n!}{r!(n-r)!} p^r q^{n-r} \qquad (2\text{-}9)$$

The symbol ! means factorial, and $n! = n(n-1)(n-2) \ldots (1)$. For example,

$$4! = (4)(3)(2)(1) = 24$$

Also, $1! = 1$, and $0! = 1$ by definition.

Solving Problems with the Binomial Formula

A common example of a binomial distribution is the tossing of a coin and counting the number of heads. For example, if we wished to find the probability of 4 heads in 5 tosses of a coin, we would have

$$n = 5, r = 4, p = 0.5, \quad \text{and} \quad q = 1 - 0.5 = 0.5$$

Thus,

$$P(4 \text{ successes in 5 trials}) = \frac{5!}{4!(5-4)!} 0.5^4 0.5^{5-4}$$

$$= \frac{5(4)(3)(2)(1)}{4(3)(2)(1)(1!)} (0.0625)(0.5) = 0.15625$$

Thus, the probability of 4 heads in 5 tosses of a coin is 0.15625 or about 16%.

Using Equation 2-9, it is also possible to find the entire probability distribution (all the possible values for r and the corresponding probabilities) for a binomial experiment. The probability distribution for the number of heads in 5 tosses of a fair coin is shown in Table 2.8 and then graphed in Figure 2.6.

TABLE 2.8

Binomial Probability Distribution for $n = 5$ and $p = 0.50$

NUMBER OF HEADS (r)	PROBABILITY $= \frac{5!}{r!(5-r)!}(0.5)^r(0.5)^{5-r}$
0	$0.03125 = \frac{5!}{0!(5-0)!}(0.5)^0(0.5)^{5-0}$
1	$0.15625 = \frac{5!}{1!(5-1)!}(0.5)^1(0.5)^{5-1}$
2	$0.31250 = \frac{5!}{2!(5-2)!}(0.5)^2(0.5)^{5-2}$
3	$0.31250 = \frac{5!}{3!(5-3)!}(0.5)^3(0.5)^{5-3}$
4	$0.15625 = \frac{5!}{4!(5-4)!}(0.5)^4(0.5)^{5-4}$
5	$0.03125 = \frac{5!}{5!(5-5)!}(0.5)^5(0.5)^{5-5}$

FIGURE 2.6

Binomial Probability Distribution for $n = 5$ and $p = 0.50$

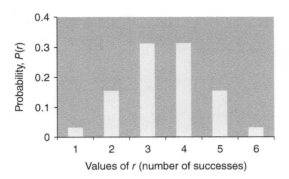

Solving Problems with Binomial Tables

MSA Electronics is experimenting with the manufacture of a new type of transistor that is very difficult to mass produce at an acceptable quality level. Every hour a supervisor takes a random sample of 5 transistors produced on the assembly line. The probability that any one transistor is defective is considered to be 0.15. MSA wants to know the probability of finding 3, 4, or 5 defectives if the true percentage defective is 15%.

For this problem, $n = 5$, $p = 0.15$, and $r = 3, 4$, or 5. Although we could use the formula for each of these values, it is easier to use binomial tables for this. Appendix B gives a binomial table for a broad range of values for n, r, and p. A portion of this appendix is shown in Table 2.9. To find these probabilities, we look through the $n = 5$ section and find the

TABLE 2.9   A Sample Table for the Binomial Distribution

						P					
n	r	0.05	0.10	0.15	0.20	0.25	0.30	0.35	0.40	0.45	0.50
1	0	0.9500	0.9000	0.8500	0.8000	0.7500	0.7000	0.6500	0.6000	0.5500	0.5000
	1	0.0500	0.1000	0.1500	0.2000	0.2500	0.3000	0.3500	0.4000	0.4500	0.5000
2	0	0.9025	0.8100	0.7225	0.6400	0.5625	0.4900	0.4225	0.3600	0.3025	0.2500
	1	0.0950	0.1800	0.2500	0.3200	0.3750	0.4200	0.4550	0.4800	0.4950	0.5000
	2	0.0025	0.0100	0.0225	0.0400	0.0625	0.0900	0.1225	0.1600	0.2025	0.2500
3	0	0.8574	0.7290	0.6141	0.5120	0.4219	0.3430	0.2746	0.2160	0.1664	0.1250
	1	0.1354	0.2430	0.3251	0.3840	0.4219	0.4410	0.4436	0.4320	0.4084	0.3750
	2	0.0071	0.0270	0.0574	0.0960	0.1406	0.1890	0.2389	0.2880	0.3341	0.3750
	3	0.0001	0.0010	0.0034	0.0080	0.0156	0.0270	0.0429	0.0640	0.0911	0.1250
4	0	0.8145	0.6561	0.5220	0.4096	0.3164	0.2401	0.1785	0.1296	0.0915	0.0625
	1	0.1715	0.2916	0.3685	0.4096	0.4219	0.4116	0.3845	0.3456	0.2995	0.2500
	2	0.0135	0.0486	0.0975	0.1536	0.2109	0.2646	0.3105	0.3456	0.3675	0.3750
	3	0.0005	0.0036	0.0115	0.0256	0.0469	0.0756	0.1115	0.1536	0.2005	0.2500
	4	0.0000	0.0001	0.0005	0.0016	0.0039	0.0081	0.0150	0.0256	0.0410	0.0625
5	0	0.7738	0.5905	0.4437	0.3277	0.2373	0.1681	0.1160	0.0778	0.0503	0.0313
	1	0.2036	0.3281	0.3915	0.4096	0.3955	0.3602	0.3124	0.2592	0.2059	0.1563
	2	0.0214	0.0729	0.1382	0.2048	0.2637	0.3087	0.3364	0.3456	0.3369	0.3125
	3	0.0011	0.0081	0.0244	0.0512	0.0879	0.1323	0.1811	0.2304	0.2757	0.3125
	4	0.0000	0.0005	0.0022	0.0064	0.0146	0.0284	0.0488	0.0768	0.1128	0.1563
	5	0.0000	0.0000	0.0001	0.0003	0.0010	0.0024	0.0053	0.0102	0.0185	0.0313
6	0	0.7351	0.5314	0.3771	0.2621	0.1780	0.1176	0.0754	0.0467	0.0277	0.0156
	1	0.2321	0.3543	0.3993	0.3932	0.3560	0.3025	0.2437	0.1866	0.1359	0.0938
	2	0.0305	0.0984	0.1762	0.2458	0.2966	0.3241	0.3280	0.3110	0.2780	0.2344
	3	0.0021	0.0146	0.0415	0.0819	0.1318	0.1852	0.2355	0.2765	0.3032	0.3125
	4	0.0001	0.0012	0.0055	0.0154	0.0330	0.0595	0.0951	0.1382	0.1861	0.2344
	5	0.0000	0.0001	0.0004	0.0015	0.0044	0.0102	0.0205	0.0369	0.0609	0.0938
	6	0.0000	0.0000	0.0000	0.0001	0.0002	0.0007	0.0018	0.0041	0.0083	0.0156

PROGRAM 2.2A

Excel Output for the Binomial Example

Using the cell references eliminates the need to retype the formula if you change a parameter such as p or r.

1	The Binomial Distribution		
2	X = random variable for number of successes		
3	n =	5	number of trials
4	p =	0.5	probability of a success
5	r =	4	specific number of successes
6			
7	Cumulative probability	$P(X \le r) = 0.9688$	
8	Probability of exactly r successes	$P(X = r) = 0.1563$	

PROGRAM 2.2B

Function in an Excel 2013 Spreadsheet for Binomial Probabilities

The function BINOM.DIST (r,n,p,TRUE) returns the cumulative probability.

	C
7	=BINOMDIST(B5,B3,B4,TRUE)
8	=BINOMDIST(B5,B3,B4,FALSE)

$p = 0.15$ column. In the row where $r = 3$, we see 0.0244. Thus, $P(r = 3) = 0.0244$. Similarly, $P(r = 4) = 0.0022$, and $P(r = 5) = 0.0001$. By adding these three probabilities, we have the probability that the number of defects is 3 or more:

$$P(3 \text{ or more defects}) = P(3) + P(4) + P(5)$$
$$= 0.0244 + 0.0022 + 0.0001 = 0.0267$$

The expected value (or mean) and the variance of a binomial random variable may be easily found. These are

$$\text{Expected value (mean)} = np \tag{2-10}$$

$$\text{Variance} = np(1 - p) \tag{2-11}$$

The expected value and variance for the MSA Electronics example are computed as follows:

$$\text{Expected value} = np = 5(0.15) = 0.75$$
$$\text{Variance} = np(1 - p) = 5(0.15)(0.85) = 0.6375$$

Programs 2.2A and 2.2B illustrate how Excel is used for binomial probabilities.

2.8 The Normal Distribution

The normal distribution affects a large number of processes in our lives (e.g., filling boxes of cereal with 32 ounces of corn flakes). Each normal distribution depends on the mean and standard deviation.

One of the most popular and useful continuous probability distributions is the **normal distribution**. The probability density function of this distribution is given by the rather complex formula

$$f(X) = \frac{1}{\sigma\sqrt{2\pi}} e^{\frac{-(x-\mu)^2}{2\sigma^2}} \tag{2-12}$$

The normal distribution is specified completely when values for the mean, μ, and the standard deviation, σ, are known. Figure 2.7 shows several different normal distributions with the same standard deviation and different means. As shown, differing values of μ will shift the average or center of the normal distribution. The overall shape of the distribution remains the same. On the other hand, when the standard deviation is varied, the normal curve either flattens out or becomes steeper. This is shown in Figure 2.8.

As the standard deviation, σ, becomes smaller, the normal distribution becomes steeper. When the standard deviation becomes larger, the normal distribution has a tendency to flatten out or become broader.

FIGURE 2.7

Normal Distribution with Different Values for μ

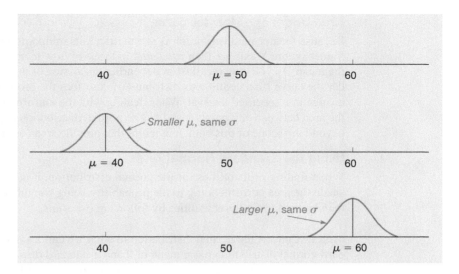

FIGURE 2.8

Normal Distribution with Different Values for σ

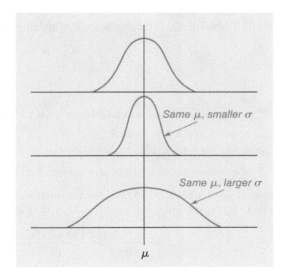

IN ACTION   **Probability Assessments of Curling Champions**

Probabilities are used every day in sporting activities. In many sporting events, there are questions involving strategies that must be answered to provide the best chance of winning the game. In baseball, should a particular batter be intentionally walked in key situations at the end of the game? In football, should a team elect to try for a two-point conversion after a touchdown? In soccer, should a penalty kick ever be aimed directly at the goal keeper? In curling, in the last round, or "end" of a game, is it better to be behind by one point and have the hammer or is it better to be ahead by one point and not have the hammer? An attempt was made to answer this last question.

In curling, a granite stone, or "rock," is slid across a sheet of ice 14 feet wide and 146 feet long. Four players on each of two teams take alternating turns sliding the rock, trying to get it as close as possible to the center of a circle called the "house." The team with the rock closest to this scores points. The team that is behind at the completion of a round or end has the advantage in

the next end by being the last team to slide the rock. This team is said to "have the hammer." A survey was taken of a group of experts in curling, including a number of former world champions. In this survey, about 58% of the respondents favored having the hammer and being down by one going into the last end. Only about 42% preferred being ahead and not having the hammer.

Data were also collected from 1985 to 1997 at the Canadian Men's Curling Championships (also called the Brier). Based on the results over this time period, it is better to be ahead by one point and not have the hammer at the end of the ninth end rather than be behind by one and have the hammer, as many people prefer. This differed from the survey results. Apparently, world champions and other experts preferred to have more control of their destiny by having the hammer even though it put them in a worse situation.

Source: Based on Keith A. Willoughby and Kent J. Kostuk. "Preferred Scenarios in the Sport of Curling," *Interfaces* 34, 2 (March–April 2004): 117–122.

Area Under the Normal Curve

Because the normal distribution is symmetrical, its midpoint (and highest point) is at the mean. Values on the X axis are then measured in terms of how many standard deviations they lie from the mean. As you may recall from our earlier discussion of probability distributions, the area under the curve (in a continuous distribution) describes the probability that a random variable has a value in a specified interval. When dealing with the uniform distribution, it is easy to compute the area between any points a and b. The normal distribution requires mathematical calculations beyond the scope of this book, but tables that provide areas or probabilities are readily available.

Using the Standard Normal Table

When finding probabilities for the normal distribution, it is best to draw the normal curve and shade the area corresponding to the probability being sought. The normal distribution table can then be used to find probabilities by following two steps.

Step 1. Convert the normal distribution to what we call a *standard normal distribution*. A standard normal distribution has a mean of 0 and a standard deviation of 1. All normal tables are set up to handle random variables with $\mu = 0$ and $\sigma = 1$. Without a standard normal distribution, a different table would be needed for each pair of μ and σ values. We call the new standard random variable Z. The value for Z for any normal distribution is computed from this equation:

$$Z = \frac{X - \mu}{\sigma} \tag{2-13}$$

where

X = value of the random variable we want to measure

μ = mean of the distribution

σ = standard deviation of the distribution

Z = number of standard deviations from X to the mean, μ

For example, if $\mu = 100$, $\sigma = 15$, and we are interested in finding the probability that the random variable X (IQ) is less than 130, we want $P(X < 130)$:

$$Z = \frac{X - \mu}{\sigma} = \frac{130 - 100}{15}$$

$$= \frac{30}{15} = 2 \text{ standard deviations}$$

This means that the point X is 2.0 standard deviations to the right of the mean. This is shown in Figure 2.9.

FIGURE 2.9

Normal Distribution Showing the Relationship Between Z Values and X Values

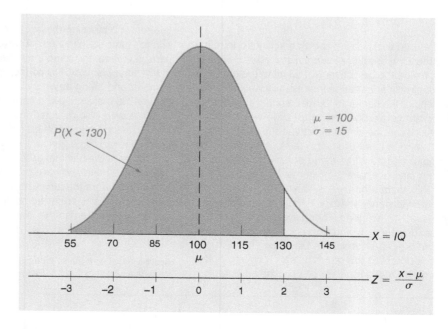

Step 2. Look up the probability from a table of normal curve areas. Table 2.10, which also appears as Appendix A, is such a table of areas for the standard normal distribution. It is set up to provide the area under the curve to the left of any specified value of Z.

Let's see how Table 2.10 can be used. The column on the left lists values of Z, with the second decimal place of Z appearing in the top row. For example, for a value of $Z = 2.00$ as just computed, find 2.0 in the left-hand column and 0.00 in the top row. In the body of the table, we find that the area sought is 0.97725, or 97.7%. Thus,

$$P(X < 130) = P(Z < 2.00) = 97.7\%$$

This suggests that if the mean IQ score is 100, with a standard deviation of 15 points, the probability that a randomly selected person's IQ is less than 130 is 97.7%. This is also the probability that the IQ is less than or equal to 130. To find the probability that the IQ is greater than 130, we simply note that this is the complement of the previous event and the total area under the curve (the total probability) is 1. Thus,

$$P(X > 130) = 1 - P(X \le 130) = 1 - P(Z \le 2) = 1 - 0.97725 = 0.02275$$

To be sure you understand the concept of symmetry in Table 2.10, try to find the probability such as $P(X < 85)$. Note that the standard normal table shows only positive Z values.

While Table 2.10 does not give negative Z values, the symmetry of the normal distribution can be used to find probabilities associated with negative Z values. For example, $P(Z < -2) = P(Z > 2)$.

To feel comfortable with the use of the standard normal probability table, we need to work a few more examples. We now use the Haynes Construction Company as a case in point.

Haynes Construction Company Example

Haynes Construction Company builds primarily three- and four-unit apartment buildings (called triplexes and quadraplexes) for investors, and it is believed that the total construction time in days follows a normal distribution. The mean time to construct a triplex is 100 days, and the standard deviation is 20 days. Recently, the president of Haynes Construction signed a contract to complete a triplex in 125 days. Failure to complete the triplex in 125 days would result in severe penalty fees. What is the probability that Haynes Construction will not be in violation of their construction contract? The normal distribution for the construction of triplexes is shown in Figure 2.10.

To compute this probability, we need to find the shaded area under the curve. We begin by computing Z for this problem:

$$Z = \frac{X - \mu}{\sigma}$$

$$= \frac{125 - 100}{20}$$

$$= \frac{25}{20} = 1.25$$

Looking in Table 2.10 for a Z value of 1.25, we find an area under the curve of 0.89435. (We do this by looking up 1.2 in the left-hand column of the table and then moving to the 0.05 column to find the value for $Z = 1.25$.) Therefore, the probability of not violating the contract is 0.89435, or about an 89% chance.

FIGURE 2.10

Normal Distribution for Haynes Construction

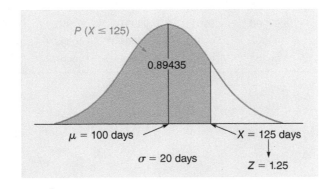

$P(X \le 125)$

0.89435

$\mu = 100$ days

$X = 125$ days

$\sigma = 20$ days

$Z = 1.25$

TABLE 2.10 Standardized Normal Distribution Function

Z	0.00	0.01	0.02	0.03	0.04	0.05	0.06	0.07	0.08	0.09
				AREA UNDER THE NORMAL CURVE						
0.0	.50000	.50399	.50798	.51197	.51595	.51994	.52392	.52790	.53188	.53586
0.1	.53983	.54380	.54776	.55172	.55567	.55962	.56356	.56749	.57142	.57535
0.2	.57926	.58317	.58706	.59095	.59483	.59871	.60257	.60642	.61026	.61409
0.3	.61791	.62172	.62552	.62930	.63307	.63683	.64058	.64431	.64803	.65173
0.4	.65542	.65910	.66276	.66640	.67003	.67364	.67724	.68082	.68439	.68793
0.5	.69146	.69497	.69847	.70194	.70540	.70884	.71226	.71566	.71904	.72240
0.6	.72575	.72907	.73237	.73565	.73891	.74215	.74537	.74857	.75175	.75490
0.7	.75804	.76115	.76424	.76730	.77035	.77337	.77637	.77935	.78230	.78524
0.8	.78814	.79103	.79389	.79673	.79955	.80234	.80511	.80785	.81057	.81327
0.9	.81594	.81859	.82121	.82381	.82639	.82894	.83147	.83398	.83646	.83891
1.0	.84134	.84375	.84614	.84849	.85083	.85314	.85543	.85769	.85993	.86214
1.1	.86433	.86650	.86864	.87076	.87286	.87493	.87698	.87900	.88100	.88298
1.2	.88493	.88686	.88877	.89065	.89251	.89435	.89617	.89796	.89973	.90147
1.3	.90320	.90490	.90658	.90824	.90988	.91149	.91309	.91466	.91621	.91774
1.4	.91924	.92073	.92220	.92364	.92507	.92647	.92785	.92922	.93056	.93189
1.5	.93319	.93448	.93574	.93699	.93822	.93943	.94062	.94179	.94295	.94408
1.6	.94520	.94630	.94738	.94845	.94950	.95053	.95154	.95254	.95352	.95449
1.7	.95543	.95637	.95728	.95818	.95907	.95994	.96080	.96164	.96246	.96327
1.8	.96407	.96485	.96562	.96638	.96712	.96784	.96856	.96926	.96995	.97062
1.9	.97128	.97193	.97257	.97320	.97381	.97441	.97500	.97558	.97615	.97670
2.0	.97725	.97778	.97831	.97882	.97932	.97982	.98030	.98077	.98124	.98169
2.1	.98214	.98257	.98300	.98341	.98382	.98422	.98461	.98500	.98537	.98574
2.2	.98610	.98645	.98679	.98713	.98745	.98778	.98809	.98840	.98870	.98899
2.3	.98928	.98956	.98983	.99010	.99036	.99061	.99086	.99111	.99134	.99158
2.4	.99180	.99202	.99224	.99245	.99266	.99286	.99305	.99324	.99343	.99361
2.5	.99379	.99396	.99413	.99430	.99446	.99461	.99477	.99492	.99506	.99520
2.6	.99534	.99547	.99560	.99573	.99585	.99598	.99609	.99621	.99632	.99643
2.7	.99653	.99664	.99674	.99683	.99693	.99702	.99711	.99720	.99728	.99736
2.8	.99744	.99752	.99760	.99767	.99774	.99781	.99788	.99795	.99801	.99807
2.9	.99813	.99819	.99825	.99831	.99836	.99841	.99846	.99851	.99856	.99861
3.0	.99865	.99869	.99874	.99878	.99882	.99886	.99889	.99893	.99896	.99900
3.1	.99903	.99906	.99910	.99913	.99916	.99918	.99921	.99924	.99926	.99929
3.2	.99931	.99934	.99936	.99938	.99940	.99942	.99944	.99946	.99948	.99950
3.3	.99952	.99953	.99955	.99957	.99958	.99960	.99961	.99962	.99964	.99965
3.4	.99966	.99968	.99969	.99970	.99971	.99972	.99973	.99974	.99975	.99976
3.5	.99977	.99978	.99978	.99979	.99980	.99981	.99981	.99982	.99983	.99983
3.6	.99984	.99985	.99985	.99986	.99986	.99987	.99987	.99988	.99988	.99989
3.7	.99989	.99990	.99990	.99990	.99991	.99991	.99992	.99992	.99992	.99992
3.8	.99993	.99993	.99993	.99994	.99994	.99994	.99994	.99995	.99995	.99995
3.9	.99995	.99995	.99996	.99996	.99996	.99996	.99996	.99996	.99997	.99997

FIGURE 2.11

Probability That Haynes Will Receive the Bonus by Finishing in 75 Days or Less

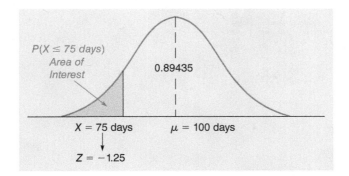

Now let us look at the Haynes problem from another perspective. If the firm finishes this triplex in 75 days or less, it will be awarded a bonus payment of $5,000. What is the probability that Haynes will receive the bonus?

Figure 2.11 illustrates the probability we are looking for in the shaded area. The first step is again to compute the Z value:

$$Z = \frac{X - \mu}{\sigma}$$

$$= \frac{75 - 100}{20}$$

$$= \frac{-25}{20} = -1.25$$

This Z value indicates that 75 days is -1.25 standard deviations to the left of the mean. But the standard normal table is structured to handle only positive Z values. To solve this problem, we observe that the curve is symmetric. The probability that Haynes will finish in *75 days or less is equivalent* to the probability that it will finish in *more than 125 days*. A moment ago (in Figure 2.10) we found the probability that Haynes will finish in less than 125 days. That value is 0.89435. So the probability it takes more than 125 days is

$$P(X > 125) = 1.0 - P(X \leq 125)$$
$$= 1.0 - 0.89435 = 0.10565$$

Thus, the probability of completing the triplex in 75 days or less is 0.10565, or about 11%.

One final example: What is the probability that the triplex will take between 110 and 125 days? We see in Figure 2.12 that

$$P(110 < X < 125) = P(X \leq 125) - P(X < 110)$$

That is, the shaded area in the graph can be computed by finding the probability of completing the building in 125 days or less *minus* the probability of completing it in 110 days or less.

FIGURE 2.12

Probability That Haynes Will Complete in 110 to 125 Days

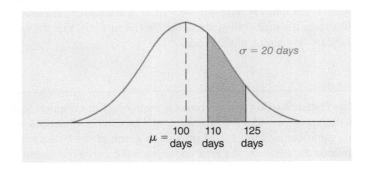

PROGRAM 2.3A

Excel 2013 Output for the Normal Distribution Example

	A	B
1	X is a normal random variable	
2	with mean, μ, and standard deviation, σ	
3	μ =	100
4	σ =	20
5	x =	75
6	P(X ≤ x) =	0.10565
7	P(X > x) =	0.89435

PROGRAM 2.3B

Function in an Excel 2013 Spreadsheet for the Normal Distribution Example

	B
6	=NORMDIST(B5,B3,B4,TRUE)
7	=1-B6

Recall that $P(X \leq 125 \text{ days})$ is equal to 0.89435. To find $P(X < 110 \text{ days})$, we follow the two steps developed earlier:

1.
$$Z = \frac{X - \mu}{\sigma} = \frac{110 - 100}{20} = \frac{10}{20}$$
$$= 0.5 \text{ standard deviations}$$

2. From Table 2.10, the area for $Z = 0.50$ is 0.69146. So the probability the triplex can be completed in less than 110 days is 0.69146. Finally,

$$P(110 \leq X \leq 125) = 0.89435 - 0.69146 = 0.20289$$

The probability that it will take between 110 and 125 days is about 20%. Programs 2.3A and 2.3B show how Excel can be used for this.

The Empirical Rule

While the probability tables for the normal distribution can provide precise probabilities, many situations require less precision. The empirical rule was derived from the normal distribution and is an easy way to remember some basic information about normal distributions. The empirical rule states that for a normal distribution

approximately 68% of the values will be within ± 1 standard deviation of the mean

approximately 95% of the values will be within ± 2 standard deviations of the mean

almost all (about 99.7%) of the values will be within ± 3 standard deviations of the mean

Figure 2.13 illustrates the empirical rule. The area from point a to point b in the first drawing represents the probability, approximately 68%, that the random variable will be within ± 1 standard deviation of the mean. The middle drawing illustrates the probability, approximately 95%, that the random variable will be within ± 2 standard deviations of the mean. The last drawing illustrates the probability, about 99.7% (almost all), that the random variable will be within ± 3 standard deviations of the mean.

2.9   The *F* Distribution

The **F distribution** is a continuous probability distribution that is helpful in testing hypotheses about variances. The *F* distribution will be used in Chapter 4 when regression models are tested for significance. Figure 2.14 provides a graph of the *F* distribution. As with a graph for any continuous distribution, the area underneath the curve represents probability. Note that for a large value of *F*, the probability is very small.

The *F* statistic is the ratio of two sample variances from independent normal distributions. Every *F* distribution has two sets of degrees of freedom associated with it. One of the degrees of freedom is associated with the numerator of the ratio, and the other is associated with the denominator of the ratio. The degrees of freedom are based on the sample sizes used in calculating the numerator and denominator.

FIGURE 2.13

Approximate Probabilities from the Empirical Rule

Figure 2.13 is very important, and you should comprehend the meanings of ±1, 2, and 3 standard deviation symmetrical areas.

Managers often speak of 95% and 99% confidence intervals, which roughly refer to ±2 and 3 standard deviation graphs.

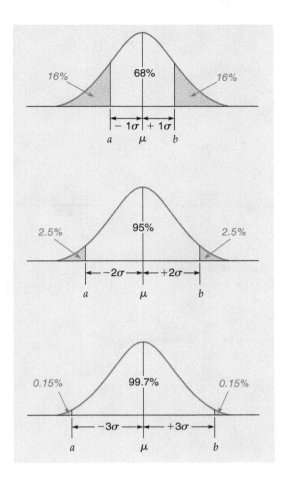

Appendix D provides values of F associated with the upper tail of the distribution for certain probabilities (denoted by α) and degrees of freedom for the numerator (df_1) and degrees of freedom for the denominator (df_2).

To find the F value that is associated with a particular probability and degrees of freedom, refer to Appendix D. The following notation will be used:

$$df_1 = \text{degrees of freedom for the numerator}$$
$$df_2 = \text{degrees of freedom for the denominator}$$

Consider the following example:

$$df_1 = 5$$
$$df_2 = 6$$
$$\alpha = 0.05$$

FIGURE 2.14

The F Distribution

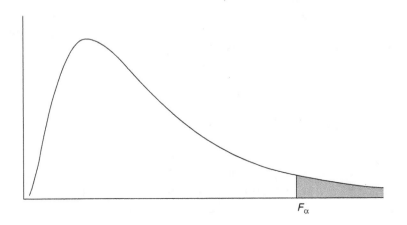

FIGURE 2.15

F Value for 0.05
Probability with 5 and
6 Degrees of Freedom

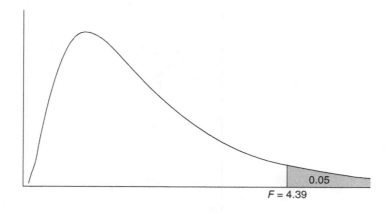

$F = 4.39$

PROGRAM 2.4A

Excel 2013 Output for
the *F* Distribution

	A	B	C	D
1	F Distribution with df1 and df2 degrees of freedom			
2	To find F given α			
3	df1 =	5		
4	df2 =	6		
5	α =	0.05		
6	F-value =	4.39		
7				
8	To find the probability to the right of a calculated value, *f*			
9	df1 =	5		
10	df2 =	6		
11	*f* =	4.2		
12	P(F > f) =	0.0548		

PROGRAM 2.4B

Functions in an Excel
2013 Spreadsheet for
the *F* Distribution

	B
6	=FINV(B5,B3,B4)
12	=FDIST(B11,B9,B10)

From Appendix D, we get

$$F_{\alpha, df1, df2} = F_{0.05, 5, 6} = 4.39$$

This means

$$P(F > 4.39) = 0.05$$

The probability is very low (only 5%) that the *F* value will exceed 4.39. There is a 95% probability that it will not exceed 4.39. This is illustrated in Figure 2.15. Appendix D also provides *F* values associated with $\alpha = 0.01$. Programs 2.4A and 2.4B illustrate Excel functions for the *F* distribution.

2.10   The Exponential Distribution

The *exponential distribution*, also called the **negative exponential distribution**, is used in dealing with queuing problems. The exponential distribution often describes the time required to service a customer. The exponential distribution is a continuous distribution. Its probability function is given by

$$f(X) = \mu e^{-\mu x} \tag{2-14}$$

where

$X =$ random variable (service times)

$\mu =$ average number of units the service facility can handle in a specific period of time

$e = 2.718$ (the base of the natural logarithm)

FIGURE 2.16
Exponential Distribution

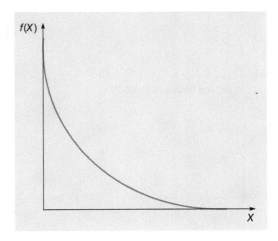

The general shape of the exponential distribution is shown in Figure 2.16. Its expected value and variance can be shown to be

$$\text{Expected value} = \frac{1}{\mu} = \text{Average service time} \qquad (2\text{-}15)$$

$$\text{Variance} = \frac{1}{\mu^2} \qquad (2\text{-}16)$$

As with any other continuous distribution, probabilities are found by determining the area under the curve. For the normal distribution, we found the area by using a table of probabilities. For the exponential distribution, the probabilities can be found using the exponent key on a calculator with the formula below. The probability that an exponentially distributed time (X) required to serve a customer is less than or equal to time t is given by the formula

$$P(X \le t) = 1 - e^{-\mu t} \qquad (2\text{-}17)$$

The time period used in describing μ determines the units for the time t. For example, if μ is the average number served per hour, the time t must be given in hours. If μ is the average number served per minute, the time t must be given in minutes.

Arnold's Muffler Example

Arnold's Muffler Shop installs new mufflers on automobiles and small trucks. The mechanic can install new mufflers at a rate of about three per hour, and this service time is exponentially distributed. What is the probability that the time to install a new muffler would be $\frac{1}{2}$ hour or less? Using Equation 2-17, we have

$$X = \text{exponentially distributed service time}$$
$$\mu = \text{average number that can be served per time period} = 3 \text{ per hour}$$
$$t = \frac{1}{2} \text{ hour} = 0.5 \text{ hour}$$
$$P(X \le 0.5) = 1 - e^{-3(0.5)} = 1 - e^{-1.5} = 1 - 0.2231 = 0.7769$$

Figure 2.17 shows the area under the curve from 0 to 0.5 to be 0.7769. Thus, there is about a 78% chance the time will be no more than 0.5 hour and about a 22% chance that the time will be longer than this. Similarly, we could find the probability that the service time is no more $\frac{1}{3}$ hour or $\frac{2}{3}$ hour, as follows:

$$P\left(X \le \frac{1}{3}\right) = 1 - e^{-3\left(\frac{1}{3}\right)} = 1 - e^{-1} = 1 - 0.3679 = 0.6321$$

$$P\left(X \le \frac{2}{3}\right) = 1 - e^{-3\left(\frac{2}{3}\right)} = 1 - e^{-2} = 1 - 0.1353 = 0.8647$$

FIGURE 2.17

Probability That the Mechanic Will Install a Muffler in 0.5 Hour

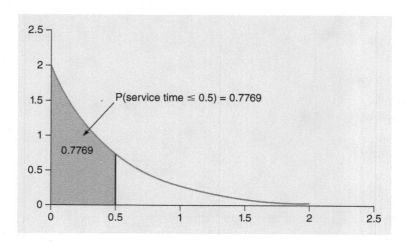

PROGRAM 2.5A

Excel 2013 Output for the Exponential Distribution

	A	B	C
1	Exponential distribution - the random variable (X) is time		
2	Average number per time period = μ =	3	per hour
3	t =	0.5000	hours
4	P(X ≤ t) =	0.7769	
5	P(X > t) =	0.2231	

Program 2.5B

Function in an Excel 2013 Spreadsheet for the Exponential Distribution

	B
4	=EXPONDIST(B3,B2,TRUE)
5	=1-B4

While Equation 2-17 provides the probability that the time (X) is less than or equal to a particular value t, the probability that the time is greater than a particular value t is found by observing that these two events are complementary. For example, to find the probability that the mechanic at Arnold's Muffler Shop would take longer than 0.5 hour, we have

$$P(X > 0.5) = 1 - P(X \le 0.5) = 1 - 0.7769 = 0.2231$$

Programs 2.5A and 2.5B illustrate how a function in Excel can find exponential probabilities.

2.11   The Poisson Distribution

An important **discrete probability distribution** is the **Poisson distribution**.[1] We examine it because of its key role in complementing the exponential distribution in queuing theory in Chapter 12. The distribution describes situations in which customers arrive independently during a certain time interval, and the number of arrivals depends on the length of the time interval. Examples are patients arriving at a health clinic, customers arriving at a bank window, passengers arriving at an airport, and telephone calls going through a central exchange.

The Poisson probability distribution is used in many queuing models to represent arrival patterns.

The formula for the Poisson distribution is

$$P(X) = \frac{\lambda^x e^{-\lambda}}{X!} \tag{2-18}$$

---

[1]This distribution, derived by Siméon Denis Poisson in 1837, is pronounced "pwah-sahn."

where

$P(X)$ = probability of exactly X arrivals or occurrences

λ = average number of arrivals per unit of time (the mean arrival rate), pronounced "lambda"

e = 2.718, the base of the natural logarithm

X = number of occurrences $(0, 1, 2, \ldots)$

The mean and variance of the Poisson distribution are equal and are computed simply as

$$\text{Expected value} = \lambda \qquad \text{(2-19)}$$

$$\text{Variance} = \lambda \qquad \text{(2-20)}$$

With the help of the table in Appendix C, the values of $e^{-\lambda}$ are easy to find. We can use these in the formula to find probabilities. For example, if $\lambda = 2$, from Appendix C we find $e^{-2} = 0.1353$. The Poisson probabilities that X is 0, 1, and 2 when $\lambda = 2$ are as follows:

$$P(X) = \frac{e^{-\lambda}\lambda^x}{X!}$$

$$P(0) = \frac{e^{-2}2^0}{0!} = \frac{(0.1353)1}{1} = 0.1353 \approx 14\%$$

$$P(1) = \frac{e^{-2}2^1}{1!} = \frac{e^{-2}2}{1} = \frac{0.1353(2)}{1} = 0.2706 \approx 27\%$$

$$P(2) = \frac{e^{-2}2^2}{2!} = \frac{e^{-2}4}{2(1)} = \frac{0.1353(4)}{2} = 0.2706 \approx 27\%$$

These probabilities, as well as others for $\lambda = 2$ and $\lambda = 4$, are shown in Figure 2.18. Notice that the chances that 9 or more customers will arrive in a particular time period are virtually nil. Programs 2.6A and 2.6B illustrate how Excel can be used to find Poisson probabilities.

It should be noted that the exponential and Poisson distributions are related. If the number of occurrences per time period follows a Poisson distribution, then the time between occurrences follows an exponential distribution. For example, if the number of phone calls arriving at a customer service center followed a Poisson distribution with a mean of 10 calls per hour, the time between each phone call would be exponentially distributed with a mean time between calls of $^1/_{10}$ hour (6 minutes).

FIGURE 2.18
Sample Poisson Distributions with $\lambda = 2$ and $\lambda = 4$

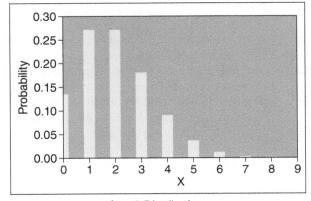

$\lambda = 2$ Distribution

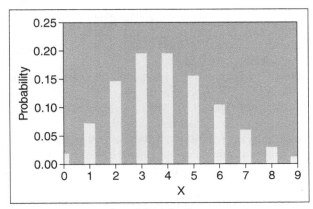

$\lambda = 4$ Distribution

PROGRAM 2.6A

Excel 2013 Output for the Poisson Distribution

	A	B	C	D	E	F	G	H
1	Poisson distribution - the random variable is the number of occurrences per time period							
2		$\lambda =$	2					
3	x		P(X)	P(X ≤ x)				
4	0		0.1353	0.1353				
5	1		0.2707	0.4060				
6	2		0.7293	0.6767				

PROGRAM 2.6B

Functions in an Excel 2013 Spreadsheet for the Poisson Distribution

	B	C
4	=POISSON(A4,$B$2,FALSE)	=POISSON(A4,$B$2,TRUE)
5	=POISSON(A5,$B$2,FALSE)	=POISSON(A5,$B$2,TRUE)
6	=1-B5	=POISSON(A6,$B$2,TRUE)

Summary

This chapter presents the fundamental concepts of probability and probability distributions. Probability values can be obtained objectively or subjectively. A single probability value must be between 0 and 1, and the sum of all probability values for all possible outcomes must be equal to 1. In addition, probability values and events can have a number of properties. These properties include mutually exclusive, collectively exhaustive, statistically independent, and statistically dependent events. Rules for computing probability values depend on these fundamental properties. It is also possible to revise probability values when new information becomes available. This can be done using Bayes' theorem.

We also covered the topics of random variables, discrete probability distributions (such as Poisson and binomial), and continuous probability distributions (such as normal, F, and exponential). A probability distribution is any statement of a probability function having a set of collectively exhaustive and mutually exclusive events. All probability distributions follow the basic probability rules mentioned previously.

The topics presented here will be very important in many of the chapters to come. Basic probability concepts and distributions are used for decision theory, inventory control, Markov analysis, project management, simulation, and statistical quality control.

Glossary

Bayes' Theorem   A formula that is used to revise probabilities based on new information.

Bernoulli Process   A process with two outcomes in each of a series of independent trials in which the probabilities of the outcomes do not change.

Binomial Distribution   A discrete distribution that describes the number of successes in independent trials of a Bernoulli process.

Classical or **Logical Method**   An objective way of assessing probabilities based on logic.

Collectively Exhaustive Events   A collection of all possible outcomes of an experiment.

Conditional Probability   The probability of one event occurring given that another has taken place.

Continuous Probability Distribution   A probability distribution with a continuous random variable.

Continuous Random Variable   A random variable that can assume an infinite or unlimited set of values.

Discrete Probability Distribution   A probability distribution with a discrete random variable.

Discrete Random Variable   A random variable that can only assume a finite or limited set of values.

Expected Value   The (weighted) average of a probability distribution.

F Distribution   A continuous probability distribution that is the ratio of the variances of samples from two independent normal distributions.

Independent Events   The situation in which the occurrence of one event has no effect on the probability of occurrence of a second event.

Intersection   The set of all outcomes that are common to both events.

Joint Probability   The probability of events occurring together (or one after the other).

Mutually Exclusive Events   A situation in which only one event can occur on any given trial or experiment.

Negative Exponential Distribution   A continuous probability distribution that describes the time between customer arrivals in a queuing situation.

Normal Distribution   A continuous bell-shaped distribution that is a function of two parameters, the mean and standard deviation of the distribution.

Objective Approach   A method of determining probability values based on historical data or logic.

Poisson Distribution   A discrete probability distribution used in queuing theory.

Prior Probability   A probability value determined before new or additional information is obtained. It is sometimes called an a priori probability estimate.

Probability A statement about the likelihood of an event occurring. It is expressed as a numerical value between 0 and 1, inclusive.

Probability Density Function The mathematical function that describes a continuous probability distribution. It is represented by $f(X)$.

Probability Distribution The set of all possible values of a random variable and their associated probabilities.

Random Variable A variable that assigns a number to every possible outcome of an experiment.

Relative Frequency Approach An objective way of determining probabilities based on observing frequencies over a number of trials.

Revised or **Posterior Probability** A probability value that results from new or revised information and prior probabilities.

Standard Deviation The square root of the variance.

Subjective Approach A method of determining probability values based on experience or judgment.

Union The set of all outcomes that are contained in either of these two events.

Variance A measure of dispersion or spread of the probability distribution.

Key Equations

(2-1) $0 \le P(\text{event}) \le 1$

A basic statement of probability.

(2-2) $P(A \text{ or } B) = P(A) + P(B) - P(A \text{ and } B)$

Probability of the union of two events.

(2-3) $P(A|B) = \dfrac{P(AB)}{P(B)}$

Conditional probability.

(2-4) $P(AB) = P(A|B)P(B)$

Probability of the intersection of two events.

(2-5) $P(A|B) = \dfrac{P(B|A)P(A)}{P(B|A)P(A) + P(B|A')P(A')}$

Bayes' theorem in general form.

(2-6) $E(X) = \sum\limits_{i=1}^{n} X_i P(X_i)$

An equation that computes the expected value (mean) of a discrete probability distribution.

(2-7) $\sigma^2 = \text{Variance} = \sum\limits_{i=1}^{n} [X_i - E(X)]^2 P(X_i)$

An equation that computes the variance of a discrete probability distribution.

(2-8) $\sigma = \sqrt{\text{Variance}} = \sqrt{\sigma^2}$

An equation that computes the standard deviation from the variance.

(2-9)   Probability of r successes in n trials $= \dfrac{n!}{r!(n-r)!} p^r q^{n-r}$

A formula that computes probabilities for the binomial probability distribution.

(2-10) Expected value (mean) $= np$

The expected value of the binomial distribution.

(2-11) Variance $= np(1 - p)$

The variance of the binomial distribution.

(2-12) $f(X) = \dfrac{1}{\sigma\sqrt{2\pi}} e^{\frac{-(x-\mu)^2}{2\sigma^2}}$

The density function for the normal probability distribution.

(2-13) $Z = \dfrac{X - \mu}{\sigma}$

An equation that computes the number of standard deviations, Z, the point X is from the mean μ.

(2-14) $f(X) = \mu e^{-\mu x}$

The exponential distribution.

(2-15) Expected value $= \dfrac{1}{\mu}$

The expected value of an exponential distribution.

(2-16) Variance $= \dfrac{1}{\mu^2}$

The variance of an exponential distribution.

(2-17) $P(X \le t) = 1 - e^{-\mu t}$

Formula to find the probability that an exponential random variable (X) is less than or equal to time t.

(2-18) $P(X) = \dfrac{\lambda^x e^{-\lambda}}{X!}$

The Poisson distribution.

(2-19) Expected value $= \lambda$

The mean of a Poisson distribution.

(2-20) Variance $= \lambda$

The variance of a Poisson distribution.

Solved Problems

Solved Problem 2-1

In the past 30 days, Roger's Rural Roundup has sold 8, 9, 10, or 11 lottery tickets. It never sold fewer than 8 or more than 11. Assuming that the past is similar to the future, find the probabilities for the number of tickets sold if sales were 8 tickets on 10 days, 9 tickets on 12 days, 10 tickets on 6 days, and 11 tickets on 2 days.

Solution

SALES	NO. DAYS	PROBABILITY
8	10	0.333
9	12	0.400
10	6	0.200
11	2	0.067
Total	30	1.000

Solved Problem 2-2

A class contains 30 students. Ten are female (F) and U.S. citizens (U); 12 are male (M) and U.S. citizens; 6 are female and non-U.S. citizens (N); 2 are male and non-U.S. citizens.

A name is randomly selected from the class roster and it is female. What is the probability that the student is a U.S. citizen?

Solution

$$P(FU) = {}^{10}\!/_{30} = 0.333$$
$$P(FN) = {}^{6}\!/_{30} = 0.200$$
$$P(MU) = {}^{12}\!/_{30} = 0.400$$
$$P(MN) = {}^{2}\!/_{30} = 0.067$$
$$P(F) = P(FU) + P(FN) = 0.333 + 0.200 = 0.533$$
$$P(M) = P(MU) + P(MN) = 0.400 + 0.067 = 0.467$$
$$P(U) = P(FU) + P(MU) = 0.333 + 0.400 = 0.733$$
$$P(N) = P(FN) + P(MN) = 0.200 + 0.067 = 0.267$$
$$P(U|F) = \frac{P(FU)}{P(F)} = \frac{0.333}{0.533} = 0.625$$

Solved Problem 2-3

Your professor tells you that if you score an 85 or better on your midterm exam, then you have a 90% chance of getting an A for the course. You think you have only a 50% chance of scoring 85 or better. Find the probability that *both* your score is 85 or better *and* you receive an A in the course.

Solution

$$P(A \text{ and } 85) = P(A|85) \times P(85) = (0.90)(0.50)$$
$$= 45\%$$

Solved Problem 2-4

A statistics class was asked if it believed that all tests on the Monday following the football game win over their archrival should be postponed automatically. The results were as follows:

Strongly agree	40
Agree	30
Neutral	20
Disagree	10
Strongly disagree	0
	100

Transform this into a numeric score, using the following random variable scale, and find a probability distribution for the results:

Strongly agree	5
Agree	4
Neutral	3
Disagree	2
Strongly disagree	1

Solution

OUTCOME	PROBABILITY, $P(X)$
Strongly agree (5)	$0.4 = 40/100$
Agree (4)	$0.3 = 30/100$
Neutral (3)	$0.2 = 20/100$
Disagree (2)	$0.1 = 10/100$
Strongly disagree (1)	$0.0 = 0/100$
Total	$1.0 = 100/100$

Solved Problem 2-5

For Solved Problem 2-4, let X be the numeric score. Compute the expected value of X.

Solution

$$E(X) = \sum_{i=1}^{5} X_i P(X_i) = X_1 P(X_1) + X_2 P(X_2)$$
$$+ X_3 P(X_3) + X_4 P(X_4) + X_5 P(X_5)$$
$$= 5(0.4) + 4(0.3) + 3(0.2) + 2(0.1) + 1(0)$$
$$= 4.0$$

Solved Problem 2-6

Compute the variance and standard deviation for the random variable X in Solved Problems 2-4 and 2-5.

Solution

$$\text{Variance} = \sum_{i=1}^{5} (X_i - E(X))^2 P(X_i)$$
$$= (5 - 4)^2(0.4) + (4 - 4)^2(0.3) + (3 - 4)^2(0.2) + (2 - 4)^2(0.1) + (1 - 4)^2(0.0)$$
$$= (1)^2(0.4) + (0)^2(0.3) + (-1)^2(0.2) + (-2)^2(0.1) + (-3)^2(0.0)$$
$$= 0.4 + 0.0 + 0.2 + 0.4 + 0.0 = 1.0$$

The standard deviation is
$$\sigma = \sqrt{\text{Variance}} = \sqrt{1} = 1$$

Solved Problem 2-7

A candidate for public office has claimed that 60% of voters will vote for her. If 5 registered voters were sampled, what is the probability that exactly 3 would say they favor this candidate?

Solution

We use the binomial distribution with $n = 5$, $p = 0.6$, and $r = 3$:

$$P(\text{exactly 3 successes in 5 trials}) = \frac{n!}{r!(n-r)!} p^r q^{n-r} = \frac{5!}{3!(5-3)!}(0.6)^3(0.4)^{5-3} = 0.3456$$

Solved Problem 2-8

The length of the rods coming out of our new cutting machine can be said to approximate a normal distribution with a mean of 10 inches and a standard deviation of 0.2 inch. Find the probability that a rod selected randomly will have a length

(a) of less than 10.0 inches
(b) between 10.0 and 10.4 inches
(c) between 10.0 and 10.1 inches
(d) between 10.1 and 10.4 inches
(e) between 9.6 and 9.9 inches
(f) between 9.9 and 10.4 inches
(g) between 9.886 and 10.406 inches

Solution

First, compute the standard normal distribution, the Z value:

$$Z = \frac{X - \mu}{\sigma}$$

Next, find the area under the curve for the given Z value by using a standard normal distribution table.

(a) $P(X < 10.0) = 0.50000$
(b) $P(10.0 < X < 10.4) = 0.97725 - 0.50000 = 0.47725$
(c) $P(10.0 < X < 10.1) = 0.69146 - 0.50000 = 0.19146$
(d) $P(10.1 < X < 10.4) = 0.97725 - 0.69146 = 0.28579$
(e) $P(9.6 < X < 9.9) = 0.97725 - 0.69146 = 0.28579$
(f) $P(9.9 < X < 10.4) = 0.19146 + 0.47725 = 0.66871$
(g) $P(9.886 < X < 10.406) = 0.47882 + 0.21566 = 0.69448$

Self-Test

- Before taking the self-test, refer to the learning objectives at the beginning of the chapter, the notes in the margins, and the glossary at the end of the chapter.
- Use the key at the back of the book to correct your answers.
- Restudy pages that correspond to any questions that you answered incorrectly or material you feel uncertain about.

1. If only one event may occur on any one trial, then the events are said to be
   a. independent.
   b. exhaustive.
   c. mutually exclusive.
   d. continuous.
2. New probabilities that have been found using Bayes' theorem are called
   a. prior probabilities.
   b. posterior probabilities.
   c. Bayesian probabilities.
   d. joint probabilities.
3. A measure of central tendency is
   a. expected value.
   b. variance.
   c. standard deviation.
   d. all of the above.

4. To compute the variance, of a discrete random variable you need to know the
   a. variable's possible values.
   b. expected value of the variable.
   c. probability of each possible value of the variable.
   d. all of the above.
5. The square root of the variance is the
   a. expected value.
   b. standard deviation.
   c. area under the normal curve.
   d. all of the above.
6. Which of the following is an example of a discrete distribution?
   a. the normal distribution
   b. the exponential distribution
   c. the Poisson distribution
   d. the Z distribution

7. The total area under the curve for any continuous distribution must equal
   a. 1.
   b. 0.
   c. 0.5.
   d. none of the above.
8. Probabilities for all the possible values of a discrete random variable
   a. may be greater than 1.
   b. may be negative on some occasions.
   c. must sum to 1.
   d. are represented by area underneath the curve.
9. In a standard normal distribution, the mean is equal to
   a. 1.
   b. 0.
   c. the variance.
   d. the standard deviation.
10. The probability of two or more independent events occurring is the
    a. marginal probability.
    b. simple probability.
    c. conditional probability.
    d. joint probability.
    e. all of the above.
11. In the normal distribution, 95.45% of the population lies within
    a. 1 standard deviation of the mean.
    b. 2 standard deviations of the mean.
    c. 3 standard deviations of the mean.
    d. 4 standard deviations of the mean.

12. If a normal distribution has a mean of 200 and a standard deviation of 10, 99.7% of the population falls within what range of values?
    a. 170–230
    b. 180–220
    c. 190–210
    d. 175–225
    e. 170–220
13. If two events are mutually exclusive, then the probability of the intersection of these two events will equal
    a. 0.
    b. 0.5.
    c. 1.0.
    d. cannot be determined without more information.
14. If $P(A) = 0.4$ and $P(B) = 0.5$ and $P(A \text{ and } B) = 0.2$, then $P(B|A) =$
    a. 0.80.
    b. 0.50.
    c. 0.10.
    d. 0.40.
    e. none of the above.
15. If $P(A) = 0.4$ and $P(B) = 0.5$ and $P(A \text{ and } B) = 0.2$, then $P(A \text{ or } B) =$
    a. 0.7.
    b. 0.9.
    c. 1.1.
    d. 0.2.
    e. none of the above.

Discussion Questions and Problems

Discussion Questions

2-1 What are the two basic laws of probability?

2-2 What is the meaning of mutually exclusive events? What is meant by collectively exhaustive? Give an example of each.

2-3 Describe the various approaches used in determining probability values.

2-4 Why is the probability of the intersection of two events subtracted in the sum of the probability of two events?

2-5 Describe what it means for two events to be independent.

2-6 What is Bayes' theorem, and when can it be used?

2-7 Describe the characteristics of a Bernoulli process. How is a Bernoulli process associated with the binomial distribution?

2-8 What is a random variable? What are the various types of random variables?

2-9 What is the difference between a discrete probability distribution and a continuous probability distribution? Give your own example of each.

2-10 What is the expected value, and what does it measure? How is it computed for a discrete probability distribution?

2-11 What is the variance, and what does it measure? How is it computed for a discrete probability distribution?

2-12 Name three business processes that can be described by the normal distribution.

2-13 A card is drawn from a standard deck of playing cards. For each of the following pairs of events, indicate if the events are mutually exclusive and indicate if the events are exhaustive.

(a) Draw a spade and draw a club.
(b) Draw a face card and draw a number card.
(c) Draw an ace and draw a three.

(d) Draw a red card and draw a black card.

(e) Draw a five and draw a diamond.

(f) Draw a red card and draw a diamond.

Problems

• 2-14 A student taking Management Science 301 at East Haven University will receive one of the five possible grades for the course: A, B, C, D, or F. The distribution of grades over the past 2 years is as follows:

GRADE	NUMBER OF STUDENTS
A	80
B	75
C	90
D	30
F	25
	Total 300

If this past distribution is a good indicator of future grades, what is the probability of a student receiving a C in the course?

• 2-15 A silver dollar is flipped twice. Calculate the probability of each of the following occurring:

(a) a head on the first flip

(b) a tail on the second flip given that the first toss was a head

(c) two tails

(d) a tail on the first and a head on the second

(e) a tail on the first and a head on the second or a head on the first and a tail on the second

(f) at least one head on the two flips

• 2-16 An urn contains 8 red chips, 10 green chips, and 2 white chips. A chip is drawn and replaced, and then a second chip drawn. What is the probability of

(a) a white chip on the first draw?

(b) a white chip on the first draw and a red on the second?

(c) two green chips being drawn?

(d) a red chip on the second, given that a white chip was drawn on the first?

• 2-17 Evertight, a leading manufacturer of quality nails, produces 1-, 2-, 3-, 4-, and 5-inch nails for various uses. In the production process, if there is an overrun or the nails are slightly defective, they are placed in a common bin. Yesterday, 651 of the 1-inch nails, 243 of the 2-inch nails, 41 of the 3-inch nails, 451 of the 4-inch nails, and 333 of the 5-inch nails were placed in the bin.

(a) What is the probability of reaching into the bin and getting a 4-inch nail?

(b) What is the probability of getting a 5-inch nail?

(c) If a particular application requires a nail that is 3 inches or shorter, what is the probability of getting a nail that will satisfy the requirements of the application?

⁑ 2-18 Last year, at Northern Manufacturing Company, 200 people had colds during the year. One hundred fifty-five people who did no exercising had colds, and the remainder of the people with colds were involved in a weekly exercise program. Half of the 1,000 employees were involved in some type of exercise.

(a) What is the probability that an employee will have a cold next year?

(b) Given that an employee is involved in an exercise program, what is the probability that he or she will get a cold next year?

(c) What is the probability that an employee who is not involved in an exercise program will get a cold next year?

(d) Are exercising and getting a cold independent events? Explain your answer.

⁑ 2-19 The Springfield Kings, a professional basketball team, has won 12 of its last 20 games and is expected to continue winning at the same percentage rate. The team's ticket manager is anxious to attract a large crowd to tomorrow's game but believes that depends on how well the Kings perform tonight against the Galveston Comets. He assesses the probability of drawing a large crowd to be 0.90 should the team win tonight. What is the probability that the team wins tonight and that there will be a large crowd at tomorrow's game?

⁑ 2-20 David Mashley teaches two undergraduate statistics courses at Kansas College. The class for Statistics 201 consists of 7 sophomores and 3 juniors. The more advanced course, Statistics 301, has 2 sophomores and 8 juniors enrolled. As an example of a business sampling technique, Professor Mashley randomly selects, from the stack of Statistics 201 registration cards, the class card of one student and then places that card back in the stack. If that student was a sophomore, Mashley draws another card from the Statistics 201 stack; if not, he randomly draws a card from the Statistics 301 group. Are these two draws independent events? What is the probability of

(a) a junior's name on the first draw?

(b) a junior's name on the second draw, given that a sophomore's name was drawn first?

(c) a junior's name on the second draw, given that a junior's name was drawn first?

(d) a sophomore's name on both draws?

(e) a junior's name on both draws?

(f) one sophomore's name and one junior's name on the two draws, regardless of order drawn?

2-21 The oasis outpost of Abu Ilan, in the heart of the Negev desert, has a population of 20 Bedouin tribesmen and 20 Farima tribesmen. El Kamin, a nearby oasis, has a population of 32 Bedouins and 8 Farima. A lost Israeli soldier, accidentally separated from his army unit, is wandering through the desert and arrives at the edge of one of the oases. The soldier has no idea which oasis he has found, but the first person he spots at a distance is a Bedouin. What is the probability that he wandered into Abu Ilan? What is the probability that he is in El Kamin?

2-22 The lost Israeli soldier mentioned in Problem 2-21 decides to rest for a few minutes before entering the desert oasis he has just found. Closing his eyes, he dozes off for 15 minutes, wakes, and walks toward the center of the oasis. The first person he spots this time he again recognizes as a Bedouin. What is the posterior probability that he is in El Kamin?

2-23 Ace Machine Works estimates that the probability its lathe tool is properly adjusted is 0.8. When the lathe is properly adjusted, there is a 0.9 probability that the parts produced pass inspection. If the lathe is out of adjustment, however, the probability of a good part being produced is only 0.2. A part randomly chosen is inspected and found to be acceptable. At this point, what is the posterior probability that the lathe tool is properly adjusted?

2-24 The Boston South Fifth Street Softball League consists of three teams: Mama's Boys, team 1; the Killers, team 2; and the Machos, team 3. Each team plays the other teams just once during the season. The win–loss record for the past 5 years is as follows:

WINNER	(1)	(2)	(3)
Mama's Boys (1)	X	3	4
The Killers (2)	2	X	1
The Machos (3)	1	4	X

Each row represents the number of wins over the past 5 years. Mama's Boys beat the Killers 3 times, beat the Machos 4 times, and so on.

(a) What is the probability that the Killers will win every game next year?

(b) What is the probability that the Machos will win at least one game next year?

(c) What is the probability that Mama's Boys will win exactly one game next year?

(d) What is the probability that the Killers will win fewer than two games next year?

2-25 The schedule for the Killers next year is as follows (refer to Problem 2-24):

Game 1: The Machos

Game 2: Mama's Boys

(a) What is the probability that the Killers will win their first game?

(b) What is the probability that the Killers will win their last game?

(c) What is the probability that the Killers will break even—win exactly one game?

(d) What is the probability that the Killers will win every game?

(e) What is the probability that the Killers will lose every game?

(f) Would you want to be the coach of the Killers?

2-26 The Northside Rifle team has two markspersons, Dick and Sally. Dick hits a bull's-eye 90% of the time, and Sally hits a bull's-eye 95% of the time.

(a) What is the probability that either Dick or Sally or both will hit the bull's-eye if each takes one shot?

(b) What is the probability that Dick and Sally will both hit the bull's-eye?

(c) Did you make any assumptions in answering the preceding questions? If you answered yes, do you think that you are justified in making the assumption(s)?

2-27 In a sample of 1,000 representing a survey from the entire population, 650 people were from Laketown, and the rest of the people were from River City. Out of the sample, 19 people had some form of cancer. Thirteen of these people were from Laketown.

(a) Are the events of living in Laketown and having some sort of cancer independent?

(b) Which city would you prefer to live in, assuming that your main objective was to avoid having cancer?

2-28 Compute the probability of "loaded die, given that a 3 was rolled," as shown in the example in Section 2.3, this time using the general form of Bayes' theorem from Equation 2-5.

2-29 Which of the following are probability distributions? Why?

(a)

RANDOM VARIABLE X	PROBABILITY
2	0.1
−1	0.2
0	0.3
1	0.25
2	0.15

(b)

RANDOM VARIABLE Y	PROBABILITY
1	1.1
1.5	0.2
2	0.3
2.5	0.25
3	−1.25

(c)

RANDOM VARIABLE Z	PROBABILITY
1	0.1
2	0.2
3	0.3
4	0.4
5	0.0

• 2-30 Harrington Health Food stocks 5 loaves of Neutro-Bread. The probability distribution for the sales of Neutro-Bread is listed in the following table. How many loaves will Harrington sell on average?

NUMBER OF LOAVES SOLD	PROBABILITY
0	0.05
1	0.15
2	0.20
3	0.25
4	0.20
5	0.15

• 2-31 What are the expected value and variance of the following probability distribution?

RANDOM VARIABLE X	PROBABILITY
1	0.05
2	0.05
3	0.10
4	0.10
5	0.15
6	0.15
7	0.25
8	0.15

✕:2-32 There are 10 questions on a true–false test. A student feels unprepared for this test and randomly guesses the answer for each of these.

(a) What is the probability that the student gets exactly 7 correct?

(b) What is the probability that the student gets exactly 8 correct?

(c) What is the probability that the student gets exactly 9 correct?

(d) What is the probability that the student gets exactly 10 correct?

(e) What is the probability that the student gets more than 6 correct?

✕:2-33 Gary Schwartz is the top salesman for his company. Records indicate that he makes a sale on 70% of his sales calls. If he calls on four potential clients, what is the probability that he makes exactly 3 sales? What is the probability that he makes exactly 4 sales?

✕:2-34 If 10% of all disk drives produced on an assembly line are defective, what is the probability that there will be exactly one defect in a random sample of 5 of these? What is the probability that there will be no defects in a random sample of 5?

✕:2-35 Trowbridge Manufacturing produces cases for personal computers and other electronic equipment. The quality control inspector for this company believes that a particular process is out of control. Normally, only 5% of all cases are deemed defective due to discolorations. If 6 such cases are sampled, what is the probability that there will be 0 defective cases if the process is operating correctly? What is the probability that there will be exactly 1 defective case?

✕:2-36 Refer to the Trowbridge Manufacturing example in Problem 2-35. The quality control inspection procedure is to select 6 items, and if there are 0 or 1 defective cases in the group of 6, the process is said to be in control. If the number of defects is more than 1, the process is out of control. Suppose that the true proportion of defective items is 0.15. What is the probability that there will be 0 or 1 defects in a sample of 6 if the true proportion of defects is 0.15?

✕:2-37 An industrial oven used to cure sand cores for a factory manufacturing engine blocks for small cars is able to maintain fairly constant temperatures. The temperature range of the oven follows a normal distribution with a mean of 450°F and a standard deviation of 25°F. Leslie Larsen, president of the factory, is concerned about the large number of defective cores that have been produced in the past several months. If the oven gets hotter than 475°F, the core is defective. What is the probability that the oven will cause a core to be defective? What is the probability that the temperature of the oven will range from 460° to 470°F?

✕:2-38 Steve Goodman, production foreman for the Florida Gold Fruit Company, estimates that the average sale of oranges is 4,700 and the standard deviation is 500 oranges. Sales follow a normal distribution.

(a) What is the probability that sales will be greater than 5,500 oranges?

(b) What is the probability that sales will be greater than 4,500 oranges?

(c) What is the probability that sales will be less than 4,900 oranges?

(d) What is the probability that sales will be less than 4,300 oranges?

✕:2-39 Susan Williams has been the production manager of Medical Suppliers, Inc., for the past 17 years. Medical Suppliers, Inc., is a producer of bandages and arm slings. During the past 5 years, the demand for No-Stick bandages has been fairly constant. On the average, sales have been about 87,000 packages of No-Stick. Susan has reason to believe that the distribution of No-Stick follows a normal curve, with a standard deviation of 4,000 packages. What is the probability that sales will be less than 81,000 packages?

⋮ 2-40 Armstrong Faber produces a standard number-two pencil called Ultra-Lite. Since Chuck Armstrong started Armstrong Faber, sales have grown steadily. With the increase in the price of wood products, however, Chuck has been forced to increase the price of the Ultra-Lite pencils. As a result, the demand for Ultra-Lite has been fairly stable over the past 6 years. On the average, Armstrong Faber has sold 457,000 pencils each year. Furthermore, 90% of the time sales have been between 454,000 and 460,000 pencils. It is expected that the sales follow a normal distribution with a mean of 457,000 pencils. Estimate the standard deviation of this distribution. (*Hint:* Work backward from the normal table to find Z. Then apply Equation 2-13.)

⋮ 2-41 The time to complete a construction project is normally distributed with a mean of 60 weeks and a standard deviation of 4 weeks.

(a) What is the probability the project will be finished in 62 weeks or less?
(b) What is the probability the project will be finished in 66 weeks or less?
(c) What is the probability the project will take longer than 65 weeks?

⋮ 2-42 A new integrated computer system is to be installed worldwide for a major corporation. Bids on this project are being solicited, and the contract will be awarded to one of the bidders. As a part of the proposal for this project, bidders must specify how long the project will take. There will be a significant penalty for finishing late. One potential contractor determines that the average time to complete a project of this type is 40 weeks with a standard deviation of 5 weeks. The time required to complete this project is assumed to be normally distributed.

(a) If the due date of this project is set at 40 weeks, what is the probability that the contractor will have to pay a penalty (i.e., the project will not be finished on schedule)?
(b) If the due date of this project is set at 43 weeks, what is the probability that the contractor will have to pay a penalty (i.e., the project will not be finished on schedule)?
(c) If the bidder wishes to set the due date in the proposal so that there is only a 5% chance of being late (and consequently only a 5% chance of having to pay a penalty), what due date should be set?

⋮ 2-43 Patients arrive at the emergency room of Costa Valley Hospital at an average of 5 per day. The demand for emergency room treatment at Costa Valley follows a Poisson distribution.

(a) Using Appendix C, compute the probability of exactly 0, 1, 2, 3, 4, and 5 arrivals per day.
(b) What is the sum of these probabilities, and why is the number less than 1?

⋮ 2-44 Using the data in Problem 2-43, determine the probability of more than 3 visits for emergency room service on any given day.

⋮ 2-45 Cars arrive at Carla's Muffler shop for repair work at an average of 3 per hour, following an exponential distribution.

(a) What is the expected time between arrivals?
(b) What is the variance of the time between arrivals?

⋮ 2-46 A particular test for the presence of steroids is to be used after a professional track meet. If steroids are present, the test will accurately indicate this 95% of the time. However, if steroids are not present, the test will indicate this 90% of the time (so it is wrong 10% of the time and predicts the presence of steroids). Based on past data, it is believed that 2% of the athletes do use steroids. This test is administered to one athlete, and the test is positive for steroids. What is the probability that this person actually used steroids?

⋮ 2-47 Market Researchers, Inc., has been hired to perform a study to determine if the market for a new product will be good or poor. In similar studies performed in the past, whenever the market actually was good, the market research study indicated that it would be good 85% of the time. On the other hand, whenever the market actually was poor, the market study incorrectly predicted it would be good 20% of the time. Before the study is performed, it is believed there is a 70% chance the market will be good. When Market Researchers, Inc., performs the study for this product, the results predict the market will be good. Given the results of this study, what is the probability that the market actually will be good?

⋮ 2-48 Policy Pollsters is a market research firm specializing in political polls. Records indicate in past elections, when a candidate was elected, Policy Pollsters had accurately predicted this 80% of the time and they were wrong 20% of the time. Records also show, for losing candidates, Policy Pollsters accurately predicted they would lose 90% of the time and they were only wrong 10% of the time. Before the poll is taken, there is a 50% chance of winning the election. If Policy Pollsters predicts a candidate will win the election, what is the probability that the candidate will actually win? If Policy Pollsters predicts that a candidate will lose the election, what is the probability that the candidate will actually lose?

⋮ 2-49 Burger City is a large chain of fast-food restaurants specializing in gourmet hamburgers. A mathematical model is now used to predict the success of new restaurants based on location and demographic information for that area. In the past, 70% of all restaurants that were opened were successful. The mathematical model has been tested in the existing restaurants to determine how effective it is. For the restaurants that were successful, 90% of the time the model predicted they would be, while 10% of the time the model predicted a failure. For the restaurants that were not successful, when the mathematical model was applied, 20% of the time it incorrectly predicted a successful restaurant while 80% of the time it was accurate and predicted an unsuccessful restaurant. If the model is used on a new location and predicts the restaurant will be successful, what is the probability that it actually is successful?

2-50   A mortgage lender attempted to increase its business by marketing its subprime mortgage. This mortgage is designed for people with a less-than-perfect credit rating, and the interest rate is higher to offset the extra risk. In the past year, 20% of these mortgages resulted in foreclosure as customers defaulted on their loans. A new screening system has been developed to determine whether to approve customers for the subprime loans. When the system is applied to a credit application, the system will classify the application as "Approve for loan" or "Reject for loan." When this new system was applied to recent customers who had defaulted on their loans, 90% of these customers were classified as "Reject." When this same system was applied to recent loan customers who had not defaulted on their loan payments, 70% of these customers were classified as "Approve for loan."

(a) If a customer did not default on a loan, what is the probability that the rating system would have classified the applicant in the reject category?

(b) If the rating system had classified the applicant in the reject category, what is the probability that the customer would not default on a loan?

2-51   Use the F table in Appendix D to find the value of F for the upper 5% of the F distribution with

(a) $df_1 = 5, df_2 = 10$
(b) $df_1 = 8, df_2 = 7$
(c) $df_1 = 3, df_2 = 5$
(d) $df_1 = 10, df_2 = 4$

2-52   Use the F table in Appendix D to find the value of F for the upper 1% of the F distribution with

(a) $df_1 = 15, df_2 = 6$
(b) $df_1 = 12, df_2 = 8$
(c) $df_1 = 3, df_2 = 5$
(d) $df_1 = 9, df_2 = 7$

2-53   For each of the following F values, determine whether the probability indicated is greater than or less than 5%:

(a) $P(F_{3,4} > 6.8)$
(b) $P(F_{7,3} > 3.6)$
(c) $P(F_{20,20} > 2.6)$
(d) $P(F_{7,5} > 5.1)$
(e) $P(F_{7,5} < 5.1)$

2-54   For each of the following F values, determine whether the probability indicated is greater than or less than 1%:

(a) $P(F_{5,4} > 14)$
(b) $P(F_{6,3} > 30)$
(c) $P(F_{10,12} > 4.2)$
(d) $P(F_{2,3} > 35)$
(e) $P(F_{2,3} < 35)$

2-55   Nite Time Inn has a toll-free telephone number so that customers can call at any time to make a reservation. A typical call takes about 4 minutes to complete, and the time required follows an exponential distribution. Find the probability that a call takes

(a) 3 minutes or less
(b) 4 minutes or less
(c) 5 minutes or less
(d) longer than 5 minutes

2-56   During normal business hours on the east coast, calls to the toll-free reservation number of the Nite Time Inn arrive at a rate of 5 per minute. It has been determined that the number of calls per minute can be described by the Poisson distribution. Find the probability that in the next minute, the number of calls arriving will be

(a) exactly 5
(b) exactly 4
(c) exactly 3
(d) exactly 6
(e) less than 2

2-57   In the Arnold's Muffler example for the exponential distribution in this chapter, the average rate of service was given as 3 per hour, and the times were expressed in hours. Convert the average service rate to the number per minute and convert the times to minutes. Find the probabilities that the service times will be less than $1/2$ hour, $1/3$ hour, and $2/3$ hour. Compare these probabilities to the probabilities found in the example.

Internet Homework Problems

See our Internet home page, at www.pearsonhighered.com/render, for additional homework problems, Problems 2-58 to 2-65.

Case Study

WTVX

WTVX, Channel 6, is located in Eugene, Oregon, home of the University of Oregon's football team. The station was owned and operated by George Wilcox, a former Duck (University of Oregon football player). Although there were other television stations in Eugene, WTVX was the only station that had a weatherperson who was a member of the American Meteorological Society (AMS). Every night, Joe Hummel would be introduced as the only weatherperson in Eugene who was a member of the AMS. This was George's idea, and he believed that this gave his station the mark of quality and helped with market share.

In addition to being a member of AMS, Joe was also the most popular person on any of the local news programs. Joe was always trying to find innovative ways to make the weather interesting, and this was especially difficult during the winter months when the weather seemed to remain the same over long periods of time. Joe's forecast for next month, for example, was that there would be a 70% chance of rain *every* day, and that what happens on one day (rain or shine) was not in any way dependent on what happened the day before.

One of Joe's most popular features of the weather report was to invite questions during the actual broadcast. Questions would be phoned in, and they were answered on the spot by Joe. Once a 10-year-old boy asked what caused fog, and Joe did an excellent job of describing some of the various causes.

Occasionally, Joe would make a mistake. For example, a high school senior asked Joe what the chances were of getting 15 days of rain in the next month (30 days). Joe made a quick calculation: $(70\%) \times (15 \text{ days}/30 \text{ days}) = (70\%)(1/2) = 35\%$. Joe quickly found out what it was like being wrong in a university town. He had over 50 phone calls from scientists, mathematicians, and other university professors, telling him that he had made a big mistake in computing the chances of getting 15 days of rain during the next 30 days. Although Joe didn't understand all of the formulas the professors mentioned, he was determined to find the correct answer and make a correction during a future broadcast.

Discussion Questions

1. What are the chances of getting 15 days of rain during the next 30 days?
2. What do you think about Joe's assumptions concerning the weather for the next 30 days?

Bibliography

Berenson, Mark, David Levine, and Timothy Krehbiel. *Basic Business Statistics*, 10th ed. Upper Saddle River, NJ: Prentice Hall, 2006.

Campbell, S. *Flaws and Fallacies in Statistical Thinking*. Upper Saddle River, NJ: Prentice Hall, 1974.

Feller, W. *An Introduction to Probability Theory and Its Applications*, Vols. 1 and 2. New York: John Wiley & Sons, Inc., 1957 and 1968.

Groebner, David, Patrick Shannon, Phillip Fry, and Kent Smith. *Business Statistics*, 8th ed. Upper Saddle River, NJ: Prentice Hall, 2011.

Hanke, J. E., A. G. Reitsch, and D. W. Wichern. *Business Forecasting*, 9th ed. Upper Saddle River, NJ: Prentice Hall, 2008.

Huff, D. *How to Lie with Statistics*. New York: W. W. Norton & Company, Inc., 1954.

Newbold, Paul, William Carlson, and Betty Thorne. *Statistics for Business and Economics*, 6th ed. Upper Saddle River, NJ: Prentice Hall, 2007.

Appendix 2.1: Derivation of Bayes' Theorem

We know that the following formulas are correct:

$$P(A \mid B) = \frac{P(AB)}{P(B)} \tag{1}$$

$$P(B \mid A) = \frac{P(AB)}{P(A)}$$

[which can be rewritten as $P(AB) = P(B|A)P(A)$] and (2)

$$P(B|A') = \frac{P(A'B)}{P(A')}$$

[which can be rewritten as $P(A'B) = P(B|A')P(A')$]. (3)

Furthermore, by definition, we know that

$$P(B) = P(AB) + P(A'B)$$
$$= P(B|A)P(A) + P(B|A')P(A') \tag{4}$$

from (2)   from (3)

Substituting Equations 2 and 4 into Equation 1, we have

$$P(A|B) = \frac{P(AB)}{P(B)}$$

from (2)

$$= \frac{P(B|A)P(A)}{P(B|A)P(A) + P(B|A')P(A')} \tag{5}$$

from (4)

This is the general form of Bayes' theorem, shown as Equation 2-5 in this chapter.

CHAPTER 3

Decision Analysis

After completing this chapter, students will be able to:

1. List the steps of the decision-making process.
2. Describe the types of decision-making environments.
3. Make decisions under uncertainty.
4. Use probability values to make decisions under risk.
5. Develop accurate and useful decision trees.

6. Revise probability estimates using Bayesian analysis.
7. Use computers to solve basic decision-making problems.
8. Understand the importance and use of utility theory in decision making.

CHAPTER OUTLINE

3.1 Introduction
3.2 The Six Steps in Decision Making
3.3 Types of Decision-Making Environments
3.4 Decision Making Under Uncertainty
3.5 Decision Making Under Risk
3.6 A Minimization Example

3.7 Using Software for Payoff Table Problems
3.8 Decision Trees
3.9 How Probability Values Are Estimated by Bayesian Analysis
3.10 Utility Theory

Summary • Glossary • Key Equations • Solved Problems • Self-Test • Discussion Questions and Problems • Internet Homework Problems • Case Study: Starting Right Corporation • Case Study: Blake Electronics • Internet Case Studies Bibliography

3.1 Introduction

Decision theory is an analytic and systematic way to tackle problems.

A good decision is based on logic.

To a great extent, the successes or failures that a person experiences in life depend on the decisions that he or she makes. The person who managed the ill-fated space shuttle *Challenger* is no longer working for NASA. The person who designed the top-selling Mustang became president of Ford. Why and how did these people make their respective decisions? In general, what is involved in making good decisions? One decision may make the difference between a successful career and an unsuccessful one. **Decision theory** is an analytic and systematic approach to the study of decision making. In this chapter, we present the mathematical models useful in helping managers make the best possible decisions.

What makes the difference between good and bad decisions? A good decision is one that is based on logic, considers all available data and possible alternatives, and applies the quantitative approach we are about to describe. Occasionally, a good decision results in an unexpected or unfavorable outcome. But if it is made properly, it is *still* a good decision. A bad decision is one that is not based on logic, does not use all available information, does not consider all alternatives, and does not employ appropriate quantitative techniques. If you make a bad decision but are lucky and a favorable outcome occurs, you have *still* made a bad decision. Although occasionally good decisions yield bad results, in the long run, using decision theory will result in successful outcomes.

3.2 The Six Steps in Decision Making

Whether you are deciding about getting a haircut today, building a multimillion-dollar plant, or buying a new camera, the steps in making a good decision are basically the same:

Six Steps in Decision Making

1. Clearly define the problem at hand.
2. List the possible alternatives.
3. Identify the possible outcomes or states of nature.
4. List the payoff (typically profit) of each combination of alternatives and outcomes.
5. Select one of the mathematical decision theory models.
6. Apply the model and make your decision.

We use the Thompson Lumber Company case as an example to illustrate these decision theory steps. John Thompson is the founder and president of Thompson Lumber Company, a profitable firm located in Portland, Oregon.

The first step is to define the problem.

Step 1. The problem that John Thompson identifies is whether to expand his product line by manufacturing and marketing a new product, backyard storage sheds.

Thompson's second step is to generate the alternatives that are available to him. In decision theory, an **alternative** is defined as a course of action or a strategy that the decision maker can choose.

The second step is to list alternatives.

Step 2. John decides that his alternatives are to construct (1) a large new plant to manufacture the storage sheds, (2) a small plant, or (3) no plant at all (i.e., he has the option of not developing the new product line).

One of the biggest mistakes that decision makers make is to leave out some important alternatives. Although a particular alternative may seem to be inappropriate or of little value, it might turn out to be the best choice.

The next step involves identifying the possible outcomes of the various alternatives. A common mistake is to forget about some of the possible outcomes. Optimistic decision makers tend to ignore bad outcomes, whereas pessimistic managers may discount a favorable outcome. If you don't consider all possibilities, you will not be making a logical decision, and the results may be undesirable. If you do not think the worst can happen, you may design another Edsel automobile. In decision theory, those outcomes over which the decision maker has little or no control are called **states of nature**.

TABLE 3.1

Decision Table with Conditional Values for Thompson Lumber

	STATE OF NATURE	
ALTERNATIVE	**FAVORABLE MARKET ($)**	**UNFAVORABLE MARKET ($)**
Construct a large plant	200,000	−180,000
Construct a small plant	100,000	−20,000
Do nothing	0	0

Note: It is important to include all alternatives, including "do nothing."

The third step is to identify possible outcomes.

Step 3. Thompson determines that there are only two possible outcomes: the market for the storage sheds could be favorable, meaning that there is a high demand for the product, or it could be unfavorable, meaning that there is a low demand for the sheds.

Once the alternatives and states of nature have been identified, the next step is to express the payoff resulting from each possible combination of alternatives and outcomes. In decision theory, we call such payoffs or profits **conditional values**. Not every decision, of course, can be based on money alone—any appropriate means of measuring benefit is acceptable.

The fourth step is to list payoffs.

During the fourth step, the decision maker can construct decision or payoff tables.

Step 4. Because Thompson wants to maximize his profits, he can use *profit* to evaluate each consequence.

John Thompson has already evaluated the potential profits associated with the various outcomes. With a favorable market, he thinks a large facility would result in a net profit of $200,000 to his firm. This $200,000 is a *conditional value* because Thompson's receiving the money is conditional upon both his building a large factory and having a good market. The conditional value if the market is unfavorable would be a $180,000 net loss. A small plant would result in a net profit of $100,000 in a favorable market, but a net loss of $20,000 would occur if the market was unfavorable. Finally, doing nothing would result in $0 profit in either market. The easiest way to present these values is by constructing a **decision table**, sometimes called a **payoff table**. A decision table for Thompson's conditional values is shown in Table 3.1. All of the alternatives are listed down the left side of the table, and all of the possible outcomes or states of nature are listed across the top. The body of the table contains the actual payoffs.

The last two steps are to select and apply the decision theory model.

Steps 5 and 6. The last two steps are to select a decision theory model and apply it to the data to help make the decision. Selecting the model depends on the environment in which you're operating and the amount of risk and uncertainty involved.

3.3 Types of Decision-Making Environments

The types of decisions people make depend on how much knowledge or information they have about the situation. There are three decision-making environments:

- Decision making under certainty
- Decision making under uncertainty
- Decision making under risk

In the environment of **decision making under certainty**, decision makers know with certainty the consequence of every alternative or decision choice. Naturally, they will choose the alternative that will maximize their well-being or will result in the best outcome. For example, let's say that you have $1,000 to invest for a 1-year period. One alternative is to open a savings account paying 4% interest and another is to invest in a government Treasury bond paying 6% interest. If both investments are secure and guaranteed, there is a certainty that the Treasury bond will pay a higher return. The return after 1 year will be $60 in interest.

In **decision making under uncertainty**, there are several possible outcomes for each alternative, and the decision maker does not know the probabilities of the various outcomes. As an example, the probability that a Democrat will be president of the United States 25 years from now is not known. Sometimes it is impossible to assess the probability of success of a new undertaking or product. The criteria for decision making under uncertainty are explained in Section 3.4.

Probabilities are not known.

Probabilities are known.

In **decision making under risk**, there are several possible outcomes for each alternative, and the decision maker knows the probability of occurrence of each outcome. We know, for example, that when playing cards using a standard deck, the probability of being dealt a club is 0.25. The probability of rolling a 5 on a die is 1/6. In decision making under risk, the decision maker usually attempts to maximize his or her expected well-being. Decision theory models for business problems in this environment typically employ two equivalent criteria: maximization of expected monetary value and minimization of expected opportunity loss.

In the Thompson Lumber example, John Thompson is faced with decision making under uncertainty. If either a large plant or a small plant is constructed, the actual payoff depends on the state of nature, and probabilities are not known. If probabilities for a favorable market and for an unfavorable market were known, the environment would change from uncertainty to risk. For the third alternative, do nothing, the payoff does not depend on the state of nature and is known with certainty.

3.4 Decision Making Under Uncertainty

The presentation in this section of the criteria for decision making under uncertainty (and also for decision making under risk) is based on the assumption that the payoff is something in which larger values are better and high values are desirable. For payoffs such as profit, total sales, total return on investment, and interest earned, the best decision would be one that resulted in some type of maximum payoff. However, there are situations in which lower payoff values (e.g., cost) are better, and these payoffs would be minimized rather than maximized. The statement of the decision criteria would be modified slightly for such minimization problems. These differences will be mentioned in this section, and an example will be provided in a later section.

Several criteria exist for making decisions under conditions of uncertainty. The ones that we cover in this section are as follows:

1. Optimistic
2. Pessimistic
3. Criterion of realism (Hurwicz)
4. Equally likely (Laplace)
5. Minimax regret

The first four criteria can be computed directly from the decision (payoff) table, whereas the minimax regret criterion requires use of the opportunity loss table. Let's take a look at each of the five models and apply them to the Thompson Lumber example.

Optimistic

Maximax is an optimistic approach.

In using the **optimistic** criterion, the best (maximum) payoff for each alternative is considered and the alternative with the best (maximum) of these is selected. Hence, the optimistic criterion is sometimes called the **maximax** criterion. In Table 3.2, we see that Thompson's optimistic choice is the first alternative, "construct a large plant." By using this criterion, the highest of all possible payoffs ($200,000 in this example) may be achieved, while if any other alternative were selected, it would be impossible to achieve a payoff this high.

In using the optimistic criterion for minimization problems in which lower payoffs (e.g., cost) are better, you would look at the best (minimum) payoff for each alternative and choose the alternative with the best (minimum) of these.

TABLE 3.2

Thompson's Maximax Decision

| | STATE OF NATURE | | |
| | FAVORABLE MARKET ($) | UNFAVORABLE MARKET ($) | MAXIMUM IN A ROW ($) |
ALTERNATIVE			
Construct a large plant	200,000	−180,000	(200,000) ← Maximax
Construct a small plant	100,000	−20,000	100,000
Do nothing	0	0	0

TABLE 3.3
Thompson's Maximin Decision

	STATE OF NATURE		
ALTERNATIVE	**FAVORABLE MARKET ($)**	**UNFAVORABLE MARKET ($)**	**MINIMUM IN A ROW ($)**
Construct a large plant	200,000	−180,000	−180,000
Construct a small plant	100,000	−20,000	−20,000
Do nothing	0	0	⓪ ◄ Maximin

Pessimistic

Maximin is a pessimistic approach.

In using the *pessimistic* criterion, the worst (minimum) payoff for each alternative is considered and the alternative with the best (maximum) of these is selected. Hence, the pessimistic criterion is sometimes called the **maximin** criterion. This criterion guarantees the payoff will be at least the maximin value (the best of the worst values). Choosing any other alternative may allow a worse (lower) payoff to occur.

Thompson's maximin choice, "do nothing," is shown in Table 3.3. This decision is associated with the maximum of the minimum number within each row or alternative.

In using the pessimistic criterion for minimization problems in which lower payoffs (e.g., cost) are better, you would look at the worst (maximum) payoff for each alternative and choose the alternative with the best (minimum) of these.

Both the maximax and maximin criteria consider only one extreme payoff for each alternative, while all other payoffs are ignored. The next criterion considers both of these extremes.

Criterion of Realism (Hurwicz Criterion)

Criterion of realism uses the weighted average approach.

Often called the **weighted average**, the **criterion of realism** (the **Hurwicz criterion**) is a compromise between an optimistic and a pessimistic decision. To begin, a **coefficient of realism**, α, is selected. This measures the degree of optimism of the decision maker and is between 0 and 1. When α is 1, the decision maker is 100% optimistic about the future. When α is 0, the decision maker is 100% pessimistic about the future. The advantage of this approach is that it allows the decision maker to build in personal feelings about relative optimism and pessimism. The weighted average is computed as follows:

$$\text{Weighted average} = \alpha(\text{best in row}) + (1 - \alpha)(\text{worst in row})$$

For a maximization problem, the best payoff for an alternative is the highest value, and the worst payoff is the lowest value. Note that when $\alpha = 1$, this is the same as the optimistic criterion, and when $\alpha = 0$ this is the same as the pessimistic criterion. This value is computed for each alternative, and the alternative with the highest weighted average is then chosen.

If we assume that John Thompson sets his coefficient of realism, α, to be 0.80, the best decision would be to construct a large plant. As seen in Table 3.4, this alternative has the highest weighted average: $124,000 = (0.80)(\$200,000) = (0.20)(-\$180,000)$.

In using the criterion of realism for minimization problems, the best payoff for an alternative would be the lowest payoff in the row and the worst would be the highest payoff in the row. The alternative with the lowest weighted average is then chosen.

TABLE 3.4
Thompson's Criterion of Realism Decision

	STATE OF NATURE		
ALTERNATIVE	**FAVORABLE MARKET ($)**	**UNFAVORABLE MARKET ($)**	**CRITERION OF REALISM OR WEIGHTED AVERAGE ($\alpha = 0.8$) $**
Construct a large plant	200,000	−180,000	124,000 ◄ Realism
Construct a small plant	100,000	−20,000	76,000
Do nothing	0	0	0

TABLE 3.5
Thompson's Equally Likely Decision

| | STATE OF NATURE | | |
| | FAVORABLE MARKET ($) | UNFAVORABLE MARKET ($) | ROW AVERAGE ($) |
ALTERNATIVE			
Construct a large plant	200,000	−180,000	10,000
Construct a small plant	100,000	−20,000	(40,000) ◄ Equally likely
Do nothing	0	0	0

Because there are only two states of nature in the Thompson Lumber example, only two payoffs for each alternative are present and both are considered. However, if there are more than two states of nature, this criterion will ignore all payoffs except the best and the worst. The next criterion will consider all possible payoffs for each decision.

Equally Likely (Laplace)

Equally likely criterion uses the average outcome.

One criterion that uses all the payoffs for each alternative is the **equally likely**, also called **Laplace**, decision criterion. This involves finding the average payoff for each alternative, and selecting the alternative with the best or highest average. The equally likely approach assumes that all probabilities of occurrence for the states of nature are equal, and thus each state of nature is equally likely.

The equally likely choice for Thompson Lumber is the second alternative, "construct a small plant." This strategy, shown in Table 3.5, is the one with the maximum average payoff.

In using the equally likely criterion for minimization problems, the calculations are exactly the same, but the best alternative is the one with the lowest average payoff.

Minimax Regret

Minimax regret criterion is based on opportunity loss.

The next decision criterion that we discuss is based on **opportunity loss** or **regret**. Opportunity loss refers to the difference between the optimal profit or payoff for a given state of nature and the actual payoff received for a particular decision for that state of nature. In other words, it's the amount lost by not picking the best alternative in a given state of nature.

The first step is to create the opportunity loss table by determining the opportunity loss for not choosing the best alternative for each state of nature. Opportunity loss for any state of nature, or any column, is calculated by subtracting each payoff in the column from the *best* payoff in the same column. For a favorable market, the best payoff is $200,000 as a result of the first alternative, "construct a large plant." The opportunity loss is 0, meaning that it is impossible to achieve a higher payoff in this state of nature. If the second alternative is selected, a profit of $100,000 would be realized in a favorable market, and this is compared to the best payoff of $200,000. Thus, the opportunity loss is 200,000 − 100,000 = 100,000. Similarly, if "do nothing" is selected, the opportunity loss would be 200,000 − 0 = 200,000.

For an unfavorable market, the best payoff is $0 as a result of the third alternative, "do nothing," so this has 0 opportunity loss. The opportunity losses for the other alternatives are found by subtracting the payoffs from this best payoff ($0) in this state of nature as shown in Table 3.6. Thompson's opportunity loss table is shown as Table 3.7.

TABLE 3.6
Determining Opportunity Losses for Thompson Lumber

| STATE OF NATURE | |
FAVORABLE MARKET ($)	UNFAVORABLE MARKET ($)
200,000 − 200,000	0 − (−180,000)
200,000 − 100,000	0 − (−20,000)
200,000 − 0	0 − 0

TABLE 3.7
Opportunity Loss Table for Thompson Lumber

| | STATE OF NATURE | |
| | FAVORABLE MARKET ($) | UNFAVORABLE MARKET ($) |
ALTERNATIVE		
Construct a large plant	0	180,000
Construct a small plant	100,000	20,000
Do nothing	200,000	0

IN ACTION

Ford Uses Decision Theory to Choose Parts Suppliers

Ford Motor Company manufactures about 5 million cars and trucks annually and employs more than 200,000 people at about 100 facilities around the globe. Such a large company often needs to make large supplier decisions under tight deadlines.

This was the situation when researchers at MIT teamed up with Ford management and developed a data-driven supplier selection tool. This computer program aids in decision making by applying some of the decision-making criteria presented in this chapter. Decision makers at Ford are asked to input data about their suppliers (part costs, distances, lead times, supplier reliability, etc.) as well as the type of decision criterion they want to use. Once these are entered, the model outputs the best set of suppliers to meet the specified needs. The result is a system that is now saving Ford Motor Company over $40 million annually.

Source: Based on E. Klampfl, Y. Fradkin, C. McDaniel, and M. Wolcott. "Ford Uses OR to Make Urgent Sourcing Decisions in a Distressed Supplier Environment," *Interfaces* 39, 5 (2009): 428–442.

TABLE 3.8

Thompson's Minimax Decision Using Opportunity Loss

| | STATE OF NATURE | | |
ALTERNATIVE	FAVORABLE MARKET ($)	UNFAVORABLE MARKET ($)	MAXIMUM IN A ROW ($)
Construct a large plant	0	180,000	180,000
Construct a small plant	100,000	20,000	100,000 ← Minimax
Do nothing	200,000	0	200,000

Using the opportunity loss (regret) table, the **minimax regret** criterion first consider the maximum (worst) opportunity loss for each alternative. Next, looking at these maximum values, pick that alternative with the minimum (or best) number. By doing this, the opportunity loss actually realized is guaranteed to be no more than this minimax value. In Table 3.8, we can see that the minimax regret choice is the second alternative, "construct a small plant." When this alternative is selected, we know the maximum opportunity loss cannot be more than 100,000 (the *mini*mum of the *maxi*mum regrets).

In calculating the opportunity loss for minimization problems such as those involving costs, the best (lowest) payoff or cost in a column is subtracted from each payoff in that column. Once the opportunity loss table has been constructed, the minimax regret criterion is applied in exactly the same way as just described. The maximum opportunity loss for each alternative is found, and the alternative with the minimum of these maximums is selected. As with maximization problems, the opportunity loss can never be negative.

We have considered several decision-making criteria to be used when probabilities of the states of nature are not known and cannot be estimated. Now we will see what to do if the probabilities are available.

3.5 Decision Making Under Risk

Decision making under risk is a decision situation in which several possible states of nature may occur, and the probabilities of these states of nature are known. In this section, we consider one of the most popular methods of making decisions under risk: selecting the alternative with the highest expected monetary value (or simply expected value). We also use the probabilities with the opportunity loss table to minimize the expected opportunity loss.

Expected Monetary Value

Given a decision table with conditional values (payoffs) that are monetary values, and probability assessments for all states of nature, it is possible to determine the **expected monetary value (EMV)** for each alternative. The *expected value*, or the *mean value*, is the long-run average value of that decision. The EMV for an alternative is just the sum of possible payoffs of the alternative, each weighted by the probability of that payoff occurring.

EMV is the weighted sum of possible payoffs for each alternative.

This could also be expressed simply as the expected value of X, or $E(X)$, which was discussed in Section 2.6 of Chapter 2.

$$\text{EMV(alternative)} = \sum X_i P(X_i) \tag{3-1}$$

TABLE 3.9

Decision Table with Probabilities and EMVs for Thompson Lumber

ALTERNATIVE	STATE OF NATURE FAVORABLE MARKET ($)	STATE OF NATURE UNFAVORABLE MARKET ($)	EMV ($)
Construct a large plant	200,000	−180,000	10,000
Construct a small plant	100,000	−20,000	40,000 ◄⌐ Best EMV ⌐
Do nothing	0	0	0
Probabilities	0.50	0.50	

where

X_i = payoff for the alternative in state of nature i

$P(X_i)$ = probability of achieving payoff X_i (i.e., probability of state of nature i)

Σ = summation symbol

If this were expanded, it would become

EMV (alternative)

= (payoff in first state of nature) × (probability of first state of nature)

+ (payoff in second state of nature) × (probability of second state of nature)

+ ⋯ + (payoff in last state of nature) × (probability of last state of nature)

The alternative with the maximum EMV is then chosen.

Suppose that John Thompson now believes that the probability of a favorable market is exactly the same as the probability of an unfavorable market; that is, each state of nature has a 0.50 probability. Which alternative would give the greatest EMV? To determine this, John has expanded the decision table, as shown in Table 3.9. His calculations follow:

EMV (large plant) = ($200,000)(0.50) + (−$180,000)(0.50) = $10,000

EMV (small plant) = ($100,000)(0.50) + (−$20,000)(0.50) = $40,000

EMV (do nothing) = ($0)(0.50) + ($0)(0.50) = $0

The largest expected value ($40,000) results from the second alternative, "construct a small plant." Thus, Thompson should proceed with the project and put up a small plant to manufacture storage sheds. The EMVs for the large plant and for doing nothing are $10,000 and $0, respectively.

When using the EMV criterion with minimization problems, the calculations are the same, but the alternative with the smallest EMV is selected.

Expected Value of Perfect Information

John Thompson has been approached by Scientific Marketing, Inc., a firm that proposes to help John make the decision about whether to build the plant to produce storage sheds. Scientific Marketing claims that its technical analysis will tell John with certainty whether the market is favorable for his proposed product. In other words, it will change his environment from one of decision making under risk to one of decision making under certainty. This information could prevent John from making a very expensive mistake. Scientific Marketing would charge Thompson $65,000 for the information. What would you recommend to John? Should he hire the firm to make the marketing study? Even if the information from the study is perfectly accurate, is it worth $65,000? What would it be worth? Although some of these questions are difficult to answer, determining the value of such *perfect information* can be very useful. It places an upper bound on what you should be willing to spend on information such as that being sold by Scientific Marketing. In this section, two related terms are investigated: the **expected value of perfect information (EVPI)** and the **expected value with perfect information (EVwPI)**. These techniques can help John make his decision about hiring the marketing firm.

EVPI places an upper bound on what to pay for information.

The expected value *with* perfect information is the expected or average return, in the long run, if we have perfect information before a decision has to be made. To calculate this value, we choose the best alternative for each state of nature and multiply its payoff times the probability of occurrence of that state of nature.

$$\text{EVwPI} = \sum (\text{best payoff in state of nature } i)(\text{probability of state of nature } i) \quad (3\text{-}2)$$

If this were expanded, it would become

EVwPI

$$= (\text{best payoff in first state of nature}) \times (\text{probability of first state of nature})$$
$$+ (\text{best payoff in second state of nature}) \times (\text{probability of second state of nature})$$
$$+ \cdots + (\text{best payoff in last state of nature}) \times (\text{probability of last state of nature})$$

The EVPI is the expected value *with* perfect information minus the expected value *without* perfect information (i.e., the best or maximum EMV). Thus, the EVPI is the improvement in EMV that results from having perfect information.

$$\text{EVPI} = \text{EVwPI} - \text{Best EMV} \quad (3\text{-}3)$$

EVPI is the expected value with perfect information minus the maximum EMV.

By referring to Table 3.9, Thompson can calculate the maximum that he would pay for information, that is, the EVPI. He follows a three-stage process. First, the best payoff in each state of nature is found. If the perfect information says the market will be favorable, the large plant will be constructed, and the profit will be $200,000. If the perfect information says the market will be unfavorable, the "do nothing" alternative is selected, and the profit will be 0. These values are shown in the "with perfect information" row in Table 3.10. Second, the expected value *with* perfect information is computed. Then, using this result, EVPI is calculated.

The expected value with perfect information is

$$\text{EVwPI} = (\$200,000)(0.50) + (\$0)(0.50) = \$100,000$$

Thus, if we had perfect information, the payoff would average $100,000.

The maximum EMV without additional information is $40,000 (from Table 3.9). Therefore, the increase in EMV is

$$\text{EVPI} = \text{EVwPI} - \text{maximum EMV}$$
$$= \$100,000 - \$40,000$$
$$= \$60,000$$

Thus, the *most* Thompson would be willing to pay for perfect information is $60,000. This, of course, is again based on the assumption that the probability of each state of nature is 0.50.

This EVPI also tells us that the most we would pay for any information (perfect or imperfect) is $60,000. In a later section, we'll see how to place a value on imperfect or sample information.

In finding the EVPI for minimization problems, the approach is similar. The best payoff in each state of nature is found, but this is the lowest payoff for that state of nature rather than the highest. The EVwPI is calculated from these lowest payoffs, and this is compared to the best (lowest) EMV without perfect information. The EVPI is the improvement that results, and this is the best EMV − EVwPI.

TABLE 3.10

Decision Table with Perfect Information

ALTERNATIVE	STATE OF NATURE		EMV ($)
	FAVORABLE MARKET ($)	UNFAVORABLE MARKET ($)	
Construct a large plant	200,000	−180,000	10,000
Construct a small plant	100,000	−20,000	40,000
Do nothing	0	0	0
With perfect information	200,000	0	100,000 ← EVwPI
Probabilities	0.50	0.50	

TABLE 3.11
EOL Table for Thompson Lumber

| | STATE OF NATURE | | |
ALTERNATIVE	FAVORABLE MARKET ($)	UNFAVORABLE MARKET ($)	EOL
Construct a large plant	0	180,000	90,000
Construct a small plant	100,000	20,000	60,000 ← Best EOL
Do nothing	200,000	0	100,000
Probabilities	0.50	0.50	

Expected Opportunity Loss

EOL is the cost of not picking the best solution.

An alternative approach to maximizing EMV is to minimize *expected opportunity loss* (EOL). First, an opportunity loss table is constructed. Then the EOL is computed for each alternative by multiplying the opportunity loss by the probability and adding these together. In Table 3.7, we presented the opportunity loss table for the Thompson Lumber example. Using these opportunity losses, we compute the EOL for each alternative by multiplying the probability of each state of nature times the appropriate opportunity loss value and adding these together:

$$EOL(\text{construct large plant}) = (0.5)(\$0) + (0.5)(\$180,000)$$
$$= \$90,000$$

$$EOL(\text{construct small plant}) = (0.5)(\$100,000) + (0.5)(\$20,000)$$
$$= \$60,000$$

$$EOL(\text{do nothing}) = (0.5)(\$200,000) + (0.5)(\$0)$$
$$= \$100,000$$

Table 3.11 gives these results. Using minimum EOL as the decision criterion, the best decision would be the second alternative, "construct a small plant."

EOL will always result in the same decision as the maximum EMV.

It is important to note that minimum EOL will always result in the same decision as maximum EMV, and that the EVPI will always equal the minimum EOL. Referring to the Thompson case, we used the payoff table to compute the EVPI to be $60,000. Note that this is the minimum EOL we just computed.

Sensitivity Analysis

Sensitivity analysis investigates how our decision might change with different input data.

In previous sections, we determined that the best decision (with the probabilities known) for Thompson Lumber was to construct the small plant, with an expected value of $40,000. This conclusion depends on the values of the economic consequences and the two probability values of a favorable and an unfavorable market. *Sensitivity analysis* investigates how our decision might change given a change in the problem data. In this section, we investigate the impact that a change in the probability values would have on the decision facing Thompson Lumber. We first define the following variable:

$$P = \text{probability of a favorable market}$$

Because there are only two states of nature, the probability of an unfavorable market must be $1 - P$.

We can now express the EMVs in terms of P, as shown in the following equations. A graph of these EMV values is shown in Figure 3.1.

$$EMV(\text{large plant}) = \$200,000P - \$180,000(1 - P)$$
$$= \$200,000P - \$180,000 + 180,000P$$
$$= \$380,000P - \$180,000$$

$$EMV(\text{small plant}) = \$100,000P - \$20,000(1 - P)$$
$$= \$100,000P - \$20,000 + 20,000P$$
$$= \$120,000P - \$20,000$$

$$EMV(\text{do nothing}) = \$0P + \$0(1 - P) = \$0$$

FIGURE 3.1
Sensitivity Analysis

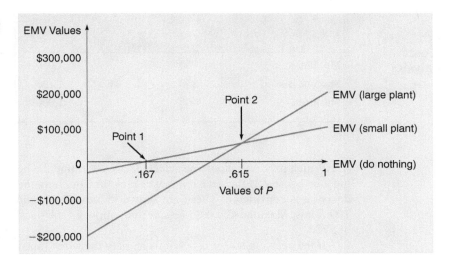

As you can see in Figure 3.1, the best decision is to do nothing as long as P is between 0 and the probability associated with point 1, where the EMV for doing nothing is equal to the EMV for the small plant. When P is between the probabilities for points 1 and 2, the best decision is to build the small plant. Point 2 is where the EMV for the small plant is equal to the EMV for the large plant. When P is greater than the probability for point 2, the best decision is to construct the large plant. Of course, this is what you would expect as P increases. The value of P at points 1 and 2 can be computed as follows:

$$\text{Point 1: EMV (do nothing)} = \text{EMV (small plant)}$$

$$0 = \$120,000P - \$20,000 \quad P = \frac{20,000}{120,000} = 0.167$$

$$\text{Point 2: EMV (small plant)} = \text{EMV (large plant)}$$

$$\$120,000P - \$20,000 = \$380,000P - \$180,000$$

$$260,000P = 160,000 \quad P = \frac{160,000}{260,000} = 0.615$$

The results of this sensitivity analysis are displayed in the following table:

BEST ALTERNATIVE	RANGE OF P VALUES
Do nothing	Less than 0.167
Construct a small plant	0.167 − 0.615
Construct a large plant	Greater than 0.615

3.6   A Minimization Example

The previous examples have illustrated how to apply the decision-making criterion when the payoffs are to be maximized. The following example illustrates how the criteria are applied to problems in which the payoffs are costs that should be minimized.

The Decision Sciences department at State University will be signing a 3-year lease for a new copy machine, and three different machines are being considered. For each of these, there is a monthly fee, which includes service on the machine, plus a charge for each copy. The number of copies that would be made each month is uncertain, but the department has estimated that the number of copies per month could be 10,000 or 20,000 or 30,000 per month. The monthly cost for each machine based on each of the three levels of activity is shown in Table 3.12.

TABLE 3.12

Payoff Table with Monthly Copy Costs for Business Analytics Department

	10,000 COPIES PER MONTH	20,000 COPIES PER MONTH	30,000 COPIES PER MONTH
Machine A	950	1,050	1,150
Machine B	850	1,100	1,350
Machine C	700	1,000	1,300

Which machine should be selected? To determine the best alternative, a specific criterion must be chosen. If the decision maker is optimistic, only the best (minimum) payoff for each decision is considered. These are shown in Table 3.13, and the best (minimum) of these is 700. Thus, Machine C would be selected, allowing the possibility of achieving this best cost of $700.

If the decision maker is pessimistic, only the worst (maximum) payoff for each decision is considered. These are also shown in Table 3.13, and the best (minimum) of these is 1,150. Thus, Machine A would be selected based on the pessimistic criterion. This would guarantee that the cost would be no more than 1,150, regardless of which state of nature occurred.

Using Hurwicz criterion, if we assume that the decision maker is 70% optimistic (the coefficient of realism is 0.7), the weighted average of the best and the worst payoff for each alternative would be calculated using the formula:

$$\text{Weighted average} = 0.7(\text{best payoff}) + (1 - 0.7)(\text{worst payoff})$$

For each of the three copy machines, we would get the following values.

$$\text{Machine A: } 0.7(950) + 0.3(1,150) = 1,010$$
$$\text{Machine B: } 0.7(850) + 0.3(1,350) = 1,000$$
$$\text{Machine C: } 0.7(700) + 0.3(1,300) = 880$$

The decision would be to select Machine C based on this criterion because it has the lowest weighted average cost.

For the equally likely criterion, the average payoff for each machine would be calculated.

$$\text{Machine A: } (950 + 1,050 + 1,150)/3 = 1,050$$
$$\text{Machine B: } (850 + 1,100 + 1,350)/3 = 1,100$$
$$\text{Machine C: } (700 + 1,000 + 1,300)/3 = 1,000$$

Based on the equally likely criterion, Machine C would be selected because it has the lowest average cost.

To apply EMV criterion, probabilities must be known for each state of nature. Past records indicate that 40% of the time the number of copies made in a month was 10,000, while 30% of the time it was 20,000 and 30% of the time it was 30,000. The probabilities for the three states of nature would be 0.4, 0.3, and 0.3. We can use these to calculate the EMVs, and the results are shown in Table 3.14. Machine C would be selected because it has the lowest EMV. The monthly cost would average $970 with this machine, while the other machines would average a higher cost.

TABLE 3.13

Best and Worst Payoffs (Costs) for Business Analytics Department

	10,000 COPIES PER MONTH	20,000 COPIES PER MONTH	30,000 COPIES PER MONTH	BEST PAYOFF (MINIMUM)	WORST PAYOFF (MAXIMUM)
Machine A	950	1,050	1,150	950	1,150
Machine B	850	1,100	1,350	850	1,350
Machine C	700	1,000	1,300	700	1,300

TABLE 3.14

Expected Monetary Values and Expected Value with Perfect Information for Business Analytics Department

	10,000 COPIES PER MONTH	20,000 COPIES PER MONTH	30,000 COPIES PER MONTH	EMV
Machine A	950	1,050	1,150	1,040
Machine B	850	1,100	1,350	1,075
Machine C	700	1,000	1,300	970
With perfect information	700	1,000	1,150	925
Probability	0.4	0.3	0.3	

TABLE 3.15

Opportunity Loss Table for Business Analytics Department

	10,000 COPIES PER MONTH	20,000 COPIES PER MONTH	30,000 COPIES PER MONTH	MAXIMUM	EOL
Machine A	250	50	0	250	115
Machine B	150	100	200	200	150
Machine C	0	0	150	150	45
Probability	0.4	0.3	0.3		

To find EVPI, we first find the payoffs (costs) that would be experienced with perfect information. The best payoff in each state of nature is the lowest value (cost) in that state of nature, as shown in the bottom row of Table 3.14. These values are used to calculate EVwPI. With these costs, we find

$$EVwPI = \$925$$
$$\text{Best EMV without perfect information} = \$970$$
$$EVPI = 970 - 925 = \$45$$

Perfect information would lower the expected value by $45.

To apply criteria based on opportunity loss, we must first develop the opportunity loss table. In each state of nature, the opportunity loss indicates how much worse each payoff is than the best possible payoff in that state of nature. The best payoff (cost) would be the lowest cost. Thus, to get the opportunity loss in this case, we subtract the lowest value in each column from all the values in that column and we obtain the opportunity loss table.

Once the opportunity loss table has been developed, the minimax regret criterion is applied exactly as it was for the Thompson Lumber example. The maximum regret for each alternative is found and the alternative with the minimum of these maximums is selected. As seen in Table 3.15, the minimum of these maximums is 150 so Machine C would be selected based on this criterion.

The probabilities are used to compute the expected opportunity losses as shown in Table 3.15. Machine C has the lowest EOL of $45, so it would be selected based on the minimum EOL criterion. As previously noted, the minimum EOL is equal to the expected value of perfect information.

3.7   Using Software for Payoff Table Problems

It is easy to use QM for Windows or Excel QM or even Excel 2013 without any add-ins to perform the calculations associated with payoff tables. The Thompson Lumber example is used in the following examples for illustration.

QM for Windows

To use QM for Windows for the Thompson Lumber example, select Modules – Decision Theory. Then enter New-Payoff Tables, and a window appears allowing you to set up the problem. Enter a title, the number of options (alternatives), the number of scenarios (states of nature),

PROGRAM 3.1A

QM for Windows Input for Thompson Lumber Example

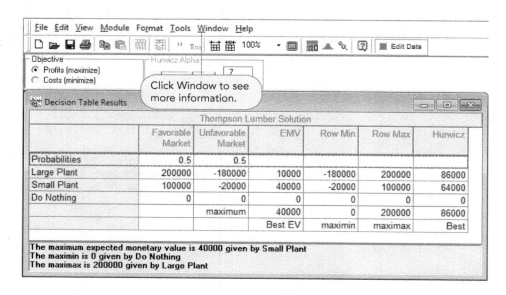

Enter data into table and type the row and column names.

	Favorable	Unfavorable
Probabilities	0.5	0.5
Large Plant	200000	-180000
Small Plant	100000	-20000
Do Nothing	0	0

PROGRAM 3.1B

QM for Windows Output Screen for Thompson Lumber Example

File Edit View Module Format Tools Window Help

Objective
○ Profits (maximize)
○ Costs (minimize)

Click Window to see more information.

Decision Table Results

Thompson Lumber Solution

	Favorable Market	Unfavorable Market	EMV	Row Min	Row Max	Hurwicz
Probabilities	0.5	0.5				
Large Plant	200000	-180000	10000	-180000	200000	86000
Small Plant	100000	-20000	40000	-20000	100000	64000
Do Nothing	0	0	0	0	0	0
		maximum	40000	0	200000	86000
			Best EV	maximin	maximax	Best

The maximum expected monetary value is 40000 given by Small Plant
The maximin is 0 given by Do Nothing
The maximax is 200000 given by Large Plant

and specify if it is to be maximized or minimized. In this example, there are three alternatives or options, and two states of nature or scenarios. When these are entered, click OK and a window appears (Program 3.1A) allowing you to enter the probabilities and payoffs. You can also change the names of the alternatives and states of nature by simply typing over the default names. When you click *Solve*, the output in Program 3.1B appears. Additional output such as EVPI and opportunity loss results are available by clicking Window on the screen where the output is displayed.

Excel QM

To use Excel QM for the Thompson Lumber example, from the Excel QM ribbon in Excel 2013, click *Alphabetical* Menu and select *Decision Analysis – Decision Tables*. When the window opens to enter the parameters of the problem, you should enter a title, the number of alternatives, the number of states of nature, and specify if it is to be maximized or minimized. Click OK and an empty payoff table is created. You simply enter the probabilities, payoffs, and names for the rows and columns. The calculations are performed automatically and the results are shown in Program 3.2A. While the formulas are automatically developed in Excel QM, Program 3.2B shows the important formulas in this example. To see the formulas in Excel, simply hold down the control key and press the grave accent (`) key (usually found above the Tab key). To return Excel 2013 spreadsheet display to the numbers instead of the formulas, simply press the keys again.

PROGRAM 3.2A

Excel QM Results for Thompson Lumber Example

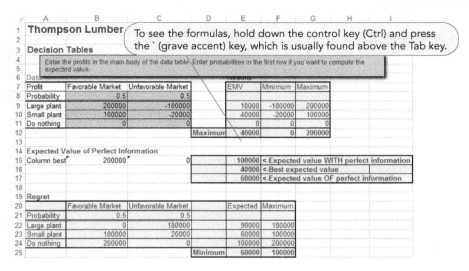

PROGRAM 3.2B

Key Formulas in Excel QM for Thompson Lumber Example

	E	F	G
9	=SUMPRODUCT($B$8:$C$8,B9:C9)	=MIN(B9:C9)	=MAX(B9:C9)
10	=SUMPRODUCT($B$8:$C$8,B10:C10)	=MIN(B10:C10)	=MAX(B10:C10)
11	=SUMPRODUCT($B$8:$C$8,B11:C11)	=MIN(B11:C11)	=MAX(B11:C11)
12	=MAX(E9:E11)	=MAX(F9:F11)	=MAX(G9:G11)
13			
14			
15	=SUMPRODUCT($B$8:$C$8,B15:C15)	<-Expected value W	
16	=E12	<-Best expected val	
17	=E15-E12	<-Expected value O	
18			
19			
20	Expected	Maximum	
21			
22	=SUMPRODUCT($B$8:$C$8,B22:C22)	=MAX(B22:C22)	
23	=SUMPRODUCT($B$8:$C$8,B23:C23)	=MAX(B23:C23)	
24	=SUMPRODUCT($B$8:$C$8,B24:C24)	=MAX(B24:C24)	
25	=MIN(E22:E24)	=MIN(F22:F24)	

3.8 Decision Trees

Any problem that can be presented in a decision table can also be graphically illustrated in a **decision tree**. All decision trees are similar in that they contain *decision points* or **decision nodes** and *state-of-nature points* or **state-of-nature nodes**:

- A decision node from which one of several alternatives may be chosen
- A state-of-nature node out of which one state of nature will occur

In drawing the tree, we begin at the left and move to the right. Thus, the tree presents the decisions and outcomes in sequential order. Lines or branches from the squares (decision nodes) represent alternatives, and branches from the circles represent the states of nature. Figure 3.2 gives the basic decision tree for the Thompson Lumber example. First, John decides whether to construct a large plant, a small plant, or no plant. Then, once that decision is made, the possible states of nature or outcomes (favorable or unfavorable market) will occur. The next step is to put the payoffs and probabilities on the tree and begin the analysis.

FIGURE 3.2

Thompson's Decision Tree

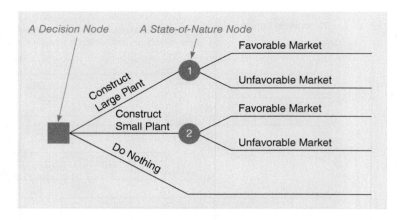

Analyzing problems with decision trees involves five steps:

Five Steps of Decision Tree Analysis

1. Define the problem.
2. Structure or draw the decision tree.
3. Assign probabilities to the states of nature.
4. Estimate payoffs for each possible combination of alternatives and states of nature.
5. Solve the problem by computing EMVs for each state-of-nature node. This is done by working backward, that is, starting at the right of the tree and working back to decision nodes on the left. Also, at each decision node, the alternative with the best EMV is selected.

The final decision tree with the payoffs and probabilities for John Thompson's decision situation is shown in Figure 3.3. Note that the payoffs are placed at the right side of each of the tree's branches. The probabilities are shown in parentheses next to each state of nature. Beginning with the payoffs on the right of the figure, the EMVs for each state-of-nature node are then calculated and placed by their respective nodes. The EMV of the first node is $10,000. This represents the branch from the decision node to construct a large plant. The

FIGURE 3.3

Completed and Solved Decision Tree for Thompson Lumber

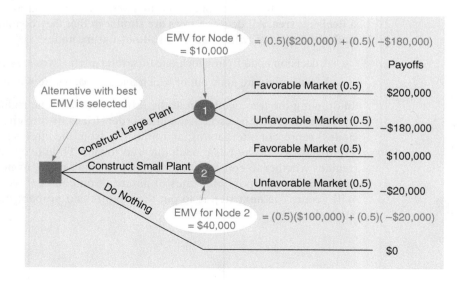

EMV for node 2, to construct a small plant, is $40,000. Building no plant or doing nothing has, of course, a payoff of $0. The branch leaving the decision node leading to the state-of-nature node with the highest EMV should be chosen. In Thompson's case, a small plant should be built.

A MORE COMPLEX DECISION FOR THOMPSON LUMBER—SAMPLE INFORMATION When **sequential decisions** need to be made, decision trees are much more powerful tools than decision tables. Let's say that John Thompson has two decisions to make, with the second decision dependent on the outcome of the first. Before deciding about building a new plant, John has the option of conducting his own marketing research survey, at a cost of $10,000. The information from his survey could help him decide whether to construct a large plant, a small plant, or not to build at all. John recognizes that such a market survey will not provide him with *perfect* information, but it may help quite a bit nevertheless.

All outcomes and alternatives must be considered.

John's new decision tree is represented in Figure 3.4. Let's take a careful look at this more complex tree. Note that *all possible outcomes and alternatives* are included in their logical sequence. This is one of the strengths of using decision trees in making decisions. The user is forced to examine all possible outcomes, including unfavorable ones. He or she is also forced to make decisions in a logical, sequential manner.

FIGURE 3.4
Larger Decision Tree with Payoffs and Probabilities for Thompson Lumber

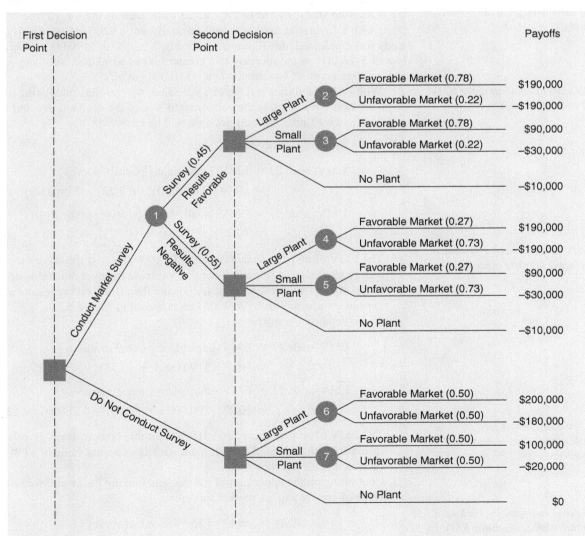

Examining the tree, we see that Thompson's first decision point is whether to conduct the $10,000 market survey. If he chooses not to do the study (the lower part of the tree), he can either construct a large plant, a small plant, or no plant. This is John's second decision point. The market will be either favorable (0.50 probability) or unfavorable (also 0.50 probability) if he builds. The payoffs for each of the possible consequences are listed along the right side. As a matter of fact, the lower portion of John's tree is *identical* to the simpler decision tree shown in Figure 3.3. Why is this so?

The upper part of Figure 3.4 reflects the decision to conduct the market survey. State-of-nature node 1 has two branches. There is a 45% chance that the survey results will indicate a favorable market for storage sheds. We also note that the probability is 0.55 that the survey results will be negative. The derivation of this probability will be discussed in the next section.

Most of the probabilities are conditional probabilities.

The rest of the probabilities shown in parentheses in Figure 3.4 are all **conditional probabilities** or **posterior probabilities** (these probabilities will also be discussed in the next section). For example, 0.78 is the probability of a favorable market for the sheds given a favorable result from the market survey. Of course, you would expect to find a high probability of a favorable market given that the research indicated that the market was good. Don't forget, though, there is a chance that John's $10,000 market survey didn't result in perfect or even reliable information. Any market research study is subject to error. In this case, there is a 22% chance that the market for sheds will be unfavorable given that the survey results are positive.

We note that there is a 27% chance that the market for sheds will be favorable given that John's survey results are negative. The probability is much higher, 0.73, that the market will actually be unfavorable given that the survey was negative.

The cost of the survey had to be subtracted from the original payoffs.

Finally, when we look to the payoff column in Figure 3.4, we see that $10,000, the cost of the marketing study, had to be subtracted from each of the top 10 tree branches. Thus, a large plant with a favorable market would normally net a $200,000 profit. But because the market study was conducted, this figure is reduced by $10,000 to $190,000. In the unfavorable case, the loss of $180,000 would increase to a greater loss of $190,000. Similarly, conducting the survey and building no plant now results in a −$10,000 payoff.

We start by computing the EMV of each branch.

With all probabilities and payoffs specified, we can start calculating the EMV at each state-of-nature node. We begin at the end, or right side of the decision tree and work back toward the origin. When we finish, the best decision will be known.

1. Given favorable survey results,

$$EMV(\text{node } 2) = EMV(\text{large plant} \mid \text{positive survey})$$
$$= (0.78)(\$190,000) + (0.22)(-\$190,000) = \$106,400$$

$$EMV(\text{node } 3) = EMV(\text{small plant} \mid \text{positive survey})$$
$$= (0.78)(\$90,000) + (0.22)(-\$30,000) = \$63,600$$

EMV calculations for favorable survey results are made first.

The EMV of no plant in this case is −$10,000. Thus, if the survey results are favorable, a large plant should be built. Note that we bring the expected value of this decision ($106,400) to the decision node to indicate that, if the survey results are positive, our expected value will be $106,400. This is shown in Figure 3.5.

2. Given negative survey results,

$$EMV(\text{node } 4) = EMV(\text{large plant} \mid \text{negative survey})$$
$$= (0.27)(\$190,000) + (0.73)(-\$190,000) = -\$87,400$$

$$EMV(\text{node } 5) = EMV(\text{small plant} \mid \text{negative survey})$$
$$= (0.27)(\$90,000) + (0.73)(-\$30,000) = \$2,400$$

EMV calculations for unfavorable survey results are done next.

The EMV of no plant is again −$10,000 for this branch. Thus, given a negative survey result, John should build a small plant with an expected value of $2,400, and this figure is indicated at the decision node.

3. Continuing on the upper part of the tree and moving backward, we compute the expected value of conducting the market survey:

We continue working backward to the origin, computing EMV values.

$$EMV(\text{node } 1) = EMV(\text{conduct survey})$$
$$= (0.45)(\$106,400) + (0.55)(\$2,400)$$
$$= \$47,880 + \$1,320 = \$49,200$$

FIGURE 3.5
Thompson's Decision Tree with EMVs Shown

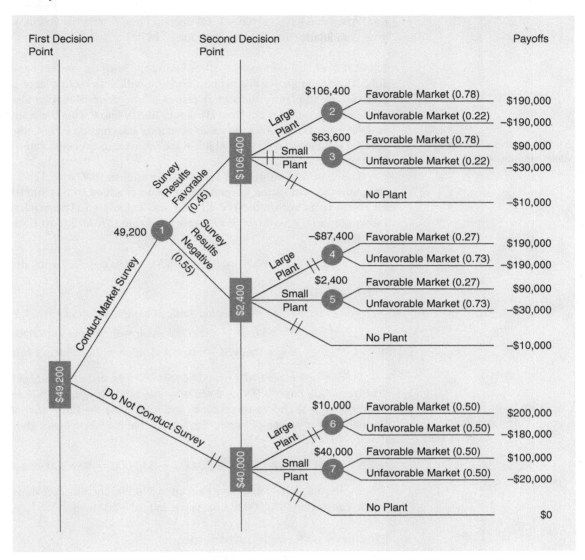

4. If the market survey is *not* conducted,

$$\text{EMV(node 6)} = \text{EMV(large plant)}$$
$$= (0.50)(\$200,000) + (0.50)(-\$180,000)$$
$$= \$10,000$$

$$\text{EMV(node 7)} = \text{EMV(small plant)}$$
$$= (0.50)(\$100,000) + (0.50)(-\$20,000)$$
$$= \$40,000$$

The EMV of no plant is $0.

Thus, building a small plant is the best choice, given that the marketing research is not performed, as we saw earlier.

5. We move back to the first decision node and choose the best alternative. The EMV of conducting the survey is $49,200, versus an EMV of $40,000 for not conducting the study, so the best choice is to *seek* marketing information. If the survey results are favorable, John should construct a large plant, but if the research is negative, John should construct a small plant.

In Figure 3.5, these expected values are placed on the decision tree. Notice on the tree that a pair of slash lines // through a decision branch indicates that a particular alternative is dropped from further consideration. This is because its EMV is lower than the EMV for the best alternative. After you have solved several decision tree problems, you may find it easier to do all of your computations on the tree diagram.

EXPECTED VALUE OF SAMPLE INFORMATION With the market survey he intends to conduct, John Thompson knows that his best decision will be to build a large plant if the survey is favorable or a small plant if the survey results are negative. But John also realizes that conducting the market research is not free. He would like to know what the actual value of doing a survey is. One way of measuring the value of market information is to compute the **expected value of sample information** (EVSI) which is the increase in expected value resulting from the sample information.

EVSI measures the value of sample information.

The expected value *with* sample information (EV with SI) is found from the decision tree, and the cost of the sample information is added to this since this was subtracted from all the payoffs before the EV with SI was calculated. The expected value *without* sample information (EV without SI) is then subtracted from this to find the value of the sample information.

$$\text{EVSI} = (\text{EV with SI} + \text{cost}) - (\text{EV without SI}) \tag{3-4}$$

where

$$\text{EVSI} = \text{expected value of sample information}$$
$$\text{EV with SI} = \text{expected value with sample information}$$
$$\text{EV without SI} = \text{expected value without sample information}$$

In John's case, his EMV would be \$59,200 *if* he hadn't already subtracted the \$10,000 study cost from each payoff. (Do you see why this is so? If not, add \$10,000 back into each payoff, as in the original Thompson problem, and recompute the EMV of conducting the market study.) From the lower branch of Figure 3.5, we see that the EMV of *not* gathering the sample information is \$40,000. Thus,

$$\text{EVSI} = (\$49,200 + \$10,000) - \$40,000 = \$59,200 - \$40,000 = \$19,200$$

This means that John could have paid up to \$19,200 for a market study and still come out ahead. Since it costs only \$10,000, the survey is indeed worthwhile.

Efficiency of Sample Information

There may be many types of sample information available to a decision maker. In developing a new product, information could be obtained from a survey, from a focus group, from other market research techniques, or from actually using a test market to see how sales will be. While none of these sources of information are perfect, they can be evaluated by comparing the EVSI with the EVPI. If the sample information was perfect, then the efficiency would be 100%. The **efficiency of sample information** is

$$\text{Efficiency of sample information} = \frac{\text{EVSI}}{\text{EVPI}} 100\% \tag{3-5}$$

In the Thompson Lumber example,

$$\text{Efficiency of sample information} = \frac{19,200}{60,000} 100\% = 32\%$$

Thus, the market survey is only 32% as efficient as perfect information.

Sensitivity Analysis

As with payoff tables, sensitivity analysis can be applied to decision trees as well. The overall approach is the same. Consider the decision tree for the expanded Thompson Lumber problem shown in Figure 3.5. How sensitive is our decision (to conduct the marketing survey) to the probability of favorable survey results?

Let p be the probability of favorable survey results. Then $(1 - p)$ is the probability of negative survey results. Given this information, we can develop an expression for the EMV of conducting the survey, which is node 1:

$$EMV(node\ 1) = (\$106,400)p + (\$2,400)(1 - p)$$
$$= \$104,000p + \$2,400$$

We are indifferent when the EMV of conducting the marketing survey, node 1, is the same as the EMV of not conducting the survey, which is $40,000. We can find the indifference point by equating EMV(node 1) to $40,000:

$$\$104,000p + \$2,400 = \$40,000$$
$$\$104,000p = \$37,600$$
$$p = \frac{\$37,600}{\$104,000} = 0.36$$

As long as the probability of favorable survey results, p, is greater than 0.36, our decision will stay the same. When p is less than 0.36, our decision will be not to conduct the survey.

We could also perform sensitivity analysis for other problem parameters. For example, we could find how sensitive our decision is to the probability of a favorable market given favorable survey results. At this time, this probability is 0.78. If this value goes up, the large plant becomes more attractive. In this case, our decision would not change. What happens when this probability goes down? The analysis becomes more complex. As the probability of a favorable market given favorable survey results goes down, the small plant becomes more attractive. At some point, the small plant will result in a higher EMV (given favorable survey results) than the large plant. This, however, does not conclude our analysis. As the probability of a favorable market given favorable survey results continues to fall, there will be a point where not conducting the survey, with an EMV of $40,000, will be more attractive than conducting the marketing survey. We leave the actual calculations to you. It is important to note that sensitivity analysis should consider *all* possible consequences.

3.9 How Probability Values Are Estimated by Bayesian Analysis

Bayes' theorem allows decision makers to revise probability values.

There are many ways of getting probability data for a problem such as Thompson's. The numbers (such as 0.78, 0.22, 0.27, 0.73 in Figure 3.4) can be assessed by a manager based on experience and intuition. They can be derived from historical data, or they can be computed from other available data using Bayes' theorem. The advantage of Bayes' theorem is that it incorporates both our initial estimates of the probabilities and information about the accuracy of the information source (e.g., market research survey).

The Bayes' theorem approach recognizes that a decision maker does not know with certainty what state of nature will occur. It allows the manager to revise his or her initial or prior probability assessments based on new information. The revised probabilities are called posterior probabilities. (Before continuing, you may wish to review Bayes' theorem in Chapter 2.)

Calculating Revised Probabilities

In the Thompson Lumber case solved in Section 3.8, we made the assumption that the following four conditional probabilities were known:

$$P(\text{favorable market(FM)} \mid \text{survey results positive}) = 0.78$$
$$P(\text{unfavorable market(UM)} \mid \text{survey results positive}) = 0.22$$
$$P(\text{favorable market(FM)} \mid \text{survey results negative}) = 0.27$$
$$P(\text{unfavorable market(UM)} \mid \text{survey results negative}) = 0.73$$

TABLE 3.16

Market Survey Reliability in Predicting States of Nature

	STATE OF NATURE	
RESULT OF SURVEY	FAVORABLE MARKET (FM)	UNFAVORABLE MARKET (UM)
Positive (predicts favorable market for product)	$P(\text{survey positive} \mid \text{FM}) = 0.70$	$P(\text{survey positive} \mid \text{UM}) = 0.20$
Negative (predicts unfavorable market for product)	$P(\text{survey negative} \mid \text{FM}) = 0.30$	$P(\text{survey negative} \mid \text{UM}) = 0.80$

We now show how John Thompson was able to derive these values with Bayes' theorem. From discussions with market research specialists at the local university, John knows that special surveys such as his can either be positive (i.e., predict a favorable market) or be negative (i.e., predict an unfavorable market). The experts have told John that, statistically, of all new products with a *favorable market* (FM), market surveys were positive and predicted success correctly 70% of the time. Thirty percent of the time the surveys falsely predicted negative results or an *unfavorable market* (UM). On the other hand, when there was actually an unfavorable market for a new product, 80% of the surveys correctly predicted negative results. The surveys incorrectly predicted positive results the remaining 20% of the time. These conditional probabilities are summarized in Table 3.16. They are an indication of the accuracy of the survey that John is thinking of undertaking.

Recall that without any market survey information, John's best estimates of a favorable and unfavorable market are

$$P(\text{FM}) = 0.50$$
$$P(\text{UM}) = 0.50$$

These are referred to as the *prior probabilities*.

We are now ready to compute Thompson's revised or posterior probabilities. These desired probabilities are the reverse of the probabilities in Table 3.16. We need the probability of a favorable or unfavorable market given a positive or negative result from the market study. The general form of Bayes' theorem presented in Chapter 2 is

$$P(A \mid B) = \frac{P(B \mid A)P(A)}{P(B \mid A)P(A) + P(B \mid A')P(A')} \tag{3-6}$$

where

$$A, B = \text{any two events}$$
$$A' = \text{complement of } A$$

We can let A represent a favorable market and B represent a positive survey. Then, substituting the appropriate numbers into this equation, we obtain the conditional probabilities, given that the market survey is positive:

$$P(\text{FM} \mid \text{survey positive}) = \frac{P(\text{survey positive} \mid \text{FM})P(\text{FM})}{P(\text{survey positive} \mid \text{FM})P(\text{FM}) + P(\text{survey positive} \mid \text{UM})P(\text{UM})}$$

$$= \frac{(0.70)(0.50)}{(0.70)(0.50) + (0.20)(0.50)} = \frac{0.35}{0.45} = 0.78$$

$$P(\text{UM} \mid \text{survey positive}) = \frac{P(\text{survey positive} \mid \text{UM})P(\text{UM})}{P(\text{survey positive} \mid \text{UM})P(\text{UM}) + P(\text{survey positive} \mid \text{FM})P(\text{FM})}$$

$$= \frac{(0.20)(0.50)}{(0.20)(0.50) + (0.70)(0.50)} = \frac{0.10}{0.45} = 0.22$$

Note that the denominator (0.45) in these calculations is the probability of a positive survey. An alternative method for these calculations is to use a probability table as shown in Table 3.17.

TABLE 3.17
Probability Revisions Given a Positive Survey

STATE OF NATURE	CONDITIONAL PROBABILITY P(SURVEY POSITIVE|STATE OF NATURE)	PRIOR PROBABILITY	POSTERIOR PROBABILITY	
			JOINT PROBABILITY	P(STATE OF NATURE|SURVEY POSITIVE)
FM	0.70	× 0.50	= 0.35	0.35/0.45 = 0.78
UM	0.20	× 0.50	= 0.10	0.10/0.45 = 0.22
		P(survey results positive)	= 0.45	1.00

The conditional probabilities, given that the market survey is negative, are

$$P(\text{FM}\mid \text{survey negative}) = \frac{P(\text{survey negative}\mid \text{FM})P(\text{FM})}{P(\text{survey negative}\mid \text{FM})P(\text{FM}) + P(\text{survey negative}\mid \text{UM})P(\text{UM})}$$

$$= \frac{(0.30)(0.50)}{(0.30)(0.50) + (0.80)(0.50)} = \frac{0.15}{0.55} = 0.27$$

$$P(\text{UM}\mid \text{survey negative}) = \frac{P(\text{survey negative}\mid \text{UM})P(\text{UM})}{P(\text{survey negative}\mid \text{UM})P(\text{UM}) + P(\text{survey negative}\mid \text{FM})P(\text{FM})}$$

$$= \frac{(0.80)(0.50)}{(0.80)(0.50) + (0.30)(0.50)} = \frac{0.40}{0.55} = 0.73$$

Note that the denominator (0.55) in these calculations is the probability of a negative survey. These computations given a negative survey could also have been performed in a table instead, as in Table 3.18.

The calculations shown in Tables 3.17 and 3.18 can easily be performed in Excel spreadsheets. Programs 3.3A and 3.3B show the final output for this example and the formulas.

New probabilities provide valuable information.

The posterior probabilities now provide John Thompson with estimates for each state of nature if the survey results are positive or negative. As you know, John's **prior probability** of success without a market survey was only 0.50. Now he is aware that the probability of successfully marketing storage sheds will be 0.78 if his survey shows positive results. His chances of success drop to 27% if the survey report is negative. This is valuable management information, as we saw in the earlier decision tree analysis.

Potential Problem in Using Survey Results

In many decision-making problems, survey results or pilot studies are done before an actual decision (such as building a new plant or taking a particular course of action) is made. As discussed earlier in this section, Bayes' analysis is used to help determine the correct

TABLE 3.18
Probability Revisions Given a Negative Survey

STATE OF NATURE	CONDITIONAL PROBABILITY P(SURVEY NEGATIVE|STATE OF NATURE)	PRIOR PROBABILITY	POSTERIOR PROBABILITY	
			JOINT PROBABILITY	P(STATE OF NATURE|SURVEY NEGATIVE)
FM	0.30	× 0.50	= 0.15	0.15/0.55 = 0.27
UM	0.80	× 0.50	= 0.40	0.40/0.55 = 0.73
		P(survey results negative)	= 0.55	

PROGRAM 3.3A

Results of Bayes' Calculations in Excel 2013

	A	B	C	D	E
1	Bayes Theorem for Thompson Lumber Example				
2					
3	Fill in cells B7, B8, and C7				
4					
5	Probability Revisions Given a Positive Survey				
6	State of Nature	P(Sur.Pos.|state of nature)	Prior Prob.	Joint Prob.	Posterior Probability
7	FM	0.7	0.5	0.35	0.78
8	UM	0.2	0.5	0.1	0.22
9			P(Sur.pos.)=	0.45	
10					
11	Probability Revisions Given a Negative Survey				
12	State of Nature	P(Sur.Pos.|state of nature)	Prior Prob.	Joint Prob.	Posterior Probability
13	FM	0.3	0.5	0.15	0.27
14	UM	0.8	0.5	0.4	0.73
15			P(Sur.neg.)=	0.55	

PROGRAM 3.3B

Formulas Used for Bayes' Calculations in Excel 2013

	B	C	D	E
7	0.7	0.5	=B7*C7	=D7/$D$9
8	0.2	=1-C7	=B8*C8	=D8/$D$9
9		P(Sur.pos.)=	=SUM(D7:D8)	
11				
13	=1-B7	=C7	=B13*C13	=D13/$D$15
14	=1-B8	=C8	=B14*C14	=D14/$D$15
15		P(Sur.neg.)=	=SUM(D13:D14)	

conditional probabilities that are needed to solve these types of decision theory problems. In computing these conditional probabilities, we need to have data about the surveys and their accuracies. If a decision to build a plant or to take another course of action is actually made, we can determine the accuracy of our surveys. Unfortunately, we cannot always get data about those situations in which the decision was not to build a plant or not to take some course of action. Thus, sometimes when we use survey results, we are basing our probabilities only on those cases in which a decision to build a plant or take some course of action is actually made. This means that, in some situations, conditional probability information may not be not quite as accurate as we would like. Even so, calculating conditional probabilities helps to refine the decision-making process and, in general, to make better decisions.

3.10   Utility Theory

We have focused on the EMV criterion for making decisions under risk. However, there are many occasions in which people make decisions that would appear to be inconsistent with the EMV criterion. When people buy insurance, the amount of the premium is greater than the expected payout to them from the insurance company because the premium includes the expected payout, the overhead cost, and the profit for the insurance company. A person involved in a lawsuit may choose to settle out of court rather than go to trial even if the expected value of going to trial is greater than the proposed settlement. A person buys a lottery ticket even though the expected return is negative. Casino games of all types have negative expected returns for the player, and yet millions of people play these games. A businessperson may rule out one potential decision because it could bankrupt the firm if things go bad, even though the expected return for this decision is better than that of all other alternatives.

Why do people make decisions that don't maximize their EMV? They do this because the monetary value is not always a true indicator of the overall value of the result of the

FIGURE 3.6

Your Decision Tree for the Lottery Ticket

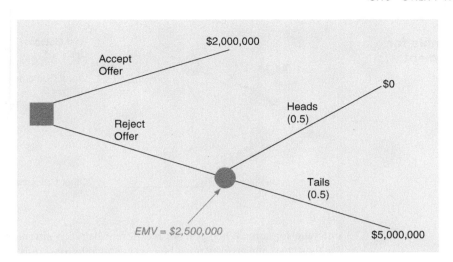

The overall value of the result of a decision is called utility.

decision. The overall worth of a particular outcome is called **utility**, and rational people make decisions that maximize the expected utility. Although at times the monetary value is a good indicator of utility, there are other times when it is not. This is particularly true when some of the values involve an extremely large payoff or an extremely large loss. Suppose that you are the lucky holder of a lottery ticket. Five minutes from now a fair coin could be flipped, and if it comes up tails, you would win $5 million. If it comes up heads, you would win nothing. Just a moment ago a wealthy person offered you $2 million for your ticket. Let's assume that you have no doubts about the validity of the offer. The person will give you a certified check for the full amount, and you are absolutely sure the check would be good.

A decision tree for this situation is shown in Figure 3.6. The EMV for rejecting the offer indicates that you should hold on to your ticket, but what would you do? Just think, $2 million for *sure* instead of a 50% chance at nothing. Suppose you were greedy enough to hold on to the ticket, and then lost. How would you explain that to your friends? Wouldn't $2 million be enough to be comfortable for a while?

Most people would choose to sell the ticket for $2 million. Most of us, in fact, would probably be willing to settle for a lot less. Just how low we would go is, of course, a matter of personal preference. People have different feelings about seeking or avoiding risk. Using the EMV alone is not always a good way to make these types of decisions.

EMV is not always the best approach.

One way to incorporate your own attitudes toward risk is through **utility theory**. In the next section, we explore first how to measure utility and then how to use utility measures in decision making.

Measuring Utility and Constructing a Utility Curve

The first step in using utility theory is to assign utility values to each monetary value in a given situation. It is convenient to begin **utility assessment** by assigning the worst outcome a utility of 0 and the best outcome a utility of 1. Although any values may be used as long as the utility for the best outcome is greater than the utility for the worst outcome, using 0 and 1 has some benefits. Because we have chosen to use 0 and 1, all other outcomes will have a utility value between 0 and 1. In determining the utilities of all outcomes, other than the best or worst outcome, a **standard gamble** is considered. This gamble is shown in Figure 3.7.

Utility assessment assigns the worst outcome a utility of 0 and the best outcome a utility of 1.

In Figure 3.7, p is the probability of obtaining the best outcome, and $(1 - p)$ is the probability of obtaining the worst outcome. Assessing the utility of any other outcome involves determining the probability (p), which makes you indifferent between alternative 1, which is the gamble between the best and worst outcomes, and alternative 2, which is obtaining the other

When you are indifferent, the expected utilities are equal.

FIGURE 3.7

Standard Gamble for Utility Assessment

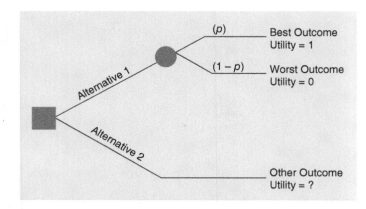

outcome for sure. When you are indifferent between alternatives 1 and 2, the expected utilities for these two alternatives must be equal. This relationship is shown as

Expected utility of alternative 2 = Expected utility of alternative 1

Utility of other outcome = (p)(utility of *best* outcome, which is 1)

$+ (1 - p)$(utility of the *worst* outcome, which is 0)

Utility of other outcome = $(p)(1) + (1 - p)(0) = p$ (3-7)

Now all you have to do is to determine the value of the probability (p) that makes you indifferent between alternatives 1 and 2. In setting the probability, you should be aware that utility assessment is completely subjective. It's a value set by the decision maker that can't be measured on an objective scale. Let's take a look at an example.

Once utility values have been determined, a utility curve can be constructed.

Jane Dickson would like to construct a utility curve revealing her preference for money between $0 and $10,000. A **utility curve** is a graph that plots utility value versus monetary value. She can invest her money either in a bank savings account or in a real estate deal.

If the money is invested in the bank, in 3 years Jane would have $5,000. If she invested in the real estate, after 3 years she could either have nothing or $10,000. Jane, however, is very conservative. Unless there is an 80% chance of getting $10,000 from the real estate deal, Jane would prefer to have her money in the bank, where it is safe. What Jane has done here is to assess her utility for $5,000. When there is an 80% chance (this means that p is 0.8) of getting $10,000, Jane is indifferent between putting her money in real estate and putting it in the bank. Jane's utility for $5,000 is thus equal to 0.8, which is the same as the value for p. This utility assessment is shown in Figure 3.8.

Other utility values can be assessed in the same way. For example, what is Jane's utility for $7,000? What value of p would make Jane indifferent between $7,000 and the gamble that would result in either $10,000 or $0? For Jane, there must be a 90% chance of getting the $10,000. Otherwise, she would prefer the $7,000 for sure. Thus, her utility for $7,000 is 0.90. Jane's utility for $3,000 can be determined in the same way. If there were a 50% chance of obtaining the $10,000, Jane would be indifferent between having $3,000 for sure and taking the gamble of either winning

FIGURE 3.8

Utility of $5,000

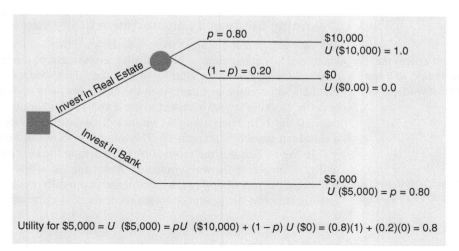

Utility for $5,000 = U ($5,000) = pU ($10,000) + $(1 - p)$ U ($0) = (0.8)(1) + (0.2)(0) = 0.8

FIGURE 3.9
Utility Curve for Jane Dickson

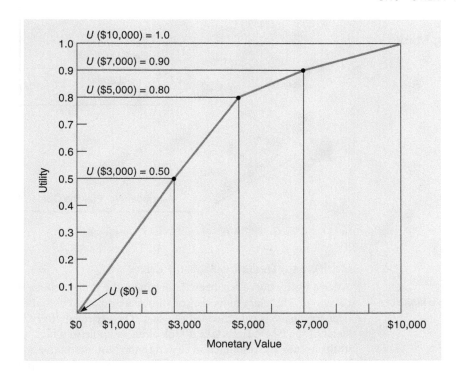

the $10,000 or getting nothing. Thus, the utility of $3,000 for Jane is 0.5. Of course, this process can be continued until Jane has assessed her utility for as many monetary values as she wants. These assessments, however, are enough to get an idea of Jane's feelings toward risk. In fact, we can plot these points in a utility curve, as is done in Figure 3.9. In the figure, the assessed utility points of $3,000, $5,000, and $7,000 are shown by dots, and the rest of the curve is inferred from these.

Jane's utility curve is typical of a **risk avoider**. A risk avoider is a decision maker who gets less utility or pleasure from a greater risk and tends to avoid situations in which high losses might occur. As monetary value increases on her utility curve, the utility increases at a slower rate.

The shape of a person's utility curve depends on many factors.

Figure 3.10 illustrates that a person who is a **risk seeker** has an opposite-shaped utility curve. This decision maker gets more utility from a greater risk and higher potential payoff. As monetary value increases on his or her utility curve, the utility increases at an increasing rate. A person who is *indifferent* to risk has a utility curve that is a straight line. The shape of a person's utility curve depends on the specific decision being considered, the monetary values involved in the situation, the person's psychological frame of mind, and how the person feels about the future. It may well be that you have one utility curve for some situations you face and completely different curves for others.

FIGURE 3.10
Preferences for Risk

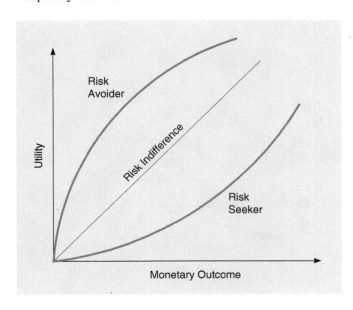

FIGURE 3.11

Decision Facing Mark Simkin

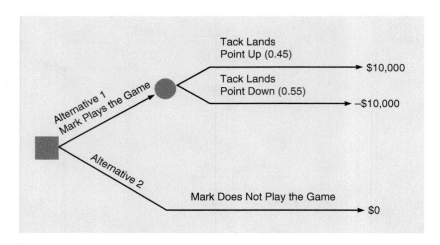

Utility as a Decision-Making Criterion

Utility values replace monetary values.

After a utility curve has been determined, the utility values from the curve are used in making decisions. Monetary outcomes or values are replaced with the appropriate utility values and then decision analysis is performed as usual. The expected utility for each alternative is computed instead of the EMV. Let's take a look at an example in which a decision tree is used and expected utility values are computed in selecting the best alternative.

Mark Simkin loves to gamble. He decides to play a game that involves tossing thumbtacks in the air. If the point on the thumbtack is facing up after it lands, Mark wins $10,000. If the point on the thumbtack is down, Mark loses $10,000. Should Mark play the game (alternative 1) or should he not play the game (alternative 2)?

Alternatives 1 and 2 are displayed in the tree shown in Figure 3.11. As can be seen, alternative 1 is to play the game. Mark believes that there is a 45% chance of winning $10,000 and a 55% chance of suffering the $10,000 loss. Alternative 2 is not to gamble. What should Mark do? Of course, this depends on Mark's utility for money. As stated previously, he likes to gamble. Using the procedure just outlined, Mark was able to construct a utility curve showing his preference for money. Mark has a total of $20,000 to gamble, so he has constructed the utility curve based on a best payoff of $20,000 and a worst payoff of a $20,000 loss. This curve appears in Figure 3.12.

Mark's objective is to maximize expected utility.

We see that Mark's utility for −$10,000 is 0.05, his utility for not playing ($0) is 0.15, and his utility for $10,000 is 0.30. These values can now be used in the decision tree. Mark's objective is to maximize his expected utility, which can be done as follows:

Step 1.
$$U(-\$10,000) = 0.05$$
$$U(\$0) = 0.15$$
$$U(\$10,000) = 0.30$$

FIGURE 3.12

Utility Curve for Mark Simkin

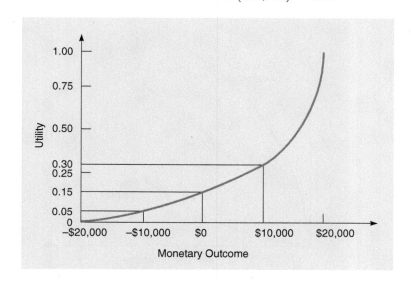

IN ACTION Multiattribute Utility Model Aids in Disposal of Nuclear Weapons

When the Cold War between the United States and the USSR ended, the two countries agreed to dismantle a large number of nuclear weapons. The exact number of weapons is not known, but the total number has been estimated to be over 40,000. The plutonium recovered from the dismantled weapons presented several concerns. The National Academy of Sciences characterized the possibility that the plutonium could fall into the hands of terrorists as a very real danger. Also, plutonium is very toxic to the environment, so a safe and secure disposal process was critical. Deciding what disposal process would be used was no easy task.

Due to the long relationship between the United States and the USSR during the Cold War, it was necessary that the plutonium disposal process for each country occur at approximately the same time. Whichever method was selected by one country would have to be approved by the other country. The U.S. Department of Energy (DOE) formed the Office of Fissile Materials Disposition (OFMD) to oversee the process of selecting the approach to use for disposal of the plutonium. Recognizing that the decision could be controversial, the OFMD used a team of operations research analysts associated with the Amarillo National Research Center. This OR group used a multiattribute utility (MAU) model to combine several performance measures into one single measure.

A total of 37 performance measures were used in evaluating 13 different possible alternatives. The MAU model combined these measures and helped to rank the alternatives as well as identify the deficiencies of some alternatives. The OFMD recommended two of the alternatives with the highest rankings, and development was begun on both of them. This parallel development permitted the United States to react quickly when the USSR's plan was developed. The USSR used an analysis based on this same MAU approach. The United States and the USSR chose to convert the plutonium from nuclear weapons into mixed oxide fuel, which is used in nuclear reactors to make electricity. Once the plutonium is converted to this form, it cannot be used in nuclear weapons.

The MAU model helped the United States and the USSR deal with a very sensitive and potentially hazardous issue in a way that considered economic, nonproliferation, and ecology issues. The framework is now being used by Russia to evaluate other policies related to nuclear energy.

Source: Based on John C. Butler et al. "The United States and Russia Evaluate Plutonium Disposition Options with Multiattribute Utility Theory," *Interfaces* 35, 1 (January–February 2005): 88–101.

Step 2. Replace monetary values with utility values. Refer to Figure 3.13. Here are the expected utilities for alternatives 1 and 2:

$$E(\text{alternative 1: play the game}) = (0.45)(0.30) + (0.55)(0.05)$$
$$= 0.135 + 0.027 = 0.162$$

$$E(\text{alternative 2: don't play the game}) = 0.15$$

Therefore, alternative 1 is the best strategy using utility as the decision criterion. If EMV had been used, alternative 2 would have been the best strategy. The utility curve is a risk-seeker utility curve, and the choice of playing the game certainly reflects this preference for risk.

FIGURE 3.13

Using Expected Utilities in Decision Making

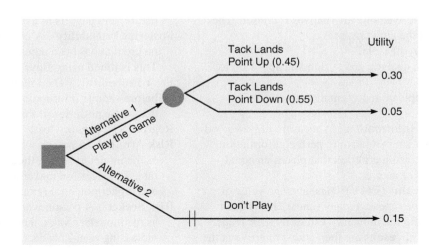

Summary

Decision theory is an analytic and systematic approach to studying decision making. Six steps are usually involved in making decisions in three environments: decision making under certainty, uncertainty, and risk. In decision making under uncertainty, decision tables are constructed to compute criteria such as maximax, maximin, criterion of realism, equally likely, and minimax regret. Methods such as determining expected monetary value (EMV), expected value of perfect information (EVPI), expected opportunity loss (EOL), and sensitivity analysis are used in decision making under risk.

Decision trees are another option, particularly for larger decision problems, when one decision must be made before other decisions can be made. For example, a decision to take a sample or to perform market research is made before we decide to construct a large plant, a small one, or no plant. In this case, we can also compute the expected value of sample information (EVSI) to determine the value of the market research. The efficiency of sample information compares the EVSI to the EVPI. Bayesian analysis can be used to revise or update probability values using both the prior probabilities and other probabilities related to the accuracy of the information source.

Glossary

Alternative A course of action or a strategy that may be chosen by a decision maker.

Coefficient of Realism (α) A number from 0 to 1. When the coefficient is close to 1, the decision criterion is optimistic. When the coefficient is close to 0, the decision criterion is pessimistic.

Conditional Probability A posterior probability.

Conditional Value or Payoff A consequence, normally expressed in a monetary value, that occurs as a result of a particular alternative and state of nature.

Criterion of Realism A decision-making criterion that uses a weighted average of the best and worst possible payoffs for each alternative.

Decision Making under Certainty A decision-making environment in which the future outcomes or states of nature are known.

Decision Making under Risk A decision-making environment in which several outcomes or states of nature may occur as a result of a decision or alternative. The probabilities of the outcomes or states of nature are known.

Decision Making under Uncertainty A decision-making environment in which several outcomes or states of nature may occur. The probabilities of these outcomes, however, are not known.

Decision Node (Point) In a decision tree, this is a point where the best of the available alternatives is chosen. The branches represent the alternatives.

Decision Table A payoff table.

Decision Theory An analytic and systematic approach to decision making.

Decision Tree A graphical representation of a decision-making situation.

Efficiency of Sample Information A measure of how good the sample information is relative to perfect information.

Equally Likely A decision criterion that places an equal weight on all states of nature.

Expected Monetary Value (EMV) The average value of a decision if it can be repeated many times. This is determined by multiplying the monetary values by their respective probabilities. The results are then added to arrive at the EMV.

Expected Value of Perfect Information (EVPI) The average or expected value of information if it were completely accurate. The increase in EMV that results from having perfect information.

Expected Value of Sample Information (EVSI) The increase in EMV that results from having sample or imperfect information.

Expected Value with Perfect Information (EVwPI) The average or expected value of a decision if perfect knowledge of the future is available.

Hurwicz Criterion The criterion of realism.

Laplace Criterion The equally likely criterion.

Maximax An optimistic decision-making criterion. This selects the alternative with the highest possible return.

Maximin A pessimistic decision-making criterion. This alternative maximizes the minimum payoff. It selects the alternative with the best of the worst possible payoffs.

Minimax Regret A criterion that minimizes the maximum opportunity loss.

Opportunity Loss The amount you would lose by not picking the best alternative. For any state of nature, this is the difference between the consequences of any alternative and the best possible alternative.

Optimistic Criterion The maximax criterion.

Payoff Table A table that lists the alternatives, states of nature, and payoffs in a decision-making situation.

Posterior Probability A conditional probability of a state of nature that has been adjusted based on sample information. This is found using Bayes' theorem.

Prior Probability The initial probability of a state of nature before sample information is used with Bayes' theorem to obtain the posterior probability.

Regret Opportunity loss.

Risk Avoider A person who avoids risk. On the utility curve, as the monetary value, the utility increases at a decreasing rate. This decision maker gets less utility for a greater risk and higher potential returns.

Risk Seeker A person who seeks risk. On the utility curve, as the monetary value increases, the utility increases at an increasing rate. This decision maker gets more pleasure for a greater risk and higher potential returns.

Sequential Decisions   Decisions in which the outcome of one decision influences other decisions.

Standard Gamble   The process used to determine utility values.

State of Nature   An outcome or occurrence over which the decision maker has little or no control.

State-of-Nature Node   In a decision tree, a point where the EMV is computed. The branches coming from this node represent states of nature.

Utility   The overall value or worth of a particular outcome.

Utility Assessment   The process of determining the utility of various outcomes. This is normally done using a standard gamble between any outcome for sure and a gamble between the worst and best outcomes.

Utility Curve   A graph or curve that reveals the relationship between utility and monetary values. When this curve has been constructed, utility values from the curve can be used in the decision-making process.

Utility Theory   A theory that allows decision makers to incorporate their risk preference and other factors into the decision-making process.

Weighted Average Criterion   Another name for the criterion of realism.

Key Equations

(3-1) $\text{EMV}(\text{alternative } i) = \Sigma X_i P(X_i)$

An equation that computes expected monetary value.

(3-2) $\text{EVwPI} = \Sigma (\text{best payoff in state of nature } i)$
$\times (\text{probability of state of nature } i)$

An equation that computes the expected value with perfect information.

(3-3) $\text{EVPI} = \text{EVwPI} - \text{Best EMV}$

An equation that computes the expected value of perfect information.

(3-4) $\text{EVSI} = (\text{EV with SI} + \text{cost}) - (\text{EV without SI})$

An equation that computes the expected value (EV) of sample information (SI).

(3-5) $\text{Efficiency of sample information} = \dfrac{\text{EVSI}}{\text{EVPI}} 100\%$

An equation that compares sample information to perfect information.

(3-6) $P(A|B) = \dfrac{P(B|A)P(A)}{P(B|A)P(A) + P(B|A')P(A')}$

Bayes' theorem—the conditional probability of event A given that event B has occurred.

(3-7) $\text{Utility of other outcome} = (p)(1) + (1 - p)(0) = p$

An equation that determines the utility of an intermediate outcome.

Solved Problems

Solved Problem 3-1

Maria Rojas is considering the possibility of opening a small dress shop on Fairbanks Avenue, a few blocks from the university. She has located a good mall that attracts students. Her options are to open a small shop, a medium-sized shop, or no shop at all. The market for a dress shop can be good, average, or bad. The probabilities for these three possibilities are 0.2 for a good market, 0.5 for an average market, and 0.3 for a bad market. The net profit or loss for the medium-sized and small shops for the various market conditions are given in the following table. Building no shop at all yields no loss and no gain.

a. What do you recommend?
b. Calculate the EVPI.
c. Develop the opportunity loss table for this situation. What decisions would be made using the minimax regret criterion and the minimum EOL criterion?

ALTERNATIVE	GOOD MARKET ($)	AVERAGE MARKET ($)	BAD MARKET ($)
Small shop	75,000	25,000	−40,000
Medium-sized shop	100,000	35,000	−60,000
No shop	0	0	0

Solution

a. Since the decision-making environment is risk (probabilities are known), it is appropriate to use the EMV criterion. The problem can be solved by developing a payoff table that contains all alternatives, states of nature, and probability values. The EMV for each alternative is also computed, as in the following table:

ALTERNATIVE	STATE OF NATURE			
	GOOD MARKET ($)	AVERAGE MARKET ($)	BAD MARKET ($)	EMV ($)
Small shop	75,000	25,000	−40,000	15,500
Medium-sized shop	100,000	35,000	−60,000	19,500
No shop	0	0	0	0
Probabilities	0.20	0.50	0.30	

$$\text{EMV(small shop)} = (0.2)(\$75,000) + (0.5)(\$25,000) + (0.3)(-\$40,000) = \$15,500$$
$$\text{EMV(medium shop)} = (0.2)(\$100,000) + (0.5)(\$35,000) + (0.3)(-\$60,000) = \$19,500$$
$$\text{EMV(no shop)} = (0.2)(\$0) + (0.5)(\$0) + (0.3)(\$0) = \$0$$

As can be seen, the best decision is to build the medium-sized shop. The EMV for this alternative is $19,500.

b. $\text{EVwPI} = (0.2)\$100,000 + (0.5)\$35,000 + (0.3)\$0 = \$37,500$
   $\text{EVPI} = \$37,500 - \$19,500 = \$18,000$

c. The opportunity loss table is shown here.

ALTERNATIVE	STATE OF NATURE				
	GOOD MARKET ($)	AVERAGE MARKET ($)	BAD MARKET ($)	MAXIMUM ($)	EOL ($)
Small shop	25,000	10,000	40,000	40,000	22,000
Medium-sized shop	0	0	60,000	60,000	18,000
No shop	100,000	35,000	0	100,000	37,500
Probabilities	0.20	0.50	0.30		

The best payoff in a good market is 100,000, so the opportunity losses in the first column indicate how much worse each payoff is than 100,000. The best payoff in an average market is 35,000, so the opportunity losses in the second column indicate how much worse each payoff is than 35,000. The best payoff in a bad market is 0, so the opportunity losses in the third column indicate how much worse each payoff is than 0.

The minimax regret criterion considers the maximum regret for each decision, and the decision corresponding to the minimum of these is selected. The decision would be to build a small shop since the maximum regret for this is 40,000, while the maximum regret for each of the other two alternatives is higher as shown in the opportunity loss table.

The decision based on the EOL criterion would be to build the medium shop. Note that the minimum EOL ($18,000) is the same as the EVPI computed in part b. The calculations are

$$\text{EOL(small)} = (0.2)25,000 + (0.5)10,000 + (0.3)40,000 = 22,000$$
$$\text{EOL(medium)} = (0.2)0 + (0.5)0 + (0.3)60,000 = 18,000$$
$$\text{EOL(no shop)} = (0.2)100,000 + (0.5)35,000 + (0.3)0 = 37,500$$

Solved Problem 3-2

Cal Bender and Becky Addison have known each other since high school. Two years ago they entered the same university and today they are taking undergraduate courses in the business school. Both hope to graduate with degrees in finance. In an attempt to make extra money and to use some of the knowledge gained from their business courses, Cal and Becky have decided to look into the possibility of starting a small company that would provide word processing services to students who needed term papers or other reports prepared in a professional manner. Using a systems approach, Cal and Becky have identified three strategies. Strategy 1 is to invest in a fairly expensive microcomputer system with a high-quality laser printer. In a favorable market, they should be able to obtain a net profit of $10,000 over the next 2 years. If the market is unfavorable, they can lose $8,000. Strategy 2 is to purchase a less expensive system. With a favorable market, they could get a return during the next 2 years of $8,000. With an unfavorable market, they would incur a loss of $4,000. Their final strategy, strategy 3, is to do nothing. Cal is basically a risk taker, whereas Becky tries to avoid risk.

a. What type of decision procedure should Cal use? What would Cal's decision be?
b. What type of decision maker is Becky? What decision would Becky make?
c. If Cal and Becky were indifferent to risk, what type of decision approach should they use? What would you recommend if this were the case?

Solution

The problem is one of decision making under uncertainty. Before answering the specific questions, a decision table should be developed showing the alternatives, states of nature, and related consequences.

ALTERNATIVE	FAVORABLE MARKET ($)	UNFAVORABLE MARKET ($)
Strategy 1	10,000	−8,000
Strategy 2	8,000	−4,000
Strategy 3	0	0

a. Since Cal is a risk taker, he should use the maximax decision criteria. This approach selects the row that has the highest or maximum value. The $10,000 value, which is the maximum value from the table, is in row 1. Thus, Cal's decision is to select strategy 1, which is an optimistic decision approach.
b. Becky should use the maximin decision criteria because she wants to avoid risk. The minimum or worst outcome for each row, or strategy, is identified. These outcomes are −$8,000 for strategy 1, −$4,000 for strategy 2, and $0 for strategy 3. The maximum of these values is selected. Thus, Becky would select strategy 3, which reflects a pessimistic decision approach.
c. If Cal and Becky are indifferent to risk, they could use the equally likely approach. This approach selects the alternative that maximizes the row averages. The row average for strategy 1 is $1,000 [i.e., $1,000 = ($10,000 − $8,000)/2]. The row average for strategy 2 is $2,000, and the row average for strategy 3 is $0. Thus, using the equally likely approach, the decision is to select strategy 2, which maximizes the row averages.

Solved Problem 3-3

Monica Britt has enjoyed sailing small boats since she was 7 years old, when her mother started sailing with her. Today, Monica is considering the possibility of starting a company to produce small sailboats for the recreational market. Unlike other mass-produced sailboats, however, these boats will be made specifically for children between the ages of 10 and 15. The boats will be of the highest quality and extremely stable, and the sail size will be reduced to prevent problems of capsizing.

Her basic decision is whether to build a large manufacturing facility, a small manufacturing facility, or no facility at all. With a favorable market, Monica can expect to make $90,000 from the large facility or $60,000 from the smaller facility. If the market is unfavorable, however, Monica estimates that she would lose $30,000 with a large facility, and she would lose only $20,000 with the small facility. Because of the expense involved in developing the initial molds and acquiring the necessary equipment

FIGURE 3.14

Monica's Decision Tree, Listing Alternatives, States of Nature, Probability Values, and Financial Outcomes for Solved Problem 3-3

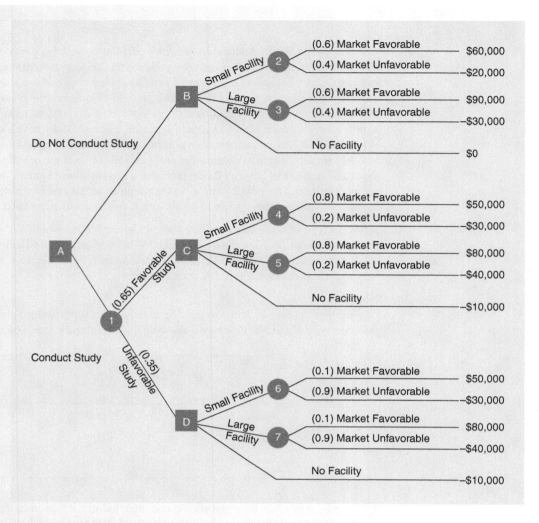

to produce fiberglass sailboats for young children, Monica has decided to conduct a pilot study to make sure that the market for the sailboats will be adequate. She estimates that the pilot study will cost her $10,000. Furthermore, the pilot study can be either favorable or unfavorable. Monica estimates that the probability of a favorable market given a favorable pilot study is 0.8. The probability of an unfavorable market given an unfavorable pilot study result is estimated to be 0.9. Monica feels that there is a 0.65 chance that the pilot study will be favorable. Of course, Monica could bypass the pilot study and simply make the decision as to whether to build a large plant, small plant, or no facility at all. Without doing any testing in a pilot study, she estimates that the probability of a favorable market is 0.6. What do you recommend? Compute the EVSI.

Solution

Before Monica starts to solve this problem, she should develop a decision tree that shows all alternatives, states of nature, probability values, and economic consequences. This decision tree is shown in Figure 3.14.

The EMV at each of the numbered nodes is calculated as follows:

$$\text{EMV(node 2)} = 60,000(0.6) + (-20,000)0.4 = 28,000$$
$$\text{EMV(node 3)} = 90,000(0.6) + (-30,000)0.4 = 42,000$$
$$\text{EMV(node 4)} = 50,000(0.8) + (-30,000)0.2 = 34,000$$
$$\text{EMV(node 5)} = 80,000(0.8) + (-40,000)0.2 = 56,000$$
$$\text{EMV(node 6)} = 50,000(0.1) + (-30,000)0.9 = -22,000$$
$$\text{EMV(node 7)} = 80,000(0.1) + (-40,000)0.9 = -28,000$$
$$\text{EMV(node 1)} = 56,000(0.65) + (-10,000)0.35 = 32,900$$

At each of the square nodes with letters, the decisions would be:

> Node B: Choose Large Facility since the EMV = $42,000.
>
> Node C: Choose Large Facility since the EMV = $56,000.
>
> Node D: Choose No Facility since the EMV = −$10,000.
>
> Node A: Choose Do Not Conduct Study since the EMV ($42,000) for this is higher than EMV(node 1), which is $32,900.

Based on the EMV criterion, Monica would select Do Not Conduct Study and then select Large Facility. The EMV of this decision is $42,000. Choosing to conduct the study would result in an EMV of only $32,900. Thus, the expected value of sample information is

$$\text{EVSI} = \$32,900 + \$10,000 - \$42,000$$
$$= \$900$$

Solved Problem 3-4

Developing a small driving range for golfers of all abilities has long been a desire of John Jenkins. John, however, believes that the chance of a successful driving range is only about 40%. A friend of John's has suggested that he conduct a survey in the community to get a better feeling of the demand for such a facility. There is a 0.9 probability that the research will be favorable if the driving range facility will be successful. Furthermore, it is estimated that there is a 0.8 probability that the marketing research will be unfavorable if indeed the facility will be unsuccessful. John would like to determine the chances of a successful driving range given a favorable result from the marketing survey.

Solution

This problem requires the use of Bayes' theorem. Before we start to solve the problem, we will define the following terms:

$P(\text{SF})$ = probability of successful driving range facility

$P(\text{UF})$ = probability of unsuccessful driving range facility

$P(\text{RF}|\text{SF})$ = probability that the research will be favorable given a successful driving range facility

$P(\text{RU}|\text{SF})$ = probability that the research will be unfavorable given a successful driving range facility

$P(\text{RU}|\text{UF})$ = probability that the research will be unfavorable given an unsuccessful driving range facility

$P(\text{RF}|\text{UF})$ = probability that the research will be favorable given an unsuccessful driving range facility

Now, we can summarize what we know:

$$P(\text{SF}) = 0.4$$
$$P(\text{RF}|\text{SF}) = 0.9$$
$$P(\text{RU}|\text{UF}) = 0.8$$

From this information we can compute three additional probabilities that we need to solve the problem:

$$P(\text{UF}) = 1 - P(\text{SF}) = 1 - 0.4 = 0.6$$
$$P(\text{RU}|\text{SF}) = 1 - P(\text{RF}|\text{SF}) = 1 - 0.9 = 0.1$$
$$P(\text{RF}|\text{UF}) = 1 - P(\text{RU}|\text{UF}) = 1 - 0.8 = 0.2$$

Now we can put these values into Bayes' theorem to compute the desired probability:

$$P(\text{SF}|\text{RF}) = \frac{P(\text{RF}|\text{SF}) \times P(\text{SF})}{P(\text{RF}|\text{SF}) \times P(\text{SF}) + P(\text{RF}|\text{UF}) \times P(\text{UF})}$$

$$= \frac{(0.9)(0.4)}{(0.9)(0.4) + (0.2)(0.6)}$$

$$= \frac{0.36}{(0.36 + 0.12)} = \frac{0.36}{0.48} = 0.75$$

In addition to using formulas to solve John's problem, it is possible to perform all calculations in a table:

Revised Probabilities Given a Favorable Research Result

STATE OF NATURE	CONDITIONAL PROBABILITY		PRIOR PROBABILITY		JOINT PROBABILITY	POSTERIOR PROBABILITY
Favorable market	0.9	×	0.4	=	0.36	0.36/0.48 = 0.75
Unfavorable market	0.2	×	0.6	=	0.12	0.12/0.48 = 0.25
					0.48	

As you can see from the table, the results are the same. The probability of a successful driving range given a favorable research result is 0.36/0.48, or 0.75.

Self-Test

- Before taking the self-test, refer to the learning objectives at the beginning of the chapter, the notes in the margins, and the glossary at the end of the chapter.
- Use the key at the back of the book to correct your answers.
- Restudy pages that correspond to any questions that you answered incorrectly or material you feel uncertain about.

1. In decision theory terminology, a course of action or a strategy that may be chosen by a decision maker is called
   a. a payoff.
   b. an alternative.
   c. a state of nature.
   d. none of the above.
2. In decision theory, probabilities are associated with
   a. payoffs.
   b. alternatives.
   c. states of nature.
   d. none of the above.
3. If probabilities are available to the decision maker, then the decision-making environment is called
   a. certainty.
   b. uncertainty.
   c. risk.
   d. none of the above.
4. Which of the following is a decision-making criterion that is used for decision making under risk?
   a. expected monetary value criterion
   b. Hurwicz criterion (criterion of realism)
   c. optimistic (maximax) criterion
   d. equally likely criterion
5. The minimum expected opportunity loss is
   a. equal to the highest expected payoff.
   b. greater than the expected value with perfect information.
   c. equal to the expected value of perfect information.
   d. computed when finding the minimax regret decision.
6. In using the criterion of realism (Hurwicz criterion), the coefficient of realism (α)
   a. is the probability of a good state of nature.

b. describes the degree of optimism of the decision maker.
c. describes the degree of pessimism of the decision maker.
d. is usually less than zero.
7. The most that a person should pay for perfect information is
   a. the EVPI.
   b. the maximum EMV minus the minimum EMV.
   c. the maximum EOL.
   d. the maximum EMV.
8. The minimum EOL criterion will always result in the same decision as
   a. the maximax criterion.
   b. the minimax regret criterion.
   c. the maximum EMV criterion.
   d. the equally likely criterion.
9. A decision tree is preferable to a decision table when
   a. a number of sequential decisions are to be made.
   b. probabilities are available.
   c. the maximax criterion is used.
   d. the objective is to maximize regret.
10. Bayes' theorem is used to revise probabilities. The new (revised) probabilities are called
    a. prior probabilities.
    b. sample probabilities.
    c. survey probabilities.
    d. posterior probabilities.
11. On a decision tree, at each state-of-nature node,
    a. the alternative with the greatest EMV is selected.
    b. an EMV is calculated.
    c. all probabilities are added together.
    d. the branch with the highest probability is selected.

12. The EVSI
    a. is found by subtracting the EMV without sample information from the EMV with sample information.
    b. is always equal to the expected value of perfect information.
    c. equals the EMV with sample information assuming no cost for the information minus the EMV without sample information.
    d. is usually negative.
13. The efficiency of sample information
    a. is the EVSI/(maximum EMV without SI) expressed as a percentage.
    b. is the EVPI/EVSI expressed as a percentage.
    c. would be 100% if the sample information were perfect.
    d. is computed using only the EVPI and the maximum EMV.
14. On a decision tree, once the tree has been drawn and the payoffs and probabilities have been placed on the tree, the analysis (computing EMVs and selecting the best alternative)
    a. working backward (starting on the right and moving to the left).
    b. working forward (starting on the left and moving to the right).
    c. starting at the top of the tree and moving down.
    d. starting at the bottom of the tree and moving up.
15. In assessing utility values,
    a. the worst outcome is given a utility of -1.
    b. the best outcome is given a utility of 0.
    c. the worst outcome is given a utility of 0.
    d. the best outcome is given a value of -1.
16. If a rational person selects an alternative that does not maximize the EMV, we would expect that this alternative
    a. minimizes the EMV.
    b. maximizes the expected utility.
    c. minimizes the expected utility.
    d. has zero utility associated with each possible payoff.

Discussion Questions and Problems

Discussion Questions

3-1 Give an example of a good decision that you made that resulted in a bad outcome. Also give an example of a bad decision that you made that had a good outcome. Why was each decision good or bad?

3-2 Describe what is involved in the decision process.

3-3 What is an alternative? What is a state of nature?

3-4 Discuss the differences among decision making under certainty, decision making under risk, and decision making under uncertainty.

3-5 What techniques are used to solve decision-making problems under uncertainty? Which technique results in an optimistic decision? Which technique results in a pessimistic decision?

3-6 Define *opportunity loss*. What decision-making criteria are used with an opportunity loss table?

3-7 What information should be placed on a decision tree?

3-8 Describe how you would determine the best decision using the EMV criterion with a decision tree.

3-9 What is the difference between prior and posterior probabilities?

3-10 What is the purpose of Bayesian analysis? Describe how you would use Bayesian analysis in the decision-making process.

3-11 What is the EVSI? How is this computed?

3-12 How is the efficiency of sample information computed?

3-13 What is the overall purpose of utility theory?

3-14 Briefly discuss how a utility function can be assessed. What is a standard gamble, and how is it used in determining utility values?

3-15 How is a utility curve used in selecting the best decision for a particular problem?

3-16 What is a risk seeker? What is a risk avoider? How does the utility curve for these types of decision makers differ?

Problems

⊘•3-17 Kenneth Brown is the principal owner of Brown Oil, Inc. After quitting his university teaching job, Ken has been able to increase his annual salary by a factor of over 100. At the present time, Ken is forced to consider purchasing some more equipment for Brown Oil because of competition. His alternatives are shown in the following table:

EQUIPMENT	FAVORABLE MARKET ($)	UNFAVORABLE MARKET ($)
Sub 100	300,000	−200,000
Oiler J	250,000	−100,000
Texan	75,000	−18,000

For example, if Ken purchases a Sub 100 and if there is a favorable market, he will realize a profit of $300,000. On the other hand, if the market is unfavorable, Ken will suffer a loss of $200,000. But Ken has always been a very optimistic decision maker.

(a) What type of decision is Ken facing?
(b) What decision criterion should he use?
(c) What alternative is best?

Q• 3-18 Although Ken Brown (discussed in Problem 3-17) is the principal owner of Brown Oil, his brother Bob is credited with making the company a financial success. Bob is vice president of finance. Bob attributes his success to his pessimistic attitude about business and the oil industry. Given the information from Problem 3-17, it is likely that Bob will arrive at a different decision. What decision criterion should Bob use, and what alternative will he select?

Q• 3-19 The *Lubricant* is an expensive oil newsletter to which many oil giants subscribe, including Ken Brown (see Problem 3-17 for details). In the last issue, the letter described how the demand for oil products would be extremely high. Apparently, the American consumer will continue to use oil products even if the price of these products doubles. Indeed, one of the articles in the *Lubricant* states that the chances of a favorable market for oil products was 70%, while the chance of an unfavorable market was only 30%. Ken would like to use these probabilities in determining the best decision.

(a) What decision model should be used?
(b) What is the optimal decision?
(c) Ken believes that the $300,000 figure for the Sub 100 with a favorable market is too high. How much lower would this figure have to be for Ken to change his decision made in part *b*?

Q: 3-20 Mickey Lawson is considering investing some money that he inherited. The following payoff table gives the profits that would be realized during the next year for each of three investment alternatives Mickey is considering:

DECISION ALTERNATIVE	STATE OF NATURE	
	GOOD ECONOMY	POOR ECONOMY
Stock market	80,000	−20,000
Bonds	30,000	20,000
CDs	23,000	23,000
Probability	0.5	0.5

(a) What decision would maximize expected profits?
(b) What is the maximum amount that should be paid for a perfect forecast of the economy?

Q: 3-21 Develop an opportunity loss table for the investment problem that Mickey Lawson faces in Problem 3-20. What decision would minimize the expected opportunity loss? What is the minimum EOL?

Q• 3-22 Allen Young has always been proud of his personal investment strategies and has done very well over the past several years. He invests primarily in the stock market. Over the past several months, however, Allen has become very concerned about the stock market as a good investment. In some cases, it would have been better for Allen to have his money in a bank than in the market. During the next year, Allen must decide whether to invest $10,000 in the stock market or in a certificate of deposit (CD) at an interest rate of 9%. If the market is good, Allen believes that he could get a 14% return on his money. With a fair market, he expects to get an 8% return. If the market is bad, he will most likely get no return at all—in other words, the return would be 0%. Allen estimates that the probability of a good market is 0.4, the probability of a fair market is 0.4, and the probability of a bad market is 0.2, and he wishes to maximize his long-run average return.

(a) Develop a decision table for this problem.
(b) What is the best decision?

Q: 3-23 In Problem 3-22, you helped Allen Young determine the best investment strategy. Now, Young is thinking about paying for a stock market newsletter. A friend of Young said that these types of letters could predict very accurately whether the market would be good, fair, or poor. Then, based on these predictions, Allen could make better investment decisions.

(a) What is the most that Allen would be willing to pay for a newsletter?
(b) Young now believes that a good market will give a return of only 11% instead of 14%. Will this information change the amount that Allen would be willing to pay for the newsletter? If your answer is yes, determine the most that Allen would be willing to pay, given this new information.

Q: 3-24 Today's Electronics specializes in manufacturing modern electronic components. It also builds the equipment that produces the components. Phyllis Weinberger, who is responsible for advising the president of Today's Electronics on electronic manufacturing equipment, has developed the following table concerning a proposed facility:

	PROFIT ($)		
	STRONG MARKET	FAIR MARKET	POOR MARKET
Large facility	550,000	110,000	−310,000
Medium-sized facility	300,000	129,000	−100,000
Small facility	200,000	100,000	−32,000
No facility	0	0	0

(a) Develop an opportunity loss table.
(b) What is the minimax regret decision?

3-25 Brilliant Color is a small supplier of chemicals and equipment that are used by some photographic stores to process 35mm film. One product that Brilliant Color supplies is BC-6. John Kubick, president of Brilliant Color, normally stocks 11, 12, or 13 cases of BC-6 each week. For each case that John sells, he receives a profit of $35. Like many photographic chemicals, BC-6 has a very short shelf life, so if a case is not sold by the end of the week, John must discard it. Since each case costs John $56, he loses $56 for every case that is not sold by the end of the week. There is a probability of 0.45 of selling 11 cases, a probability of 0.35 of selling 12 cases, and a probability of 0.2 of selling 13 cases.

   (a) Construct a decision table for this problem. Include all conditional values and probabilities in the table.
   (b) What is your recommended course of action?
   (c) If John is able to develop BC-6 with an ingredient that stabilizes it so that it no longer has to be discarded, how would this change your recommended course of action?

3-26 Megley Cheese Company is a small manufacturer of several different cheese products. One of the products is a cheese spread that is sold to retail outlets. Jason Megley must decide how many cases of cheese spread to manufacture each month. The probability that the demand will be six cases is 0.1, seven cases is 0.3, eight cases is 0.5, and nine cases is 0.1. The cost of every case is $45, and the price that Jason gets for each case is $95. Unfortunately, any cases not sold by the end of the month are of no value, due to spoilage. How many cases of cheese should Jason manufacture each month?

3-27 Farm Grown, Inc., produces cases of perishable food products. Each case contains an assortment of vegetables and other farm products. Each case costs $5 and sells for $15. If there are any cases not sold by the end of the day, they are sold to a large food processing company for $3 a case. The probability that daily demand will be 100 cases is 0.3, the probability that daily demand will be 200 cases is 0.4, and the probability that daily demand will be 300 cases is 0.3. Farm Grown has a policy of always satisfying customer demands. If its own supply of cases is less than the demand, it buys the necessary vegetables from a competitor. The estimated cost of doing this is $16 per case.

   (a) Draw a decision table for this problem.
   (b) What do you recommend?

3-28 In Problem 3-27, Farm Grown, Inc. has reason to believe the probabilities may not be reliable due to changing conditions. If these probabilities are ignored, what decision would be made using the optimistic criterion? What decision would be made using the pessimistic criterion?

3-29 Mick Karra is the manager of MCZ Drilling Products, which produces a variety of specialty valves for oil field equipment. Recent activity in the oil fields has caused demand to increase drastically, and a decision has been made to open a new manufacturing facility. Three locations are being considered, and the size of the facility would not be the same in each location. Thus, overtime might be necessary at times. The following table gives the total monthly cost (in $1,000s) for each possible location under each demand possibility. The probabilities for the demand levels have been determined to be 20% for low demand, 30% for medium demand, and 50% for high demand.

	DEMAND IS LOW	DEMAND IS MEDIUM	DEMAND IS HIGH
Ardmore, OK	85	110	150
Sweetwater, TX	90	100	120
Lake Charles, LA	110	120	130

   (a) Which location would be selected based on the optimistic criterion?
   (b) Which location would be selected based on the pessimistic criterion?
   (c) Which location would be selected based on the minimax regret criterion?
   (d) Which location should be selected to minimize the expected cost of operation?
   (e) How much is a perfect forecast of the demand worth?
   (f) Which location would minimize the expected opportunity loss?
   (g) What is the expected value of perfect information in this situation?

3-30 Even though independent gasoline stations have been having a difficult time, Susan Solomon has been thinking about starting her own independent gasoline station. Susan's problem is to decide how large her station should be. The annual returns will depend on both the size of her station and a number of marketing factors related to the oil industry and demand for gasoline. After a careful analysis, Susan developed the following table:

SIZE OF FIRST STATION	GOOD MARKET ($)	FAIR MARKET ($)	POOR MARKET ($)
Small	50,000	20,000	−10,000
Medium	80,000	30,000	−20,000
Large	100,000	30,000	−40,000
Very large	300,000	25,000	−160,000

For example, if Susan constructs a small station and the market is good, she will realize a profit of $50,000.

(a) Develop a decision table for this decision.
(b) What is the maximax decision?
(c) What is the maximin decision?
(d) What is the equally likely decision?
(e) What is the criterion of realism decision? Use an α value of 0.8.
(f) Develop an opportunity loss table.
(g) What is the minimax regret decision?

3-31 Beverly Mills has decided to lease a hybrid car to save on gasoline expenses and to do her part to help keep the environment clean. The car she selected is available from only one dealer in the local area, but that dealer has several leasing options to accommodate a variety of driving patterns. All the leases are for 3 years and require no money at the time of signing the lease. The first option has a monthly cost of $330, a total mileage allowance of 36,000 miles (an average of 12,000 miles per year), and a cost of $0.35 per mile for any miles over 36,000. The following table summarizes each of the three lease options:

3-YEAR LEASE	MONTHLY COST	MILEAGE ALLOWANCE	COST PER EXCESS MILE
Option 1	$330	36,000	$0.35
Option 2	$380	45,000	$0.25
Option 3	$430	54,000	$0.15

Beverly has estimated that, during the 3 years of the lease, there is a 40% chance she will drive an average of 12,000 miles per year, a 30% chance she will drive an average of 15,000 miles per year, and a 30% chance that she will drive 18,000 miles per year. In evaluating these lease options, Beverly would like to keep her costs as low as possible.

(a) Develop a payoff (cost) table for this situation.
(b) What decision would Beverly make if she were optimistic?
(c) What decision would Beverly make if she were pessimistic?
(d) What decision would Beverly make if she wanted to minimize her expected cost (monetary value)?
(e) Calculate the expected value of perfect information for this problem.

3-32 Refer to the leasing decision facing Beverly Mills in Problem 3-31. Develop the opportunity loss table for this situation. Which option would be chosen based on the minimax regret criterion? Which alternative would result in the lowest expected opportunity loss?

3-33 The game of roulette is popular in many casinos around the world. In Las Vegas, a typical roulette wheel has the numbers 1–36 in slots on the wheel. Half of these slots are red, and the other half are black. In the United States, the roulette wheel typically also has the numbers 0 (zero) and 00 (double zero), and both of these are on the wheel in green slots. Thus, there are 38 slots on the wheel. The dealer spins the wheel and sends a small ball in the opposite direction of the spinning wheel. As the wheel slows, the ball falls into one of the slots, and that is the winning number and color. One of the bets available is simply red or black, for which the odds are 1 to 1. If the player bets on either red or black, and that happens to be the winning color, the player wins the amount of her bet. For example, if the player bets $5 on red and wins, she is paid $5 and she still has her original bet. On the other hand, if the winning color is black or green when the player bets red, the player loses the entire bet.

(a) What is the probability that a player who bets red will win the bet?
(b) If a player bets $10 on red every time the game is played, what is the expected monetary value (expected win)?
(c) In Europe, there is usually no 00 on the wheel, just the 0. With this type of game, what is the probability that a player who bets red will win the bet? If a player bets $10 on red every time in this game (with no 00), what is the expected monetary value?
(d) Since the expected profit (win) in a roulette game is negative, why would a rational person play the game?

3-34 Refer to the Problem 3-33 for details about the game of roulette. Another bet in a roulette game is called a "straight up" bet, which means that the player is betting that the winning number will be the number that she chose. In a game with 0 and 00, there are a total of 38 possible outcomes (the numbers 1 to 36 plus 0 and 00), and each of these has the same chance of occurring. The payout on this type of bet is 35 to 1, which means the player is paid 35 and gets to keep the original bet. If a player bets $10 on the number 7 (or any single number), what is the expected monetary value (expected win)?

3-35 The Technically Techno company has several patents for a variety of different Flash memory devices that are used in computers, cell phones, and a variety of other things. A competitor has recently introduced a product based on technology very similar to something patented by Technically Techno last year. Consequently, Technically Techno has sued the other company for copyright infringement. Based on the facts in the case as well as the record of the lawyers involved, Technically Techno believes there is a 40%

chance that it will be awarded $300,000 if the lawsuit goes to court. There is a 30% chance that they would be awarded only $50,000 if they go to court and win, and there is a 30% chance they would lose the case and be awarded nothing. The estimated cost of legal fees if they go to court is $50,000. However, the other company has offered to pay Technically Techno $75,000 to settle the dispute without going to court. The estimated legal cost of this would only be $10,000. If Technically Techno wished to maximize the expected gain, should they accept the settlement offer?

3-36 A group of medical professionals is considering the construction of a private clinic. If the medical demand is high (i.e., there is a favorable market for the clinic), the physicians could realize a net profit of $100,000. If the market is not favorable, they could lose $40,000. Of course, they don't have to proceed at all, in which case there is no cost. In the absence of any market data, the best the physicians can guess is that there is a 50–50 chance the clinic will be successful. Construct a decision tree to help analyze this problem. What should the medical professionals do?

3-37 The physicians in Problem 3-36 have been approached by a market research firm that offers to perform a study of the market at a fee of $5,000. The market researchers claim their experience enables them to use Bayes' theorem to make the following statements of probability:

probability of a favorable market given
a favorable study = 0.82

probability of an unfavorable market given
a favorable study = 0.18

probability of a favorable market given
an unfavorable study = 0.11

probability of an unfavorable market given
an unfavorable study = 0.89

probability of a favorable research study = 0.55

probability of an unfavorable research study = 0.45

(a) Develop a new decision tree for the medical professionals to reflect the options now open with the market study.
(b) Use the EMV approach to recommend a strategy.
(c) What is the expected value of sample information? How much might the physicians be willing to pay for a market study?
(d) Calculate the efficiency of this sample information.

3-38 Jerry Smith is thinking about opening a bicycle shop in his hometown. Jerry loves to take his own bike on 50-mile trips with his friends, but he believes that any small business should be started only if there is a good chance of making a profit. Jerry can open a small shop, a large shop, or no shop at all. The profits will depend on the size of the shop and whether the market is favorable or unfavorable for his products. Because there will be a 5-year lease on the building that Jerry is thinking about using, he wants to make sure that he makes the correct decision. Jerry is also thinking about hiring his old marketing professor to conduct a marketing research study. If the study is conducted, the study could be favorable (i.e., predicting a favorable market) or unfavorable (i.e., predicting an unfavorable market). Develop a decision tree for Jerry.

3-39 Jerry Smith (see Problem 3-38) has done some analysis about the profitability of the bicycle shop. If Jerry builds the large bicycle shop, he will earn $60,000 if the market is favorable, but he will lose $40,000 if the market is unfavorable. The small shop will return a $30,000 profit in a favorable market and a $10,000 loss in an unfavorable market. At the present time, he believes that there is a 50–50 chance that the market will be favorable. His old marketing professor will charge him $5,000 for the marketing research. It is estimated that there is a 0.6 probability that the survey will be favorable. Furthermore, there is a 0.9 probability that the market will be favorable given a favorable outcome from the study. However, the marketing professor has warned Jerry that there is only a probability of 0.12 of a favorable market if the marketing research results are not favorable. Jerry is confused.

(a) Should Jerry use the marketing research?
(b) Jerry, however, is unsure the 0.6 probability of a favorable marketing research study is correct. How sensitive is Jerry's decision to this probability value? How far can this probability value deviate from 0.6 without causing Jerry to change his decision?

3-40 Bill Holliday is not sure what she should do. He can build a quadplex (i.e., a building with four apartments), build a duplex, gather additional information, or simply do nothing. If he gathers additional information, the results could be either favorable or unfavorable, but it would cost him $3,000 to gather the information. Bill believes that there is a 50–50 chance that the information will be favorable. If the rental market is favorable, Bill will earn $15,000 with the quadplex or $5,000 with the duplex. Bill doesn't have the financial resources to do both. With an unfavorable rental market, however, Bill could lose $20,000 with the quadplex or $10,000 with the duplex. Without gathering additional information, Bill estimates that the probability of a favorable rental market is 0.7. A favorable report from the study would increase the probability of a favorable rental market to 0.9. Furthermore, an unfavorable report from the additional information would decrease the probability of a favorable rental market to 0.4. Of course, Bill could forget all of these numbers and do nothing. What is your advice to Bill?

3-41 Peter Martin is going to help his brother who wants to open a food store. Peter initially believes that there is a 50–50 chance that his brother's food store would be a success. Peter is considering doing a market research study. Based on historical data, there is a 0.8 probability that the marketing research will be favorable given a successful food store. Moreover, there is a 0.7 probability that the marketing research will be unfavorable given an unsuccessful food store.

  (a) If the marketing research is favorable, what is Peter's revised probability of a successful food store for his brother?
  (b) If the marketing research is unfavorable, what is Peter's revised probability of a successful food store for his brother?
  (c) If the initial probability of a successful food store is 0.60 (instead of 0.50), find the probabilities in parts *a* and *b*.

3-42 Mark Martinko has been a class A racquetball player for the past 5 years, and one of his biggest goals is to own and operate a racquetball facility. Unfortunately, Mark's thinks that the chance of a successful racquetball facility is only 30%. Mark's lawyer has recommended that he employ one of the local marketing research groups to conduct a survey concerning the success or failure of a racquetball facility. There is a 0.8 probability that the research will be favorable given a successful racquetball facility. In addition, there is a 0.7 probability that the research will be unfavorable given an unsuccessful facility. Compute revised probabilities of a successful racquetball facility given a favorable and given an unfavorable survey.

3-43 A financial advisor has recommended two possible mutual funds for investment: Fund A and Fund B. The return that will be achieved by each of these depends on whether the economy is good, fair, or poor. A payoff table has been constructed to illustrate this situation:

| | STATE OF NATURE | | |
| | GOOD | FAIR | POOR |
INVESTMENT	ECONOMY	ECONOMY	ECONOMY
Fund A	$10,000	$2,000	−$5,000
Fund B	$6,000	$4,000	0
Probability	0.2	0.3	0.5

  (a) Draw the decision tree to represent this situation.
  (b) Perform the necessary calculations to determine which of the two mutual funds is better. Which one should you choose to maximize the expected value?
  (c) Suppose there is question about the return of Fund A in a good economy. It could be higher or

lower than $10,000. What value for this would cause a person to be indifferent between Fund A and Fund B (i.e., the EMVs would be the same)?

3-44 Jim Sellers is thinking about producing a new type of electric razor for men. If the market were favorable, he would get a return of $100,000, but if the market for this new type of razor were unfavorable, he would lose $60,000. Since Ron Bush is a good friend of Jim Sellers, Jim is considering the possibility of using Bush Marketing Research to gather additional information about the market for the razor. Ron has suggested that Jim use either a survey or a pilot study to test the market. The survey would be a sophisticated questionnaire administered to a test market. It will cost $5,000. Another alternative is to run a pilot study. This would involve producing a limited number of the new razors and trying to sell them in two cities that are typical of American cities. The pilot study is more accurate but is also more expensive. It will cost $20,000. Ron Bush has suggested that it would be a good idea for Jim to conduct either the survey or the pilot before Jim makes the decision concerning whether to produce the new razor. But Jim is not sure if the value of the survey or the pilot is worth the cost.

Jim estimates that the probability of a successful market without performing a survey or pilot study is 0.5. Furthermore, the probability of a favorable survey result given a favorable market for razors is 0.7, and the probability of a favorable survey result given an unsuccessful market for razors is 0.2. In addition, the probability of an unfavorable pilot study given an unfavorable market is 0.9, and the probability of an unsuccessful pilot study result given a favorable market for razors is 0.2.

  (a) Draw the decision tree for this problem without the probability values.
  (b) Compute the revised probabilities needed to complete the decision, and place these values in the decision tree.
  (c) What is the best decision for Jim? Use EMV as the decision criterion.

3-45 Jim Sellers has been able to estimate his utility for a number of different values. He would like to use these utility values in making the decision in Problem 3-44: $U(-\$80,000) = 0$, $U(-\$65,000) = 0.5$, $U(-\$60,000) = 0.55$, $U(-\$20,000) = 0.7$, $U(-\$5,000) = 0.8$, $U(\$0) = 0.81$, $U(\$80,000) = 0.9$, $U(\$95,000) = 0.95$, and $U(\$100,000) = 1$. Resolve Problem 3-44 using utility values. Is Jim a risk avoider?

3-46. Two states of nature exist for a particular situation: a good economy and a poor economy. An economic study may be performed to obtain more information about which of these will actually occur in the coming year. The study may forecast either a good economy or a poor economy. Currently there is a 60% chance that the economy will be good and a 40% chance that it will be poor. In the past, whenever the economy was good, the economic study predicted it would be good 80% of the time. (The other 20% of the time the prediction was wrong.) In the past, whenever the economy was poor, the economic study predicted it would be poor 90% of the time. (The other 10% of the time the prediction was wrong.)

(a) Use Bayes' theorem and find the following:

$P(\text{good economy} \mid \text{prediction of good economy})$
$P(\text{poor economy} \mid \text{prediction of good economy})$
$P(\text{good economy} \mid \text{prediction of poor economy})$
$P(\text{poor economy} \mid \text{prediction of poor economy})$

(b) Suppose the initial (prior) probability of a good economy is 70% (instead of 60%), and the probability of a poor economy is 30% (instead of 40%). Find the posterior probabilities in part a based on these new values.

3-47 The Long Island Life Insurance Company sells a term life insurance policy. If the policy holder dies during the term of the policy, the company pays $100,000. If the person does not die, the company pays out nothing and there is no further value to the policy. The company uses actuarial tables to determine the probability that a person with certain characteristics will die during the coming year. For a particular individual, it is determined that there is a 0.001 chance that the person will die in the next year and a 0.999 chance that the person will live and the company will pay out nothing. The cost of this policy is $200 per year. Based on the EMV criterion, should the individual buy this insurance policy? How would utility theory help explain why a person would buy this insurance policy?

3-48 In Problem 3-37, you helped the medical professionals analyze their decision using expected monetary value as the decision criterion. This group has also assessed their utility for money: $U(-\$45,000) = 0$, $U(-\$40,000) = 0.1$, $U(-\$5,000) = 0.7$, $U(\$0) = 0.9$, $U(\$95,000) = 0.99$, and $U(\$100,000) = 1$. Use expected utility as the decision criterion, and determine the best decision for the medical professionals. Are the medical professionals risk seekers or risk avoiders?

3-49 In this chapter, a decision tree was developed for John Thompson (see Figure 3.5 for the complete decision tree analysis). After completing the analysis, John was not completely sure that he is indifferent to risk. After going through a number of standard gambles, John was able to assess his utility for money. Here are some of the utility assessments: $U(-\$190,000) = 0$, $U(-\$180,000) = 0.05$, $U(-\$30,000) = 0.10$, $U(-\$20,000) = 0.15$, $U(-\$10,000) = 0.2$, $U(\$0) = 0.3$, $U(\$90,000) =$

0.15, $U(\$100,000) = 0.6$, $U(\$190,000) = 0.95$, and $U(\$200,000) = 1.0$. If John maximizes his expected utility, does his decision change?

3-50 In the past few years, the traffic problems in Lynn McKell's hometown have gotten worse. Now, Broad Street is congested about half the time. The normal travel time to work for Lynn is only 15 minutes when Broad Street is used and there is no congestion. With congestion, however, it takes Lynn 40 minutes to get to work. If Lynn decides to take the expressway, it will take 30 minutes regardless of the traffic conditions. Lynn's utility for travel time is: $U(15 \text{ minutes}) = 0.9$, $U(30 \text{ minutes}) = 0.7$, and $U(40 \text{ minutes}) = 0.2$.

(a) Which route will minimize Lynn's expected travel time?
(b) Which route will maximize Lynn's utility?
(c) When it comes to travel time, is Lynn a risk seeker or a risk avoider?

3-51 Coren Chemical, Inc., develops industrial chemicals that are used by other manufacturers to produce photographic chemicals, preservatives, and lubricants. One of their products, K-1000, is used by several photographic companies to make a chemical that is used in the film-developing process. To produce K-1000 efficiently, Coren Chemical uses the batch approach, in which a certain number of gallons is produced at one time. This reduces setup costs and allows Coren Chemical to produce K-1000 at a competitive price. Unfortunately, K-1000 has a very short shelf life of about 1 month.

Coren Chemical produces K-1000 in batches of 500 gallons, 1,000 gallons, 1,500 gallons, and 2,000 gallons. Using historical data, David Coren was able to determine that the probability of selling 500 gallons of K-1000 is 0.2. The probabilities of selling 1,000, 1,500, and 2,000 gallons are 0.3, 0.4, and 0.1, respectively. The question facing David is how many gallons to produce of K-1000 in the next batch run. K-1000 sells for $20 per gallon. Manufacturing cost is $12 per gallon, and handling costs and warehousing costs are estimated to be $1 per gallon. In the past, David has allocated advertising costs to K-1000 at $3 per gallon. If K-1000 is not sold after the batch run, the chemical loses much of its important properties as a developer. It can, however, be sold at a salvage value of $13 per gallon. Furthermore, David has guaranteed to his suppliers that there will always be an adequate supply of K-1000. If David does run out, he has agreed to purchase a comparable chemical from a competitor at $25 per gallon. David sells all of the chemical at $20 per gallon, so his shortage means that David loses the $5 to buy the more expensive chemical.

(a) Develop a decision tree of this problem.
(b) What is the best solution?
(c) Determine the expected value of perfect information.

3-52   The Jamis Corporation is involved with waste management. During the past 10 years it has become one of the largest waste disposal companies in the Midwest, serving primarily Wisconsin, Illinois, and Michigan. Bob Jamis, president of the company, is considering the possibility of establishing a waste treatment plant in Mississippi. From past experience, Bob believes that a small plant in northern Mississippi would yield a $500,000 profit regardless of the market for the facility. The success of a medium-sized waste treatment plant would depend on the market. With a low demand for waste treatment, Bob expects a $200,000 return. A medium demand would yield a $700,000 return in Bob's estimation, and a high demand would return $800,000. Although a large facility is much riskier, the potential return is much greater. With a high demand for waste treatment in Mississippi, the large facility should return a million dollars. With a medium demand, the large facility will return only $400,000. Bob estimates that the large facility would be a big loser if there were a low demand for waste treatment. He estimates that he would lose approximately $200,000 with a large treatment facility if demand were indeed low. Looking at the economic conditions for the upper part of the state of Mississippi and using his experience in the field, Bob estimates that the probability of a low demand for treatment plants is 0.15. The probability for a medium-demand facility is approximately 0.40, and the probability of a high demand for a waste treatment facility is 0.45.

Because of the large potential investment and the possibility of a loss, Bob has decided to hire a market research team that is based in Jackson, Mississippi. This team will perform a survey to get a better feeling for the probability of a low, medium, or high demand for a waste treatment facility. The cost of the survey is $50,000. To help Bob determine whether to go ahead with the survey, the marketing research firm has provided Bob with the following information:

P(survey results | possible outcomes)

	SURVEY RESULTS		
POSSIBLE OUTCOME	LOW SURVEY RESULTS	MEDIUM SURVEY RESULTS	HIGH SURVEY RESULTS
Low demand	0.7	0.2	0.1
Medium demand	0.4	0.5	0.1
High demand	0.1	0.3	0.6

As you see, the survey could result in three possible outcomes. Low survey results mean that a low demand is likely. In a similar fashion, medium survey results or high survey results would mean a medium or a high demand, respectively. What should Bob do?

3-53   Mary is considering opening a new grocery store in town. She is evaluating three sites: downtown, the mall, and out at the busy traffic circle. Mary calculated the value of successful stores at these locations as follows: downtown, $250,000; the mall, $300,000; the circle, $400,000. Mary calculated the losses if unsuccessful to be $100,000 at either downtown or the mall and $200,000 at the circle. Mary figures her chance of success to be 50% downtown, 60% at the mall, and 75% at the traffic circle.

(a) Draw a decision tree for Mary and select her best alternative.

(b) Mary has been approached by a marketing research firm that offers to study the area to determine if another grocery store is needed. The cost of this study is $30,000. Mary believes there is a 60% chance that the survey results will be positive (show a need for another grocery store). SRP = survey results positive, SRN = survey results negative, SD = success downtown, SM = success at mall, SC = success at circle, SD′ = don't succeed downtown, and so on. For studies of this nature:
$P(\text{SRP} \mid \text{success}) = 0.7$,
$P(\text{SRN} \mid \text{success}) = 0.3$,
$P(\text{SRP} \mid \text{not success}) = 0.2$; and
$P(\text{SRN} \mid \text{not success}) = 0.8$.
Calculate the revised probabilities for success (and not success) for each location, depending on survey results.

(c) How much is the marketing research worth to Mary? Calculate the EVSI.

3-54.   Sue Reynolds has to decide if she should get information (at a cost of $20,000) to invest in a retail store. If she gets the information, there is a 0.6 probability that the information will be favorable and a 0.4 probability that the information will not be favorable. If the information is favorable, there is a 0.9 probability that the store will be a success. If the information is not favorable, the probability of a successful store is only 0.2. Without any information, Sue estimates that the probability of a successful store will be 0.6. A successful store will give a return of $100,000. If the store is built but is not successful, Sue will see a loss of $80,000. Of course, she could always decide not to build the retail store.

(a) What do you recommend?

(b) What impact would a 0.7 probability of obtaining favorable information have on Sue's decision? The probability of obtaining unfavorable information would be 0.3.

(c) Sue believes that the probabilities of a successful and an unsuccessful retail store given favorable information might be 0.8 and 0.2, respectively, instead of 0.9 and 0.1, respectively. What impact, if any, would this have on Sue's decision and the best EMV?

(d) Sue had to pay $20,000 to get information. Would her decision change if the cost of the information increased to $30,000?

(e) Using the data in this problem and the following utility table, compute the expected utility. Is this the curve of a risk seeker or a risk avoider?

MONETARY VALUE	UTILITY
$100,000	1
$80,000	0.4
$0	0.2
−$20,000	0.1
−$80,000	0.05
−$100,000	0

(f) Compute the expected utility given the following utility table. Does this utility table represent a risk seeker or a risk avoider?

MONETARY VALUE	UTILITY
$100,000	1
$80,000	0.9
$0	0.8
−$20,000	0.6
−$80,000	0.4
−$100,000	0

 Internet Homework Problems

See our Internet home page, at **www.pearsonhighered.com/render**, for additional homework problems, Problems 3-55 to 3-60.

Case Study

Starting Right Corporation

After watching a movie about a young woman who quit a successful corporate career to start her own baby food company, Julia Day decided that she wanted to do the same. In the movie, the baby food company was very successful. Julia knew, however, that it is much easier to make a movie about a successful woman starting her own company than to actually do it. The product had to be of the highest quality, and Julia had to get the best people involved to launch the new company. Julia resigned from her job and launched her new company—Starting Right.

Julia decided to target the upper end of the baby food market by producing baby food that contained no preservatives but had a great taste. Although the price would be slightly higher than for existing baby food, Julia believed that parents would be willing to pay more for a high-quality baby food. Instead of putting baby food in jars, which would require preservatives to stabilize the food, Julia decided to try a new approach. The baby food would be frozen. This would allow for natural ingredients, no preservatives, and outstanding nutrition.

Getting good people to work for the new company was also important. Julia decided to find people with experience in finance, marketing, and production to get involved with Starting Right. With her enthusiasm and charisma, Julia was able to find such a group. Their first step was to develop prototypes of the new frozen baby food and to perform a small pilot test of the new product. The pilot test received rave reviews.

The final key to getting the young company off to a good start was to raise funds. Three options were considered: corporate bonds, preferred stock, and common stock. Julia decided that each investment should be in blocks of $30,000. Furthermore, each investor should have an annual income of at least $40,000 and a net worth of $100,000 to be eligible to invest in Starting Right. Corporate bonds would return 13% per year for the next 5 years. Julia furthermore guaranteed that investors in the corporate bonds would get at least $20,000 back at the end of 5 years. Investors in preferred stock should see their initial investment increase by a factor of 4 with a good market or see the investment worth only half of the initial investment with an unfavorable market. The common stock had the greatest potential. The initial investment was expected to increase by a factor of 8 with a good market, but investors would lose everything if the market was unfavorable. During the next 5 years, it was expected that inflation would increase by a factor of 4.5% each year.

Discussion Questions

1. Sue Pansky, a retired elementary school teacher, is considering investing in Starting Right. She is very conservative and is a risk avoider. What do you recommend?
2. Ray Cahn, who is currently a commodities broker, is also considering an investment, although he believes that there is only an 11% chance of success. What do you recommend?
3. Lila Battle has decided to invest in Starting Right. While she believes that Julia has a good chance of being

successful, Lila is a risk avoider and very conservative. What is your advice to Lila?

4. George Yates believes that there is an equally likely chance for success. What is your recommendation?

5. Peter Metarko is extremely optimistic about the market for the new baby food. What is your advice for Pete?

6. Julia Day has been told that developing the legal documents for each fundraising alternative is expensive. Julia would like to offer alternatives for both risk-averse and risk-seeking investors. Can Julia delete one of the financial alternatives and still offer investment choices for risk seekers and risk avoiders?

Case Study

Blake Electronics

In 1979, Steve Blake founded Blake Electronics in Long Beach, California, to manufacture resistors, capacitors, inductors, and other electronic components. During the Vietnam War, Steve was a radio operator, and it was during this time that he became proficient at repairing radios and other communications equipment. Steve viewed his 4-year experience with the army with mixed feelings. He hated army life, but this experience gave him the confidence and the initiative to start his own electronics firm.

Over the years, Steve kept the business relatively unchanged. By 1992, total annual sales were in excess of $2 million. In 1996, Steve's son, Jim, joined the company after finishing high school and 2 years of courses in electronics at Long Beach Community College. Jim was always aggressive in high school athletics, and he became even more aggressive as general sales manager of Blake Electronics. This aggressiveness bothered Steve, who was more conservative. Jim would make deals to supply companies with electronic components before he bothered to find out if Blake Electronics had the ability or capacity to produce the components. On several occasions this behavior caused the company some embarrassing moments when Blake Electronics was unable to produce the electronic components for companies with which Jim had made deals.

In 2000, Jim started to go after government contracts for electronic components. By 2002, total annual sales had increased to more than $10 million, and the number of employees exceeded 200. Many of these employees were electronic specialists and graduates of electrical engineering programs from top colleges and universities. But Jim's tendency to stretch Blake Electronics to contracts continued as well, and by 2007, Blake Electronics had a reputation with government agencies as a company that could not deliver what it promised. Almost overnight, government contracts stopped, and Blake Electronics was left with an idle workforce and unused manufacturing equipment. This high overhead started to melt away profits, and in 2009, Blake Electronics was faced with the possibility of sustaining a loss for the first time in its history.

In 2010, Steve decided to look at the possibility of manufacturing electronic components for home use. Although this was a totally new market for Blake Electronics, Steve was convinced that this was the only way to keep Blake

Figure 3.15   Master Control Center

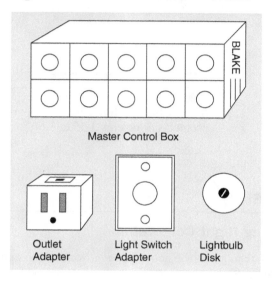

Electronics from dipping into the red. The research team at Blake Electronics was given the task of developing new electronic devices for home use. The first idea from the research team was the Master Control Center. The basic components for this system are shown in Figure 3.15.

The heart of the system is the master control box. This unit, which would have a retail price of $250, has two rows of five buttons. Each button controls one light or appliance and can be set as either a switch or a rheostat. When set as a switch, a light finger touch on the button turns a light or appliance on or off. When set as a rheostat, a finger touching the button controls the intensity of the light. Leaving your finger on the button makes the light go through a complete cycle ranging from off to bright and back to off again.

To allow for maximum flexibility, each master control box is powered by two D-sized batteries that can last up to a year, depending on usage. In addition, the research team has developed three versions of the master control box—versions A, B, and C. If a family wants to control more than 10 lights or appliances, another master control box can be purchased.

The lightbulb disk, which would have a retail price of $2.50, is controlled by the master control box and is used to control the intensity of any light. A different disk is available for each button position for all three master control boxes. By inserting the lightbulb disk between the lightbulb and the socket, the appropriate button on the master control box can completely control the intensity of the light. If a standard light switch is used, it must be on at all times for the master control box to work.

One disadvantage of using a standard light switch is that only the master control box can be used to control the particular light. To avoid this problem, the research team developed a special light switch adapter that would sell for $15. When this device is installed, either the master control box or the light switch adapter can be used to control the light.

When used to control appliances other than lights, the master control box must be used in conjunction with one or more outlet adapters. The adapters are plugged into a standard wall outlet, and the appliance is then plugged into the adapter. Each outlet adapter has a switch on top that allows the appliance to be controlled from the master control box or the outlet adapter. The price of each outlet adapter would be $25.

The research team estimated that it would cost $500,000 to develop the equipment and procedures needed to manufacture the master control box and accessories. If successful, this venture could increase sales by approximately $2 million. But will the master control boxes be a successful venture? With a 60% chance of success estimated by the research team, Steve had serious doubts about trying to market the master control boxes even though he liked the basic idea. Because of his reservations, Steve decided to send requests for proposals (RFPs) for additional marketing research to 30 marketing research companies in southern California.

The first RFP to come back was from a small company called Marketing Associates, Inc. (MAI), which would charge $100,000 for the survey. According to its proposal, MAI has been in business for about 3 years and has conducted about 100 marketing research projects. MAI's major strengths appeared to be individual attention to each account, experienced staff, and

TABLE 3.19   Success Figures for MAI

| | SURVEY RESULTS | | |
OUTCOME	FAVORABLE	UNFAVORABLE	TOTAL
Successful venture	35	20	55
Unsuccessful venture	15	30	45

fast work. Steve was particularly interested in one part of the proposal, which revealed MAI's success record with previous accounts. This is shown in Table 3.19.

The only other proposal to be returned was by a branch office of Iverstine and Walker, one of the largest marketing research firms in the country. The cost for a complete survey would be $300,000. While the proposal did not contain the same success record as MAI, the proposal from Iverstine and Walker did contain some interesting information. The chance of getting a favorable survey result, given a successful venture, was 90%. On the other hand, the chance of getting an unfavorable survey result, given an unsuccessful venture, was 80%. Thus, it appeared to Steve that Iverstine and Walker would be able to predict the success or failure of the master control boxes with a great amount of certainty.

Steve pondered the situation. Unfortunately, both marketing research teams gave different types of information in their proposals. Steve concluded that there would be no way that the two proposals could be compared unless he got additional information from Iverstine and Walker. Furthermore, Steve wasn't sure what he would do with the information, and if it would be worth the expense of hiring one of the marketing research firms.

Discussion Questions

1. Does Steve need additional information from Iverstine and Walker?
2. What would you recommend?

Internet Case Studies

See our Internet home page, at **www.pearsonhighered.com/render**, for these additional case studies:

(1) **Drink-At-Home, Inc.:** This case involves the development and marketing of a new beverage.
(2) **Ruth Jones' Heart Bypass Operation:** This case deals with a medical decision regarding surgery.
(3) **Ski Right:** This case involves the development and marketing of a new ski helmet.
(4) **Study Time:** This case is about a student who must budget time while studying for a final exam.

Bibliography

Abbas, Ali E. "Invariant Utility Functions and Certain Equivalent Transformations," *Decision Analysis* 4, 1(March 2007): 17–31.

Carassus, Laurence, and Miklós Rásonyi. "Optimal Strategies and Utility-Based Prices Converge When Agents' Preferences Do," *Mathematics of Operations Research* 32, 1 (February 2007): 102–117.

Congdon, Peter. *Bayesian Statistical Modeling.* New York: John Wiley & Sons, Inc., 2001.

Ewing, Paul L., Jr. "Use of Decision Analysis in the Army Base Realignment and Closure (BRAC) 2005 Military Value Analysis," *Decision Analysis* 3 (March 2006): 33–49.

Hammond, J. S., R. L. Kenney, and H. Raiffa. "The Hidden Traps in Decision Making," *Harvard Business Review* (September–October 1998): 47–60.

Hurley, William J. "The 2002 Ryder Cup: Was Strange's Decision to Put Tiger Woods in the Anchor Match a Good One?" *Decision Analysis* 4, 1 (March 2007): 41–45.

Kirkwood, C. W. "An Overview of Methods for Applied Decision Analysis," *Interfaces* 22, 6 (November–December 1992): 28–39.

Kirkwood, C. W. "Approximating Risk Aversion in Decision Analysis Applications," *Decision Analysis* 1 (March 2004): 51–67.

Luce, R., and H. Raiffa. *Games and Decisions.* New York: John Wiley & Sons, Inc., 1957.

Maxwell, Daniel T. "Improving Hard Decisions," *OR/MS Today* 33, 6 (December 2006): 51–61.

Patchak, William M. "Software Survey: Decision Analysis." *OR/MS Today* 39, 5 (October 2012).

Paté-Cornell, M. Elisabeth, and Robin L. Dillon. "The Respective Roles of Risk and Decision Analyses in Decision Support," *Decision Analysis* 3 (December 2006): 220–232.

Pennings, Joost M. E., and Ale Smidts. "The Shape of Utility Functions and Organizational Behavior," *Management Science* 49, 9 (September 2003): 1251–1263.

Raiffa, Howard, John W. Pratt, and Robert Schlaifer. *Introduction to Statistical Decision Theory.* Boston: MIT Press, 1995.

Raiffa, Howard, and Robert Schlaifer. *Applied Statistical Decision Theory.* New York: John Wiley & Sons, Inc., 2000.

Render, B., and R. M. Stair. *Cases and Readings in Management Science,* 2nd ed. Boston: Allyn & Bacon, Inc., 1988.

Schlaifer, R. *Analysis of Decisions Under Uncertainty.* New York: McGraw-Hill Book Company, 1969.

Smith, James E., and Robert L. Winkler. "The Optimizer's Curse: Skepticism and Postdecision Surprise in Decision Analysis," *Management Science* 52 (March 2006): 311–322.

van Binsbergen, Jules H., and Leslie M. Marx. "Exploring Relations Between Decision Analysis and Game Theory," *Decision Analysis* 4, 1 (March 2007): 32–40.

Wallace, Stein W. "Decision Making Under Uncertainty: Is Sensitivity Analysis of Any Use?" *Operations Research* 48, 1 (2000): 20–25.

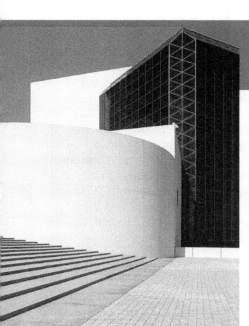

CHAPTER 7

Linear Programming Models: Graphical and Computer Methods

CHAPTER OUTLINE

7.1   Introduction
7.2   Requirements of a Linear Programming Problem
7.3   Formulating LP Problems
7.4   Graphical Solution to an LP Problem

7.5   Solving Flair Furniture's LP Problem Using QM for Windows, Excel 2013, and Excel QM
7.6   Solving Minimization Problems
7.7   Four Special Cases in LP
7.8   Sensitivity Analysis

Summary • Glossary • Solved Problems • Self-Test • Discussion Questions and Problems • Internet Homework Problems • Case Study: Mexicana Wire Works • Internet Case Study • Bibliography

7.1 Introduction

Linear programming is a technique that helps in resource allocation decisions.

Many management decisions involve trying to make the most effective use of an organization's resources. Resources typically include machinery, labor, money, time, warehouse space, and raw materials. These resources may be used to make products (such as machinery, furniture, food, or clothing) or services (such as schedules for airlines or production, advertising policies, or investment decisions). **Linear programming (LP)** is a widely used mathematical modeling technique designed to help managers in planning and decision making relative to resource allocation. We devote this and the next chapter to illustrating how and why linear programming works.

Despite its name, LP and the more general category of techniques called **"mathematical" programming** have very little to do with computer programming. In the world of management science, *programming* refers to modeling and solving a problem mathematically. Computer programming has, of course, played an important role in the advancement and use of LP. Real-life LP problems are too cumbersome to solve by hand or with a calculator. So throughout the chapters on LP we give examples of how valuable a computer program can be in solving an LP problem.

7.2 Requirements of a Linear Programming Problem

In the past 60 years, LP has been applied extensively to military, industrial, financial, marketing, accounting, and agricultural problems. Even though these applications are diverse, all LP problems have several properties and assumptions in common.

Problems seek to maximize or minimize an objective.

All problems seek to *maximize* or *minimize* some quantity, usually profit or cost. We refer to this property as the **objective function** of an LP problem. The major objective of a typical manufacturer is to maximize dollar profits. In the case of a trucking or railroad distribution system, the objective might be to minimize shipping costs. In any event, this objective must be stated clearly and defined mathematically. It does not matter, by the way, whether profits and costs are measured in cents, dollars, or millions of dollars.

Constraints limit the degree to which the objective can be obtained.

The second property that LP problems have in common is the presence of restrictions, or **constraints**, that limit the degree to which we can pursue our objective. For example, deciding how many units of each product in a firm's product line to manufacture is restricted by available personnel and machinery. Selection of an advertising policy or a financial portfolio is limited by the amount of money available to be spent or invested. We want, therefore, to maximize or minimize a quantity (the objective function) subject to limited resources (the constraints).

There must be alternatives available.

There must be alternative courses of action to choose from. For example, if a company produces three different products, management may use LP to decide how to allocate among them its limited production resources (of personnel, machinery, and so on). Should it devote all manufacturing capacity to make only the first product, should it produce equal amounts of each product, or should it allocate the resources in some other ratio? If there were no alternatives to select from, we would not need LP.

Mathematical relationships are linear.

The objective and constraints in LP problems must be expressed in terms of *linear* equations or inequalities. Linear mathematical relationships just mean that all terms used in the objective function and constraints are of the first degree (i.e., not squared, or to the third or higher power, or appearing more than once). Hence, the equation $2A + 5B = 10$ is an acceptable linear function, while the equation $2A^2 + 5B^3 + 3AB = 10$ is not linear because the variable A is squared, the variable B is cubed, and the two variables appear again as a product of each other.

The term *linear* implies both proportionality and additivity. Proportionality means that if production of 1 unit of a product uses 3 hours, production of 10 units would use 30 hours. Additivity means that the total of all activities equals the sum of the individual activities. If the production of one product generated $3 profit and the production of another product generated $8 profit, the total profit would be the sum of these two, which would be $11.

We assume that conditions of *certainty* exist: that is, number in the objective and constraints are known with certainty and do not change during the period being studied.

We make the *divisibility* assumption that solutions need not be in whole numbers (integers). Instead, they are divisible and may take any fractional value. In production problems, we often define variables as the number of units produced per week or per month, and a fractional value

TABLE 7.1
LP Properties and Assumptions

PROPERTIES OF LINEAR PROGRAMS
1. One objective function
2. One or more constraints
3. Alternative courses of action
4. Objective function and constraints are linear—proportionality and divisibility
5. Certainty
6. Divisibility
7. Nonnegative variables

(e.g., 0.3 chair) would simply mean that there is work in process. Something that was started in one week can be finished in the next. However, in other types of problems, fractional values do not make sense. If a fraction of a product cannot be purchased (for example, one-third of a submarine), an integer programming problem exists. Integer programming is discussed in more detail in Chapter 10.

Finally, we assume that all answers or variables are *nonnegative*. Negative values of physical quantities are impossible; you simply cannot produce a negative number of chairs, shirts, lamps, or computers. However, there are some variables that can have negative values, such as profit, where a negative value indicates a loss. A simple mathematical operation can transform such a variable into two nonnegative variables, and that process can be found in books on linear programming. However, when working with linear programming in this book, we will only work with nonnegative variables. Table 7.1 summarizes these properties and assumptions.

7.3 Formulating LP Problems

Formulating a linear program involves developing a mathematical model to represent the managerial problem. Thus, in order to formulate a linear program, it is necessary to completely understand the managerial problem being faced. Once this is understood, we can begin to develop the mathematical statement of the problem. The steps in formulating a linear program follow:

1. Completely understand the managerial problem being faced.
2. Identify the objective and the constraints.
3. Define the decision variables.
4. Use the decision variables to write mathematical expressions for the objective function and the constraints.

Product mix problems use LP to decide how much of each product to make, given a series of resource restrictions.

One of the most common LP applications is the **product mix problem**. Two or more products are usually produced using limited resources such as personnel, machines, raw materials, and so on. The profit that the firm seeks to maximize is based on the profit contribution per unit of each product. (Profit contribution, you may recall, is just the selling price per unit minus the variable cost per unit.*) The company would like to determine how many units of each product it should produce so as to maximize overall profit given its limited resources. A problem of this type is formulated in the following example.

Flair Furniture Company

The Flair Furniture Company produces inexpensive tables and chairs. The production process for each is similar in that both require a certain number of hours of carpentry work and a certain number of labor hours in the painting and varnishing department. Each table takes 4 hours of carpentry and 2 hours in the painting and varnishing shop. Each chair requires 3 hours in carpentry and 1 hour in painting and varnishing. During the current production period, 240 hours of carpentry time are available and 100 hours in painting and varnishing time are available. Each table sold yields a profit of $70; each chair produced is sold for a $50 profit.

---

*Technically, we maximize total contribution margin, which is the difference between unit selling price and costs that vary in proportion to the quantity of the item produced. Depreciation, fixed general expense, and advertising are excluded from calculations.

HISTORY **The Beginning of Linear Programming**

Prior to 1945, some conceptual problems regarding the allocation of scarce resources had been suggested by economists and others. Two of these people, Leonid Kantorovich and Tjalling Koopmans, shared the 1975 Nobel Prize in Economics for advancing the concepts of optimal planning in their work that began during the 1940s. In 1945, George Stigler proposed the "diet problem" which is now the name given to a major category of linear programming applications. However, Stigler relied on heuristic techniques to find a good solution to this problem as there was no method available to find the optimal solution.

Major progress in the field, however, took place in 1947 when George D. Dantzig, often called the "Father of Linear Programming," published his work on the solution procedure known as the simplex algorithm. Dantzig had been an Air Force mathematician during World War II and was assigned to work on logistics problems. He saw that many problems involving limited resources and more than one demand could be set up in terms of a series of equations and inequalities, and he subsequently developed the simplex algorithm for solving these problems.

Although early applications of linear programming were military in nature, industrial applications rapidly became apparent with the widespread use of business computers. As problems became larger, research continued to find even better ways to solve linear programs. The work of Leonid Kachiyan in 1979 and Narendra Karmarkar in 1984 spurred others to study the use of interior point methods for solving linear programs, some of which are used today. However, the simplex algorithm developed by Dantzig is still the basis for much of the software used for solving linear programs today.

Flair Furniture's problem is to determine the best possible combination of tables and chairs to manufacture in order to reach the maximum profit. The firm would like this production mix situation formulated as an LP problem.

We begin by summarizing the information needed to formulate and solve this problem (see Table 7.2). This helps us understand the problem being faced. Next we identify the objective and the constraints. The objective is

Maximize profit

The constraints are

1. The hours of carpentry time used cannot exceed 240 hours per week.
2. The hours of painting and varnishing time used cannot exceed 100 hours per week.

The **decision variables** that represent the actual decisions we will make are defined as

$$T = \text{number of tables to be produced per week}$$
$$C = \text{number of chairs to be produced per week}$$

Now we can create the LP objective function in terms of T and C. The objective function is Maximize profit = $70T + $50C.

Our next step is to develop mathematical relationships to describe the two constraints in this problem. One general relationship is that the amount of a resource used is to be less than or equal to ($\leq$) the amount of resource *available*.

In the case of the carpentry department, the total time used is

$$(4 \text{ hours per table})(\text{Number of tables produced})$$
$$+ (3 \text{ hours per chair})(\text{Number of chairs produced})$$

TABLE 7.2
Flair Furniture Company Data

| DEPARTMENT | HOURS REQUIRED TO PRODUCE 1 UNIT | | AVAILABLE HOURS THIS WEEK |
	(T) TABLES	(C) CHAIRS	
Carpentry	4	3	240
Painting and varnishing	2	1	100
Profit per unit	$70	$50	

The resource constraints put limits on the carpentry labor resource and the painting labor resource mathematically.

So the first constraint may be stated as follows:

Carpentry time used $\leq$ Carpentry time available

$$4T + 3C \leq 240 \text{ (hours of carpentry time)}$$

Similarly, the second constraint is as follows:

Painting and varnishing time used $\leq$ Painting and varnishing time available

$\rightarrow$ ②$T + 1C \leq 100$ (hours of painting and varnishing time)

(This means that each table produced takes two hours of the painting and varnishing resource.)

Both of these constraints represent production capacity restrictions and, of course, affect the total profit. For example, Flair Furniture cannot produce 80 tables during the production period because if $T = 80$, both constraints will be violated. It also cannot make $T = 50$ tables and $C = 10$ chairs. Why? Because this would violate the second constraint that no more than 100 hours of painting and varnishing time be allocated.

To obtain meaningful solutions, the values for T and C must be nonnegative numbers. That is, all potential solutions must represent real tables and real chairs. Mathematically, this means that

$$T \geq 0 \text{ (number of tables produced is greater than or equal to 0)}$$
$$C \geq 0 \text{ (number of chairs produced is greater than or equal to 0)}$$

The complete problem may now be restated mathematically as

$$\text{Maximize profit} = \$70T + \$50C$$

Here is a complete mathematical statement of the LP problem.

subject to the constraints

$$4T + 3C \leq 240 \quad \text{(carpentry constraint)}$$
$$2T + 1C \leq 100 \quad \text{(painting and varnishing constraint)}$$
$$T \geq 0 \quad \text{(first nonnegativity constraint)}$$
$$C \geq 0 \quad \text{(second nonnegativity constraint)}$$

While the nonnegativity constraints are technically separate constraints, they are often written on a single line with the variables separated by commas. In this example, this would be written as

$$T, C \geq 0$$

7.4 Graphical Solution to an LP Problem

The graphical method works only when there are two decision variables, but it provides valuable insight into how larger problems are structured.

The easiest way to solve a small LP problem such as that of the Flair Furniture Company is with the graphical solution approach. The graphical procedure is useful only when there are two decision variables (such as number of tables to produce, T, and number of chairs to produce, C) in the problem. When there are more than two variables, it is not possible to plot the solution on a two-dimensional graph and we must turn to more complex approaches. But the graphical method is invaluable in providing us with insights into how other approaches work. For that reason alone, it is worthwhile to spend the rest of this chapter exploring graphical solutions as an intuitive basis for the chapters on mathematical programming that follow.

Graphical Representation of Constraints

To find the optimal solution to an LP problem, we must first identify a set, or region, of feasible solutions. The first step in doing so is to plot each of the problem's constraints on a graph. The variable T (tables) is plotted as the horizontal axis of the graph and the variable C (chairs) is plotted as the vertical axis of the graph. The notation (T, C) is used to identify the points on the graph. The

Nonnegativity constraints mean $T \geq 0$ and $C \geq 0$.

nonnegativity constraints mean that we are always working in the first (or northeast) quadrant of a graph (see Figure 7.1).

To represent the first constraint graphically, $4T + 3C \leq 240$, we must first graph the equality portion of this, which is

$$4T + 3C = 240$$

FIGURE 7.1

**Quadrant Containing
All Positive Values**

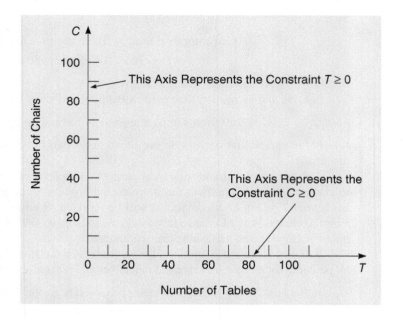

*Plotting the first constraint
involves finding points at which
the line intersects the* T *and* C
axes.

As you may recall from elementary algebra, a linear equation in two variables is a straight line. The easiest way to plot the line is to find any two points that satisfy the equation, then draw a straight line through them.

The two easiest points to find are generally the points at which the line intersects the T and C axes.

When Flair Furniture produces no tables, namely $T = 0$, it implies that

$$4(0) + 3C = 240$$

or

$$3C = 240$$

or

$$C = 80$$

In other words, if *all* of the carpentry time available is used to produce chairs, 80 chairs *could* be made. Thus, this constraint equation crosses the vertical axis at 80.

To find the point at which the line crosses the horizontal axis, we assume that the firm makes no chairs, that is, $C = 0$. Then

$$4T + 3(0) = 240$$

or

$$4T = 240$$

or

$$T = 60$$

Hence, when $C = 0$, we see that $4T = 240$ and that $T = 60$.

The carpentry constraint is illustrated in Figure 7.2. It is bounded by the line running from point $(T = 0, C = 80)$ to point $(T = 60, C = 0)$.

Recall, however, that the actual carpentry constraint was the **inequality** $4T + 3C \leq 240$. How can we identify all of the solution points that satisfy this constraint? It turns out that there are three possibilities. First, we know that any point that lies on the line $4T + 3C = 240$ satisfies the constraint. Any combination of tables and chairs on the line will use up all 240 hours of carpentry time.* Now we must find the set of solution points that would use less than

---

*Thus, what we have done is to plot the constraint equation in its most binding position, that is, using all of the carpentry resource.

FIGURE 7.2

Graph of Carpentry Constraint Equation $4T + 3C = 240$

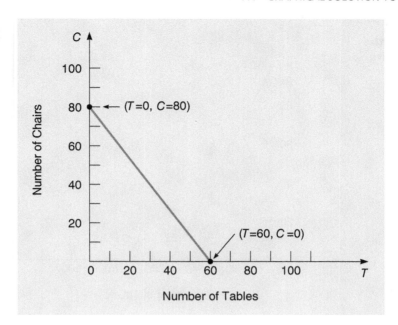

the 240 hours. The points that satisfy the $<$ portion of the constraint (i.e., $4T + 3C < 240$) will be all the points on one side of the line, while all the points on the other side of the line will not satisfy this condition. To determine which side of the line this is, simply choose any point on either side of the constraint line shown in Figure 7.2 and check to see if it satisfies this condition. For example, choose the point (30, 20), as illustrated in Figure 7.3:

$$4(30) + 3(20) = 180$$

Since $180 < 240$, this point satisfies the constraint, and all points on this side of the line will also satisfy the constraint. This set of points is indicated by the shaded region in Figure 7.3.

To see what would happen if the point did not satisfy the constraint, select a point on the other side of the line, such as (70, 40). This constraint would not be met at this point as

$$4(70) + 3(40) = 400$$

Since $400 > 240$, this point and every other point on that side of the line would not satisfy this constraint. Thus, the solution represented by the point (70, 40) would require more than the 240 hours that are available. There are not enough carpentry hours to produce 70 tables and 40 chairs.

FIGURE 7.3

Region That Satisfies the Carpentry Constraint

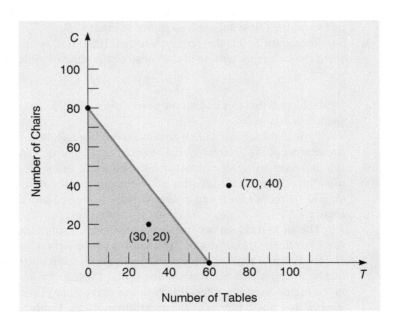

FIGURE 7.4

Region That Satisfies the Painting and Varnishing Constraint

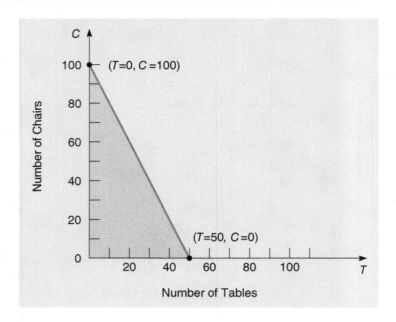

Next, let us identify the solution corresponding to the second constraint, which limits the time available in the painting and varnishing department. That constraint was given as $2T + 1C \leq 100$. As before, we start by graphing the equality portion of this constraint, which is

$$2T + 1C = 100$$

To find two points on the line, select $T = 0$ and solve for C:

$$2(0) + 1C = 100$$
$$C = 100$$

So, one point on the line is $(0, 100)$. To find the second point, select $C = 0$ and solve for T:

$$2T + 1(0) = 100$$
$$T = 50$$

The second point used to graph the line is $(50, 0)$. Plotting this point, $(50, 0)$, and the other point, $(0, 100)$, results in the line representing all the solutions in which exactly 100 hours of painting and varnishing time are used, as shown in Figure 7.4.

To find the points that require less than 100 hours, select a point on either side of this line to see if the inequality portion of the constraint is satisfied. Selecting $(0, 0)$ gives us

$$2(0) + 1(0) = 0 < 100$$

This indicates that this and all the points below the line satisfy the constraint, and this region is shaded in Figure 7.4.

Now that each individual constraint has been plotted on a graph, it is time to move on to the next step. We recognize that to produce a chair or a table, both the carpentry and painting and varnishing departments must be used. In an LP problem we need to find that set of solution points that satisfies all of the constraints *simultaneously*. Hence, the constraints should be redrawn on one graph (or superimposed one upon the other). This is shown in Figure 7.5.

In LP problems we are interested in satisfying all constraints at the same time.

The shaded region now represents the area of solutions that does not exceed either of the two Flair Furniture constraints. It is known by the term *area of feasible solutions* or, more simply, the **feasible region**. The feasible region in an LP problem must satisfy *all* conditions specified by the problem's constraints, and is thus the region where all constraints overlap. Any point in the region would be a **feasible solution** to the Flair Furniture problem; any point outside the shaded area would represent an **infeasible solution**. Hence, it would be feasible to manufacture

The feasible region is the set of points that satisfy all the constraints.

FIGURE 7.5

Feasible Solution Region for the Flair Furniture Company Problem

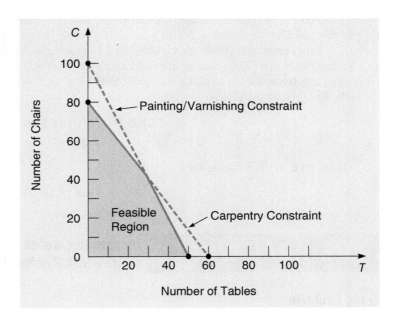

30 tables and 20 chairs ($T = 30$, $C = 20$) during a production period because both constraints are observed:

> *Carpentry constraint* $4T + 3C \leq 240$ hours available
>
> $(4)(30) + (3)(20) = 180$ hours used   ⊘
>
> *Painting constraint* $2T + 1C \leq 100$ hours available
>
> $(2)(30) + (1)(20) = 80$ hours used   ⊘

But it would violate both of the constraints to produce 70 tables and 40 chairs, as we see here mathematically:

> *Carpentry constraint* $4T + 3C \leq 240$ hours available
>
> $(4)(70) + (3)(40) = 400$ hours used   ⊗
>
> *Painting constraint* $2T + 1C \leq 100$ hours available
>
> $(2)(70) + (1)(40) = 180$ hours used   ⊗

Furthermore, it would also be infeasible to manufacture 50 tables and 5 chairs ($T = 50$, $C = 5$). Can you see why?

> *Carpentry constraint* $4T + 3C \leq 240$ hours available
>
> $(4)(50) + (3)(5) = 215$ hours used   ⊘
>
> *Painting constraint* $2T + 1C \leq 100$ hours available
>
> $(2)(50) + (1)(5) = 105$ hours used   ⊗

This possible solution falls within the time available in carpentry but exceeds the time available in painting and varnishing and thus falls outside the feasible region.

Isoprofit Line Solution Method

Now that the feasible region has been graphed, we may proceed to find the optimal solution to the problem. The optimal solution is the point lying in the feasible region that produces the highest profit. Yet there are many, many possible solution points in the region. How do we go about selecting the best one, the one yielding the highest profit?

The isoprofit method is the first method we introduce for finding the optimal solution.

There are a few different approaches that can be taken in solving for the optimal solution when the feasible region has been established graphically. The speediest one to apply is called the *isoprofit line method.*

We start the technique by letting profits equal some arbitrary but small dollar amount. For the Flair Furniture problem we may choose a profit of $2,100. This is a profit level that can be obtained easily without violating either of the two constraints. The objective function can be written as $\$2,100 = 70T + 50C$.

This expression is just the equation of a line; we call it an **isoprofit line**. It represents all combinations of (T, C) that would yield a total profit of $\$2,100$. To plot the profit line, we proceed exactly as we did to plot a constraint line. First, let $T = 0$ and solve for the point at which the line crosses the C axis:

$$\$2,100 = \$70(0) = \$50C$$

$$C = 42 \text{ chairs}$$

Then, let $C = 0$ and solve for T:

$$\$2,100 = \$70T + 50(0)$$

$$T = 30 \text{ tables}$$

MODELING IN THE REAL WORLD — Increasing Sales at Hewlett Packard

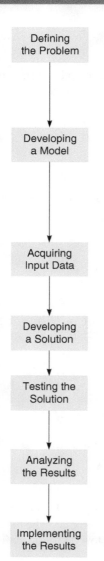

Defining the Problem

Hewlett Packard (HP) launched HPDirect.com in the late 1990s and opened online sales of HP products including computers, printers, accessories, and supplies. In 2008, the management of HPDirect.com were told that online sales had to grow 150% in the next three years, and this had to be done without exceeding marketing budgets. To do this, they had to attract more visitors to the site, they had to convert the visitors into customers by targeted marketing efforts, and they had to retain loyal customers by providing a satisfying experience in a cost-efficient manner.

Developing a Model

The massive nature of this project required the use of a variety of operations research models to achieve the objectives. Multiple regression was used to identify the key drivers of online visitors, and it was combined with time-series models (which identified seasonality and trend) to forecast the number of visits across all Web pages as well as the sales of the large variety of products. Bayesian models and Markov models were used to help predict the likelihood of a making a purchase. Linear programming was used to determine which marketing channels to use for different customers and to optimize these decisions.

Acquiring Input Data

Data was collected over a 2-year period not only on visitors to the website and their behavior, but also on sales and marketing activities over this same 2-year period. The data was separated into two groups: a training set to develop the model and a test set to validate the model.

Developing a Solution

The training set of data was used to develop the models that would be used in this project, including the linear programs to optimally allocate the marketing budget.

Testing the Solution

The data in the test set was then used to validate the models to make sure that the models were working as planned. When the different parts of the project were implemented, a test group of customers received customized marketing material based on their segment profile, while a control group received generic material.

Analyzing the Results

The test group performed better than the control group on all key metrics, including average order size, conversion rate, and total sales per dollar spent on marketing. During one particular period, the conversion rate of the targeted group was 58% higher than for the control group and dollar sales per marketing item up 33%.

Implementing the Results

At the beginning of each quarter, the models are run to help the marketing team plan efforts for that quarter. The models themselves are refreshed every quarter. Since 2009, the models have been credited with increasing incremental revenue by $117 million, increasing order size, and reducing overall inventory cost.

Source: Based on R. Randon et al., "Hewlett Packard: Delivering Profitable Growth for HPDirect.com Using Operations Research," *Interfaces* 43, 1 (January–February 2013): 48–61.

FIGURE 7.6

Profit Line of $2,100 Plotted for the Flair Furniture Company

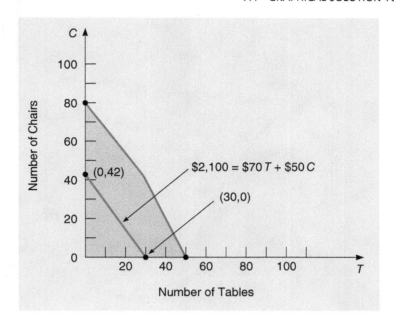

Isoprofit involves graphing parallel profit lines.

We can now connect these two points with a straight line. This profit line is illustrated in Figure 7.6. All points on the line represent feasible solutions that produce a profit of $2,100.*

Now, obviously, the isoprofit line for $2,100 does not produce the highest possible profit to the firm. In Figure 7.7 we try graphing two more lines, each yielding a higher profit. The middle equation, $2,800 = $70T + $50C$, was plotted in the same fashion as the lower line. When $T = 0$,

$$\$2,800 = \$70(0) + \$50C$$
$$C = 56$$

When $C = 0$,

$$\$2,800 = \$70T + \$50(C)$$
$$T = 40$$

FIGURE 7.7

Four Isoprofit Lines Plotted for the Flair Furniture Company

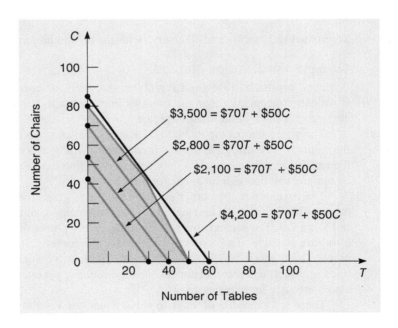

Iso means "equal" or "similar." Thus, an isoprofit line represents a line with all profits the same, in this case $2,100.

FIGURE 7.8

Optimal Solution to the Flair Furniture Problem

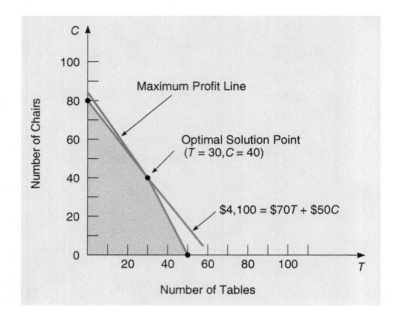

We draw a series of parallel isoprofit lines until we find the highest isoprofit line, that is, the one with the optimal solution.

Again, any combination of tables (T) and chairs (C) on this isoprofit line produces a total profit of $2,800. Note that the third line generates a profit of $3,500, even more of an improvement. The farther we move from the origin, the higher our profit will be. Another important point is that these isoprofit lines are parallel. We now have two clues as to how to find the optimal solution to the original problem. We can draw a series of parallel lines (by carefully moving our ruler in a plane parallel to the first profit line). The highest profit line that still touches some point of the feasible region pinpoints the optimal solution. Notice that the fourth line ($4,200) is too high to be considered.

The last point that an isoprofit line would touch in this feasible region is the corner point where the two constraint lines intersect, so this point will result in the maximum possible profit. To find the coordinates of this point, solve the two equations simultaneously (as detailed in the next section). This results in the point (30, 40) as shown in Figure 7.8. Calculating the profit at this point, we get

$$\text{Profit} = 70T + 50C = 70(30) + 50(40) = \$4,100$$

So producing 30 tables and 40 chairs yields the maximum profit of $4,100.

Corner Point Solution Method

A second approach to solving LP problems employs the **corner point method**. This technique is simpler conceptually than the isoprofit line approach, but it involves looking at the profit at every corner point of the feasible region.

The mathematical theory behind LP is that the optimal solution must lie at one of the corner points in the feasible region.

The mathematical theory behind LP states that an optimal solution to any problem (that is, the values of T, C that yield the maximum profit) will lie at a **corner point**, or **extreme point**, of the feasible region. Hence, it is only necessary to find the values of the variables at each corner; an optimal solution will lie at one (or more) of them.

The first step in the corner point method is to graph the constraints and find the feasible region. This was also the first step in the isoprofit method, and the feasible region is shown again in Figure 7.9. The second step is to find the corner points of the feasible region. For the Flair Furniture example, the coordinates of three of the corner points are obvious from observing the graph. These are (0, 0), (50, 0), and (0, 80). The fourth corner point is where the two constraint lines intersect, and the coordinates must be found algebraically by solving the two equations simultaneously for two variables.

There are a number of ways to solve equations simultaneously, and any of these may be used. We will illustrate the elimination method here. To begin the elimination method, select a variable to be eliminated. We will select T in this example. Then multiply or divide one equation

FIGURE 7.9

Four Corner Points of the Feasible Region

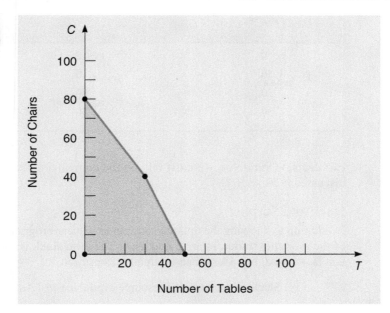

by a number so that the coefficient of that variable (T) in one equation will be the negative of the coefficient of that variable in the other equation. The two constraint equations are

$$4T + 3C = 240 \quad \text{(carpentry)}$$
$$2T + 1C = 100 \quad \text{(painting)}$$

To eliminate T, we multiply the second equation by -2:

$$-2(2T + 1C = 100) = -4T - 2C = -200$$

and then add it to the first equation:

$$\begin{array}{r} +4T + 3C = \quad 240 \\ \hline + 1C = \quad 40 \end{array}$$

or

$$C = 40$$

Doing this has enabled us to eliminate one variable, T, and to solve for C. We can now substitute 40 for C in either of the original equations and solve for T. Let's use the first equation. When $C = 40$, then

$$4T + (3)(40) = 240$$
$$4T + 120 = 240$$

or

$$4T = 120$$
$$T = 30$$

Thus, the last corner point is (30, 40).

The next step is to calculate the value of the objective function at each of the corner points. The final step is to select the corner with the best value, which would be the highest profit in this example. Table 7.3 lists these corners points with their profits. The highest profit is found to be $4,100, which is obtained when 30 tables and 40 chairs are produced. This is exactly what was obtained using the isoprofit method.

Table 7.4 provides a summary of both the isoprofit method and the corner point method. Either of these can be used when there are two decision variables. If a problem has more than

TABLE 7.3

Feasible Corner Points and Profits for Flair Furniture

NUMBER OF TABLES (*T*)	NUMBER OF CHAIRS (*C*)	Profit = $70*T* + $50*C*
0	0	$0
50	0	$3,500
0	80	$4,000
30	40	$4,100

two decision variables, we must rely on the computer software or use the simplex algorithm discussed in Module 7.

Slack and Surplus

The term slack is associated with ≤ constraints.

In addition to knowing the optimal solution to a linear program, it is helpful to know whether all of the available resources are being used. The term **slack** is used for the amount of a resource that is not used. For a less-than-or-equal to constraint,

$$\text{Slack} = (\text{Amount of resource available}) - (\text{Amount of resource used})$$

In the Flair Furniture example, there were 240 hours of carpentry time available. If the company decided to produce 20 tables and 25 chairs instead of the optimal solution, the amount of carpentry time used ($4T + 3C$) would be $4(20) + 3(25) = 155$. So,

$$\text{Slack time in carpentry} = 240 - 155 = 85$$

For the optimal solution $(30, 40)$ to the Flair Furniture problem, the slack is 0 since all 240 hours are used.

The term surplus is associated with ≥ constraints.

The term **surplus** is used with greater-than-or-equal-to constraints to indicate the amount by which the right-hand side of a constraint is exceeded. For a greater-than-or-equal-to constraint,

$$\text{Surplus} = (\text{Actual amount}) - (\text{Minimum amount})$$

Suppose there had been a constraint in the example that required the total number of tables and chairs combined to be at least 42 units (i.e., $T + C \geq 42$), and the company decided to produce 20 tables and 25 chairs. The total amount produced would be $20 + 25 = 45$, so the surplus would be

$$\text{Surplus} = 45 - 42 = 3$$

meaning that 3 units more than the minimum were produced. For the optimal solution $(30, 40)$ in the Flair Furniture problem, if this constraint had been in the problem, the surplus would be $70 - 42 = 28$.

TABLE 7.4

Summaries of Graphical Solution Methods

ISOPROFIT METHOD

1. Graph all constraints and find the feasible region.
2. Select a specific profit (or cost) line and graph it to find the slope.
3. Move the objective function line in the direction of increasing profit (or decreasing cost) while maintaining the slope. The last point it touches in the feasible region is the optimal solution.
4. Find the values of the decision variables at this last point and compute the profit (or cost).

CORNER POINT METHOD

1. Graph all constraints and find the feasible region.
2. Find the corner points of the feasible region.
3. Compute the profit (or cost) at each of the feasible corner points.
4. Select the corner point with the best value of the objective function found in step 3. This is the optimal solution.

So the slack and surplus represent the difference between the left-hand side (LHS) and the right-hand side (RHS) of a constraint. The term *slack* is used when referring to less-than-or-equal-to constraints, and the term *surplus* is used when referring to greater-than-or-equal-to constraints. Most computer software for linear programming will provide the amount of slack and surplus that exist for each constraint in the optimal solution.

A constraint that has zero slack or surplus for the optimal solution is called a **binding constraint**. A constraint with positive slack or surplus for the optimal solution is called a **nonbinding constraint**. Some computer outputs will specify whether a constraint is binding or nonbinding.

7.5   Solving Flair Furniture's LP Problem Using QM for Windows, Excel 2013, and Excel QM

Almost every organization has access to computer programs that are capable of solving enormous LP problems. Although each computer program is slightly different, the approach each takes toward handling LP problems is basically the same. The format of the input data and the level of detail provided in output results may differ from program to program and computer to computer, but once you are experienced in dealing with computerized LP algorithms, you can easily adjust to minor changes.

Using QM for Windows

Let us begin by demonstrating QM for Windows on the Flair Furniture Company problem. To use QM for Windows, select the Linear Programming module. Then specify the number of constraints (other than the nonnegativity constraints, as it is assumed that the variables must be nonnegative), the number of variables, and whether the objective is to be maximized or minimized. For the Flair Furniture Company problem, there are two constraints and two variables. Once these numbers are specified, the input window opens as shown in Program 7.1A. Then you can enter the coefficients for the objective function and the constraints. Placing the cursor over the X1 or X2 and typing a new name such as *T* and *C* will change the variable names. The constraint names can be similarly modified. Program 7.1B shows the QM for Windows screen after the data has been input and before the problem is solved. When you click the *Solve* button, you get the output shown in Program 7.1C.

PROGRAM 7.1A

QM for Windows Linear Programming Input Screen

PROGRAM 7.1B

QM for Windows Data Input for Flair Furniture Problem

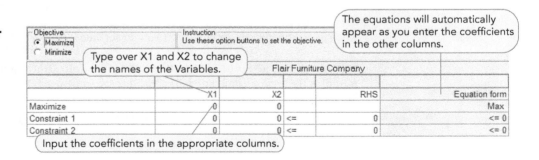

PROGRAM 7.1C

QM for Windows Output and Graph for Flair Furniture Problem

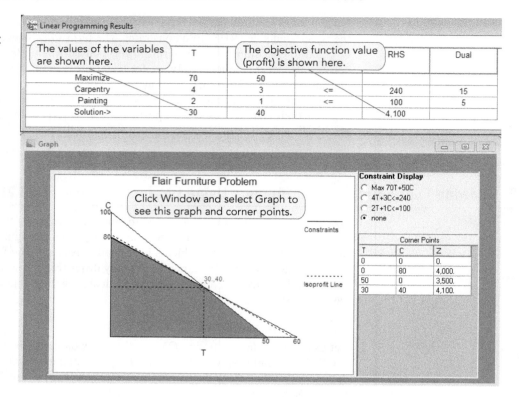

	T		RHS	Dual
Maximize	70	50		
Carpentry	4	3	<= 240	15
Painting	2	1	<= 100	5
Solution->	30	40	4,100	

The values of the variables are shown here.

The objective function value (profit) is shown here.

Graph

Flair Furniture Problem

Click Window and select Graph to see this graph and corner points.

Constraints

Isoprofit Line

Constraint Display
- Max 70T+50C
- 4T+3C<=240
- 2T+1C<=100
- none

Corner Points		
T	C	Z
0	0	0.
0	80	4,000.
50	0	3,500.
30	40	4,100.

Once the problem has been solved, a graph may be displayed by selecting *Window—Graph* from the menu bar in QM for Windows. Program 7.1C shows the output for the graphical solution. Notice that in addition to the graph, the corner points and the original problem are also shown. Later we return to see additional information related to sensitivity analysis that is provided by QM for Windows.

Using Excel's Solver Command to Solve LP Problems

Excel 2013 (as well as earlier versions) has an add-in called Solver that can be used to solve linear programs. If this add-in doesn't appear on the Data tab in Excel 2013, it has not been activated. See Appendix F for details on how to activate it.

PREPARING THE SPREADSHEET FOR SOLVER   The spreadsheet must be prepared with data and formulas for certain calculations before Solver can be used. Excel QM can be used to simplify this process (see Appendix 7.1). We will briefly describe the steps, and further discussion and suggestions will be provided when the Flair Furniture example is presented. Here is a summary of the steps to prepare the spreadsheet:

1. Enter the problem data. The problem data consist of the coefficients of the objective function and the constraints, plus the RHS values for each of the constraints. It is best to organize this in a logical and meaningful way. The coefficients will be used when writing formulas in steps 3 and 4, and the RHS will be entered into Solver.
2. Designate specific cells for the values of the decision variables. Later, these cell addresses will be input into Solver.
3. Write a formula to calculate the value of the objective function, using the coefficients for the objective function (from step 1) that you have entered and the cells containing the values of the decision variables (from step 2). Later, this cell address will be input into Solver.
4. Write a formula to calculate the value of the LHS of each constraint, using the coefficients for the constraints (from step 1) that you have entered and the cells containing the values of the decision variables (from step 2). Later, these cell addresses and the cell addresses for the corresponding RHS value will be input into Solver.

PROGRAM 7.2A

Excel Data Input for Flair Furniture Example

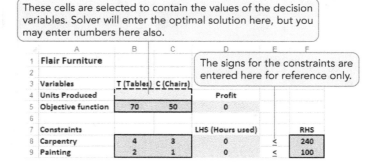

PROGRAM 7.2B

Formulas for Flair Furniture Example

PROGRAM 7.2C

Excel Spreadsheet for Flair Furniture Example

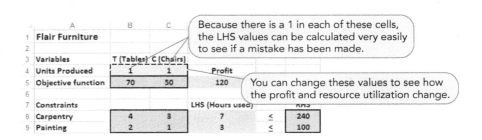

These four steps must be completed in some way with all linear programs in Excel. Additional information may be put into the spreadsheet for clarification purposes. Let's illustrate these with an example.

1. Program 7.2A provides the input data for the Flair Furniture example. You should enter the numbers in the cells shown. The words can be any description that you choose. The "≤" symbols are entered for reference only. They are not specifically used by Excel Solver.

2. The cells designated for the values of the variables are B4 for T (tables) and C4 for C (chairs). These cell addresses will be entered into Solver as the *By Changing Variable Cells.* Solver will change the values in these cells to find the optimal solution. It is sometimes helpful to enter a 1 in each of these to help identify any obvious errors when the formulas for the objective and the constraints are written.

3. A formula is written in Excel for the objective function (D5), and this is displayed in Program 7.2B. The Sumproduct function is very helpful, although there are other ways to write this. This cell address will be entered into Solver as the *Set Objective* location.

4. The hours used in carpentry (the LHS of the carpentry constraint) is calculated with the formula in cell D8, while cell D9 calculates the hours used in painting as illustrated in Program 7.2B. These cells and the cells containing the RHS values will be used when the constraints are entered into Solver.

The problem is now ready for the use of Solver. However, even if the optimal solution is not found, this spreadsheet has benefits. You can enter different values for *T* and *C* into cells B4 and C4 just to see how the resource utilization (LHS) and profit change.

PROGRAM 7.2D

Starting Solver in Excel 2013

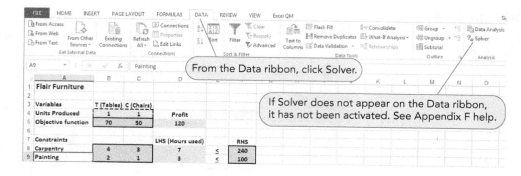

From the Data ribbon, click Solver.

If Solver does not appear on the Data ribbon, it has not been activated. See Appendix F help.

PROGRAM 7.2E   Solver Parameters Dialog Box

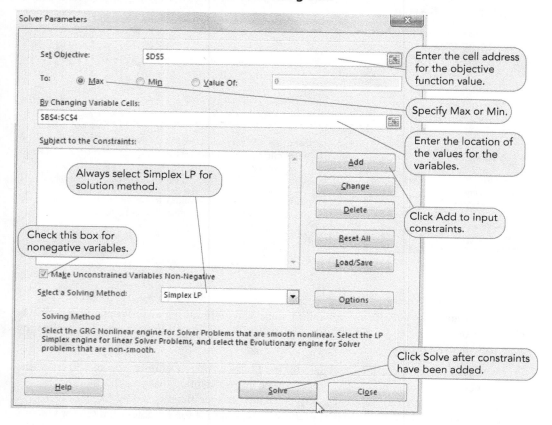

Enter the cell address for the objective function value.

Specify Max or Min.

Enter the location of the values for the variables.

Always select Simplex LP for solution method.

Click Add to input constraints.

Check this box for nonegative variables.

Click Solve after constraints have been added.

USING SOLVER   To begin using Solver, go to the *Data* tab in Excel 2013 and click *Solver*, as shown in Program 7.2D. If Solver does not appear on the Data tab, see Appendix F for instructions on how to activate this add-in. Once you click Solver, the Solver Parameters dialog box opens, as shown in Program 7.2E, and the following inputs should be entered, although the order is not important:

1. In the *Set Objective* box, enter the cell address for the total profit (D5).
2. In the *By Changing Variable Cells* box, enter the cell addresses for the variable values (B4:C4). Solver will allow the values in these cells to change while searching for the best value in the Set Objective cell reference.

PROGRAM 7.2F
Solver Add Constraint Dialog Box

3. Click *Max* for a maximization problem and *Min* for a minimization problem.
4. Check the box for *Make Unconstrained Variables Non-Negative* since the variables *T* and *C* must be greater than or equal to zero.
5. Click the *Select Solving Method* button and select *Simplex LP* from the menu that appears.
6. Click *Add* to add the constraints. When you do this, the dialog box shown in Program 7.2F appears.
7. In the *Cell Reference* box, enter the cell references for the LHS values (D8:D9). Click the button to open the drop-down menu to select <=, which is for ≤ constraints. Then enter the cell references for the RHS values (F8:F9). Since these are all less-than- or-equal-to constraints, they can all be entered at one time by specifying the ranges. If there were other types of constraints, such as ≥ constraints, you could click *Add* after entering these first constraints, and the Add Constraint dialog box would allow you to enter additional constraints. When preparing the spreadsheet for Solver, it is easier if all the ≤ constraints are together and the ≥ constraints are together. After entering all the constraints, click *OK*. The Add Constraint dialog box closes, and the Solver Parameters dialog box reopens.
8. Click *Solve* on the Solver Parameters dialog box, and the solution is found. The Solver Results dialog box opens and indicates that a solution was found, as shown in Program 7.2G. In situations where there is no feasible solution, this box will indicate this. Additional information may be obtained from the Reports section of this as will be seen later. Program 7.2H shows the results of the spreadsheet with the optimal solution.

Using Excel QM

Using the Excel QM add-in can help you easily solve linear programming problems. Not only are all formulas automatically created by Excel QM, the spreadsheet preparation for the use of

PROGRAM 7.2G
Solver Results Dialog Box

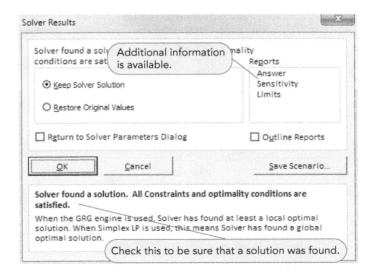

PROGRAM 7.2H

Flair Furniture Solution Found by Solver

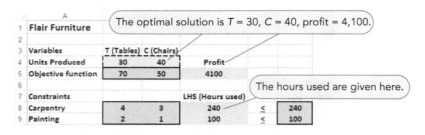

the Solver add-in is also automatically performed. We will illustrate this using the Flair Furniture example.

To begin, from the Excel QM ribbon in Excel 2013, click the *Alphabetical* menu and then select *Linear, Integer & Mixed Integer Programming* from the drop-down menu, as shown in Program 7.3A. The Excel QM Spreadsheet Initialization window opens, and in it you enter the problem title, the number of variables, and the number of constraints (do not count the nonnegativity constraints). Specify whether the problem is a maximization or minimization problem, and then click *OK*. When the initialization process is finished, a spreadsheet is prepared for data input, as shown in Program 7.3B. In this worksheet, enter the data in the section labeled Data. Specify the type of constraint (less-than, greater-than, or equal-to) and change the variable names and the constraint names, if desired. You do not have to write any formulas.

Once the data have been entered, from the *Data* tab, select *Solver*. The Solver Parameters window opens (refer back to Program 7.2E to see what input is normally required in a typical Solvers Parameters window), and you will see that Excel QM has made all the necessary inputs and selections. You do not enter any information, and you simply click *Solve* to find the solution. The solution is displayed in Program 7.3C.

Program 7.3A   Using Excel QM in Excel 2013 for the Flair Furniture Example

PROGRAM 7.3B   Excel QM Data Input for the Flair Furniture Example

After entering the problem, click the Data tab and select Solver from the Data ribbon. When the window for Solver opens, simply click Solve as all the necessary inputs have been entered by Excel QM.

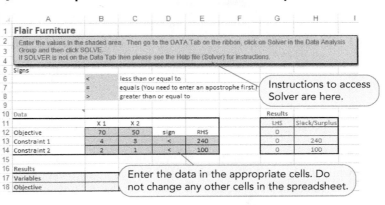

PROGRAM 7.3C

Excel QM Output for the Flair Furniture Example

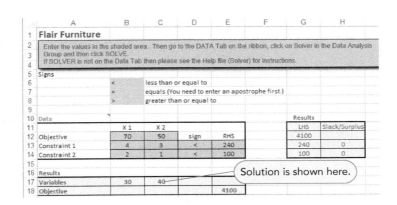

7.6 Solving Minimization Problems

Many LP problems involve minimizing an objective such as cost instead of maximizing a profit function. A restaurant, for example, may wish to develop a work schedule to meet staffing needs while minimizing the total number of employees. A manufacturer may seek to distribute its products from several factories to its many regional warehouses in such a way as to minimize total shipping costs. A hospital may want to provide a daily meal plan for its patients that meets certain nutritional standards while minimizing food purchase costs.

Minimization problems with only two variables can be solved graphically by first setting up the feasible solution region and then using either the corner point method or an isocost line approach (which is analogous to the isoprofit approach in maximization problems) to find the values of the decision variables (e.g., X_1 and X_2) that yield the minimum cost. Let's take a look at a common LP problem referred to as the diet problem. This situation is similar to the one that the hospital faces in feeding its patients at the least cost.

Holiday Meal Turkey Ranch

The Holiday Meal Turkey Ranch is considering buying two different brands of turkey feed and blending them to provide a good, low-cost diet for its turkeys. Each feed contains, in varying proportions, some or all of the three nutritional ingredients essential for fattening turkeys. Each pound of brand 1 purchased, for example, contains 5 ounces of ingredient A, 4 ounces of ingredient B, and 0.5 ounce of ingredient C. Each pound of brand 2 contains 10 ounces of ingredient A,

TABLE 7.5
Holiday Meal Turkey Ranch Data

INGREDIENT	COMPOSITION OF EACH POUND OF FEED (OZ.)		MINIMUM MONTHLY REQUIREMENT PER TURKEY (OZ.)
	BRAND 1 FEED	BRAND 2 FEED	
A	5	10	90
B	4	3	48
C	0.5	0	1.5
Cost per pound	2 cents	3 cents	

3 ounces of ingredient B, but no ingredient C. The brand 1 feed costs the ranch 2 cents a pound, while the brand 2 feed costs 3 cents a pound. The owner of the ranch would like to use LP to determine the lowest-cost diet that meets the minimum monthly intake requirement for each nutritional ingredient.

Table 7.5 summarizes the relevant information. If we let

X_1 = number of pounds of brand 1 feed purchased

X_2 = number of pounds of brand 2 feed purchased

then we may proceed to formulate this linear programming problem as follows:

$$\text{Minimize cost (in cents)} = 2X_1 + 3X_2$$

subject to these constraints:

$$5X_1 + 10X_2 \geq 90 \text{ ounces} \quad \text{(ingredient A constraint)}$$
$$4X_1 + 3X_2 \geq 48 \text{ ounces} \quad \text{(ingredient B constraint)}$$
$$0.5\,X_1 \geq 1.5 \text{ ounces} \quad \text{(ingredient C constraint)}$$
$$X_1 \geq 0 \quad \text{(nonnegativity constraint)}$$
$$X_2 \geq 0 \quad \text{(nonnegativity constraint)}$$

Before solving this problem, we want to be sure to note three features that affect its solution. First, you should be aware that the third constraint implies that the farmer *must* purchase enough brand 1 feed to meet the minimum standards for the C nutritional ingredient. Buying only brand 2 would not be feasible because it lacks C. Second, as the problem is formulated, we will be solving for the best blend of brands 1 and 2 to buy per turkey per month. If the ranch houses 5,000 turkeys in a given month, it need simply multiply the X_1 and X_2 quantities by 5,000 to decide how much feed to order overall. Third, we are now dealing with a series of greater-than-or-equal-to constraints. These cause the feasible solution area to be above the constraint lines in this example.

USING THE CORNER POINT METHOD ON A MINIMIZATION PROBLEM   To solve the Holiday Meal Turkey Ranch problem, we first construct the feasible solution region. This is done by plotting each of the three constraint equations as in Figure 7.10. Note that the third constraint, $0.5\,X_1 \geq 1.5$, can be rewritten and plotted as $X_1 \geq 3$. (This involves multiplying both sides of the inequality by 2 but does not change the position of the constraint line in any way.) Minimization problems are often unbounded outward (i.e., on the right side and on top), but this causes no difficulty in solving them. As long as they are bounded inward (on the left side and the bottom), corner points may be established. The optimal solution will lie at one of the corners as it would in a maximization problem.

We plot the three constraints to develop a feasible solution region for the minimization problem.

Note that minimization problems often have unbounded feasible regions.

In this case, there are three corner points: *a*, *b*, and *c*. For point *a*, we find the coordinates at the intersection of the ingredient C and B constraints, that is, where the line $X_1 = 3$ crosses the line $4X_1 + 3X_2 = 48$. If we substitute $X_1 = 3$ into the B constraint equation, we get

$$4(3) + 3X_2 = 48$$

or

$$X_2 = 12$$

Thus, point *a* has the coordinates ($X_1 = 3, X_2 = 12$).

FIGURE 7.10

Feasible Region for the Holiday Meal Turkey Ranch Problem

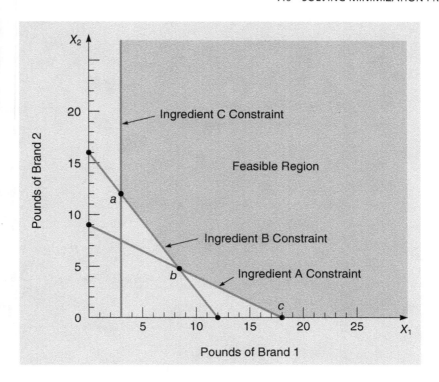

To find the coordinates of point b algebraically, we solve the equations $4X_1 + 3X_2 = 48$ and $5X_1 + 10X_2 = 90$ simultaneously. This yields $(X_1 = 8.4, X_2 = 4.8)$.

The coordinates at point c are seen by inspection to be $(X_1 = 18, X_2 = 0)$. We now evaluate the objective function at each corner point, and we get

$$\text{Cost} = 2X_1 + 3X_2$$
$$\text{Cost at point } a = 2(3) + 3(12) = 42$$
$$\text{Cost at point } b = 2(8.4) + 3(4.8) = 31.2$$
$$\text{Cost at point } c = 2(18) + 3(0) = 36$$

Hence, the minimum cost solution is to purchase 8.4 pounds of brand 1 feed and 4.8 pounds of brand 2 feed per turkey per month. This will yield a cost of 31.2 cents per turkey.

 IN ACTION **NBC Uses Linear, Integer, and Goal Programming in Selling Advertising Slots**

The National Broadcasting Company (NBC) sells over $4 billion in television advertising each year. About 60% to 80% of the air time for an upcoming season is sold in a 2- to 3-week period in late May. The advertising agencies approach the networks to purchase advertising time for their clients. Included in each request are the dollar amount, the demographic (e.g., age of the viewing audience) in which the client is interested, the program mix, weekly weighting, unit-length distribution, and a negotiated cost per 1,000 viewers. NBC must then develop detailed sales plans to meet these requirements. Traditionally, NBC developed these plans manually, and this required several hours per plan. These usually had to be reworked due to the complexity involved. With more than 300 such plans to be developed and reworked in a 2- to 3-week period, this was very time intensive and did not necessarily result in the maximum possible revenue.

In 1996, a project in the area of yield management was begun. Through this effort, NBC was able to create plans that more accurately meet customers' requirements, respond to customers more quickly, make the most profitable use of its limited inventory of advertising time slots, and reduce rework. The success of this system led to the development of a full-scale optimization system based on linear, integer, and goal programming. It is estimated that sales revenue between the years 1996 and 2000 increased by over $200 million due largely to this effort. Improvements in rework time, sales force productivity, and customer satisfaction were also benefits of this system.

Source: Based on Srinivas Bollapragada, et al. "NBC's Optimization Systems Increase Revenues and Productivity," *Interfaces* 32, 1 (January–February 2002): 47–60.

FIGURE 7.11

Graphical Solution to the Holiday Meal Turkey Ranch Problem Using the Isocost Line

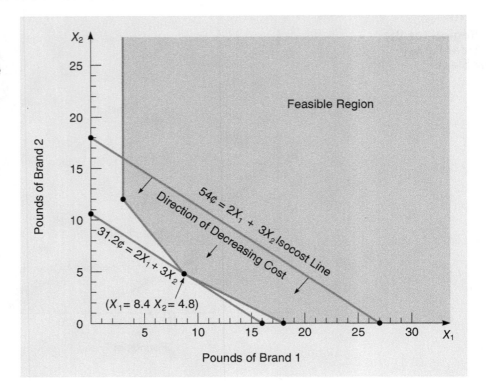

The isocost line method is analogous to the isoprofit line method we used in maximization problems.

ISOCOST LINE APPROACH As mentioned before, the **isocost line** approach may also be used to solve LP minimization problems such as that of the Holiday Meal Turkey Ranch. As with isoprofit lines, we need not compute the cost at each corner point, but instead draw a series of parallel cost lines. The lowest cost line (i.e., the one closest toward the origin) to touch the feasible region provides us with the optimal solution corner.

For example, we start in Figure 7.11 by drawing a 54-cent cost line, namely $54 = 2X_1 + 3X_2$. Obviously, there are many points in the feasible region that would yield a lower total cost. We proceed to move our isocost line toward the lower left, in a plane parallel to the 54-cent solution line. The last point we touch while still in contact with the feasible region is the same as corner point b of Figure 7.10. It has the coordinates $(X_1 = 8.4, X_2 = 4.8)$ and an associated cost of 31.2 cents.

This could be solved using QM for Windows by selecting the *Linear Programming* Module and selecting *New* problem. Specify that there are 2 variables and 3 constraints. When the input window opens, enter the data and click *Solve*. The output is shown in Program 7.4.

To solve this in Excel 2013, determine the cells where the solution will be, enter the coefficients from the objective function and the constraints, and write formulas for the total cost and the total of each ingredient (constraint). The input values and solution are shown in Program 7.5A, with Column D containing the formulas. These formulas are shown in Program 7.5B. When the Solver Parameters window opens, the *Set Objective* cell is D5; the *By Changing Variable Cells* are B4:C4; the Simplex LP method is used; the box for variables to be nonnegative is checked; and Min is selected because this is a minimization problem.

PROGRAM 7.4

Solution to the Holiday Meal Turkey Ranch Problem in QM for Windows

Linear Programming Results						
Holiday Meal Solution						
	X1	X2			RHS	Dual
Minimize	2	3				
Ingredient A	5	10	>=		90	-0.24
Ingredient B	4	3	>=		48	-0.2
Ingredient C	0.5	0	>=		1.5	0
Solution->	8.4	4.8			31.2	

PROGRAM 7.5A

Excel 2013 Solution for Holiday Meal Turkey Ranch Problem

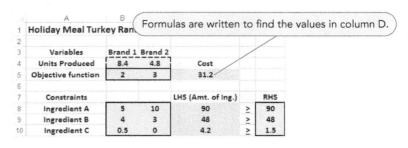

Formulas are written to find the values in column D.

	Brand 1	Brand 2		
Variables				
Units Produced	8.4	4.8	Cost	
Objective function	2	3	31.2	
Constraints			LHS (Amt. of Ing.)	RHS
Ingredient A	5	10	90 ≥	90
Ingredient B	4	3	48 ≥	48
Ingredient C	0.5	0	4.2 ≥	1.5

PROGRAM 7.5B

Excel 2013 Formulas for Holiday Meal Turkey Ranch Problem

	D
4	Cost
5	=SUMPRODUCT($B$4:$C$4,B5:C5)
6	
7	LHS (Amt. of Ing.)
8	=SUMPRODUCT($B$4:$C$4,B8:C8)
9	=SUMPRODUCT($B$4:$C$4,B9:C9)
10	=SUMPRODUCT($B$4:$C$4,B10:C10)

7.7 Four Special Cases in LP

Four special cases and difficulties arise at times when using the graphical approach to solving LP problems: (1) infeasibility, (2) unboundedness, (3) redundancy, and (4) alternate optimal solutions.

No Feasible Solution

Lack of a feasible solution region can occur if constraints conflict with one another.

When there is no solution to an LP problem that satisfies all of the constraints given, then no feasible solution exists. Graphically, it means that no feasible solution region exists—a situation that might occur if the problem was formulated with conflicting constraints. This, by the way, is a frequent occurrence in real-life, large-scale LP problems that involve hundreds of constraints. For example, if one constraint is supplied by the marketing manager who states that at least 300 tables must be produced (namely, $X_1 \geq 300$) to meet sales demand, and a second restriction is supplied by the production manager, who insists that no more than 220 tables be produced (namely, $X_1 \leq 220$) because of a lumber shortage, no feasible solution region results. When the operations research analyst coordinating the LP problem points out this conflict, one manager or the other must revise his or her inputs. Perhaps more raw materials could be procured from a new source, or perhaps sales demand could be lowered by substituting a different model table to customers.

As a further graphic illustration of this, let us consider the following three constraints:

$$X_1 + 2X_2 \leq 6$$
$$2X_1 + X_2 \leq 8$$
$$X_1 \geq 7$$

As seen in Figure 7.12, there is no feasible solution region for this LP problem because of the presence of conflicting constraints.

Unboundedness

When the profit in a maximization problem can be infinitely large, the problem is unbounded and is missing one or more constraints.

Sometimes a linear program will not have a finite solution. This means that in a maximization problem, for example, one or more solution variables, and the profit, can be made infinitely large without violating any constraints. If we try to solve such a problem graphically, we will note that the feasible region is open ended.

FIGURE 7.12

A Problem with No Feasible Solution

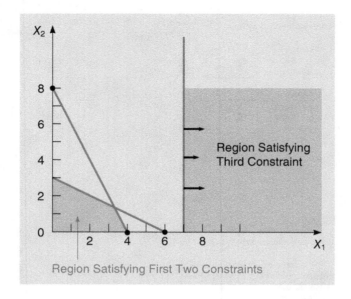

Let us consider a simple example to illustrate the situation. A firm has formulated the following LP problem:

$$\text{Maximize profit} = \$3X_1 + \$5X_2$$

$$\text{subject to} \quad X_1 \qquad \geq 5$$

$$X_2 \leq 10$$

$$X_1 + 2X_2 \geq 10$$

$$X_1, X_2 \geq 0$$

As you see in Figure 7.13, because this is a maximization problem and the feasible region extends infinitely to the right, there is **unboundedness**, or an unbounded solution. This implies that the problem has been formulated improperly. It would indeed be wonderful for the company to be able to produce an infinite number of units of X_1 (at a profit of \$3 each!), but obviously no firm has infinite resources available or infinite product demand.

Redundancy

A redundant constraint is one that does not affect the feasible solution region.

The presence of redundant constraints is another common situation that occurs in large LP formulations. **Redundancy** causes no major difficulties in solving LP problems graphically, but you should be able to identify its occurrence. A redundant constraint is simply one that does

FIGURE 7.13

A Feasible Region That Is Unbounded to the Right

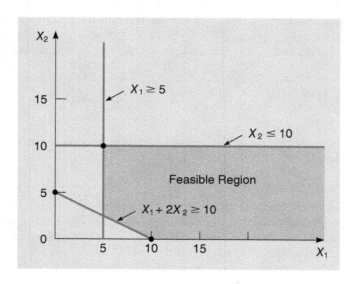

FIGURE 7.14

Example of a Redundant Constraint

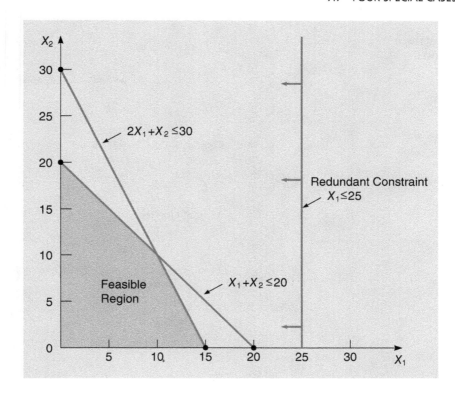

not affect the feasible solution region. In other words, other constraints may be more binding or restrictive than the redundant constraint.

Let's look at the following example of an LP problem with three constraints:

$$\text{Maximize profit} = \$1X_1 + \$2X_2$$
$$\text{subject to} \qquad X_1 + X_2 \leq 20$$
$$2X_1 + X_2 \leq 30$$
$$X_1 \qquad \leq 25$$
$$X_1, X_2 \geq 0$$

The third constraint, $X_1 \leq 25$, is less binding but the first two constraints are indeed more restrictive constraints (see Figure 7.14).

Alternate Optimal Solutions

Multiple optimal solutions are possible in LP problems.

An LP problem may, on occasion, have two or more **alternate optimal solutions**. Graphically, this is the case when the objective function's isoprofit or isocost line runs perfectly parallel to one of the problem's constraints—in other words, when they have the same slope.

Management of a firm noticed the presence of more than one optimal solution when they formulated this simple LP problem:

$$\text{Maximize profit} = \$3X_1 + \$2X_2$$
$$\text{subject to} \qquad 6X_1 + 4X_2 \leq 24$$
$$X_1 \qquad \leq 3$$
$$X_1, X_2 \geq 0$$

As we see in Figure 7.15, our first isoprofit line of $8 runs parallel to the first constraint equation. At a profit level of $12, the isoprofit line will rest directly on top of the segment of the first constraint line. This means that any point along the line between *A* and *B* provides an optimal X_1 and X_2 combination. Far from causing problems, the existence of more than one optimal solution

FIGURE 7.15

Example of Alternate Optimal Solutions

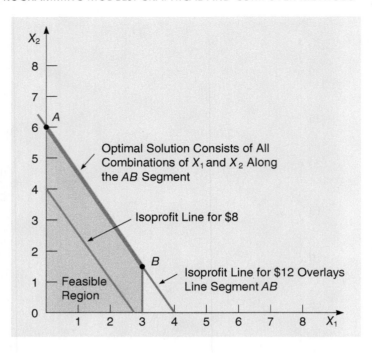

allows management great flexibility in deciding which combination to select. The profit remains the same at each alternate solution.

7.8 Sensitivity Analysis

Optimal solutions to LP problems have thus far been found under what are called *deterministic assumptions*. This means that we assume complete certainty in the data and relationships of a problem—namely, prices are fixed, resources known, time needed to produce a unit exactly set. But in the real world, conditions are dynamic and changing. How can we handle this apparent discrepancy?

How sensitive is the optimal solution to changes in profits, resources, or other input parameters?

One way we can do so is by continuing to treat each particular LP problem as a deterministic situation. However, when an optimal solution is found, we recognize the importance of seeing just how *sensitive* that solution is to model assumptions and data. For example, if a firm realizes that profit per unit is not $5 as estimated but instead is closer to $5.50, how will the final solution mix and total profit change? If additional resources, such as 10 labor hours or 3 hours of machine time, should become available, will this change the problem's answer? Such analyses are used to examine the effects of changes in three areas: (1) contribution rates for each variable, (2) technological coefficients (the numbers in the constraint equations), and (3) available resources (the right-hand-side quantities in each constraint). This task is alternatively called **sensitivity analysis**, *postoptimality analysis*, *parametric programming*, or *optimality analysis*.

An important function of sensitivity analysis is to allow managers to experiment with values of the input parameters.

Sensitivity analysis also often involves a series of what-if? questions. What if the profit on product 1 increases by 10%? What if less money is available in the advertising budget constraint? What if workers each stay one hour longer every day at $1\frac{1}{2}$-time pay to provide increased production capacity? What if new technology will allow a product to be wired in one-third the time it used to take? So we see that sensitivity analysis can be used to deal not only with errors in estimating input parameters to the LP model but also with management's experiments with possible future changes in the firm that may affect profits.

There are two approaches to determining just how sensitive an optimal solution is to changes. The first is simply a trial-and-error approach. This approach usually involves resolving the entire problem, preferably by computer, each time one input data item or parameter is changed. It can take a long time to test a series of possible changes in this way.

Postoptimality analysis means examining changes after the optimal solution has been reached.

The approach we prefer is the analytic postoptimality method. After an LP problem has been solved, we attempt to determine a range of changes in problem parameters that will not affect the optimal solution or change the variables in the solution. This is done without resolving the whole problem.

Let's investigate sensitivity analysis by developing a small production mix problem. Our goal will be to demonstrate graphically and through the simplex tableau how sensitivity analysis can be used to make linear programming concepts more realistic and insightful.

High Note Sound Company

The High Note Sound Company manufactures quality speakers and stereo receivers. Each of these products requires a certain amount of skilled artisanship, of which there is a limited weekly supply. The firm formulates the following LP problem in order to determine the best production mix of speakers (X_1) and receivers (X_2):

$$\text{Maximize profit} = \$50X_1 + \$120X_2$$

$$\begin{array}{ll} \text{subject to} & 2X_1 + 4X_2 \leq 80 \quad \text{(hours of electricians' time available)} \\ & 3X_1 + 1X_2 \leq 60 \quad \text{(hours of audio technicians' time available)} \\ & X_1, X_2 \geq 0 \end{array}$$

The solution to this problem is illustrated graphically in Figure 7.16. Given this information and deterministic assumptions, the firm should produce only stereo receivers (20 of them), for a weekly profit of $2,400.

For the optimal solution, $(0, 20)$, the electrician hours used are

$$2X_1 + 4X_2 = 2(0) + 4(20) = 80$$

and this equals the amount available, so there is 0 slack for this constraint. Thus, it is a binding constraint. If a constraint is binding, obtaining additional units of that resource will usually result in higher profits. The audio technician hours used for the optimal solution $(0, 20)$ are

$$3X_1 + 1X_2 = 3(0) + 1(20) = 20$$

but the hours available are 60. Thus, there is a slack of $60 - 20 = 40$ hours. Because there are extra hours available that are not being used, this is a nonbinding constraint. For a nonbinding constraint, obtaining additional units of that resource will not result in higher profits and will only increase the slack.

FIGURE 7.16

High Note Sound Company Graphical Solution

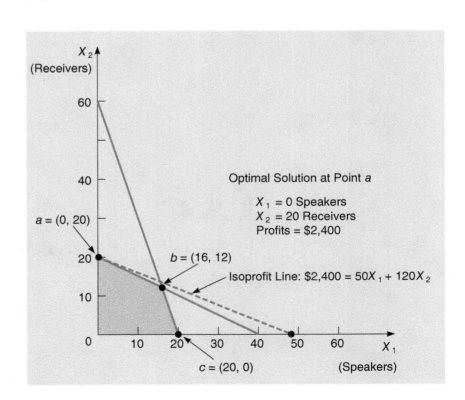

Changes in the Objective Function Coefficient

Changes in contribution rates are examined first.

In real-life problems, contribution rates (usually profit or cost) in the objective functions fluctuate periodically, as do most of a firm's expenses. Graphically, this means that although the feasible solution region remains exactly the same, the slope of the isoprofit or isocost line will change. It is easy to see in Figure 7.17 that the High Note Sound Company's profit line is optimal at point a. But what if a technical breakthrough just occurred that raised the profit per stereo receiver (X_2) from \$120 to \$150? Is the solution still optimal? The answer is definitely yes, for in this case the slope of the profit line accentuates the profitability at point a. The new profit is $\$3,000 = 0(\$50) + 20(\$150)$.

On the other hand, if X_2's profit coefficient was overestimated and should only have been \$80, the slope of the profit line changes enough to cause a new corner point (b) to become optimal. Here the profit is $\$1,760 = 16(\$50) + 12(\$80)$.

A new corner point becomes optimal if an objective function coefficient is decreased or increased too much.

This example illustrates a very important concept about changes in objective function coefficients. We can increase or decrease the objective function coefficient (profit) of any variable, and the current corner point may remain optimal if the change is not too large. However, if we increase or decrease this coefficient by too much, then the optimal solution would be at a different corner point. How much can the objective function coefficient change before another corner point becomes optimal? Both QM for Windows and Excel provide the answer.

QM for Windows and Changes in Objective Function Coefficients

The current solution remains optimal unless an objective function coefficient is increased to a value above the upper bound or decreased to a value below the lower bound.

The QM for Windows input for the High Note Sound Company example is shown in Program 7.6A. When the solution has been found, selecting *Window* and *Ranging* allows us to see additional information on sensitivity analysis. Program 7.6B provides the output related to sensitivity analysis.

From Program 7.6B, we see the profit on speakers was \$50, which is indicated as the original value in the output. This objective function coefficient has a lower bound of negative infinity

Figure 7.17   Changes in the Receiver Contribution Coefficients

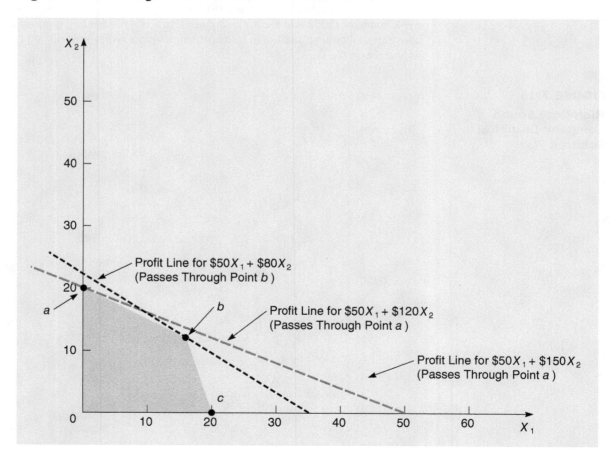

PROGRAM 7.6A

Input to QM for Windows High Note Sound Company Data

Objective					
⦿ Maximize	Instruction				
○ Minimize	Use these option buttons to set the objective.				

High Note Sound Company					
	X1	X2		RHS	Equation form
Maximize	50	120			Max 50X1 + 120X2
Electrician hours	2	4	<=	80	2X1 + 4X2 <= 80
Audio technician hours	3	1	<=	60	3X1 + X2 <= 60

PROGRAM 7.6B

High Note Sound Company Sensitivity Analysis Output

◈ Ranging   □ ▭

High Note Sound Company Solution					
Variable	Value	Reduced Cost	Original Val	Lower Bound	Upper Bound
X1	0	10	50	-Infinity	60
X2	20	0	120	100	Infinity
Constraint	Dual Value	Slack/Surplus	Original Val	Lower Bound	Upper Bound
Electrician hours	30	0	80	0	240
Audio technician hours	0	40	60	20	Infinity

and an upper bound of $60. This means that the current corner point solution remains optimal as long as the profit on speakers does not go above $60. If it equals $60, there would be two optimal solutions as the objective function would be parallel to the first constraint. The points (0, 20) and (16, 12) would both give a profit of $2,400. The profit on speakers may decrease any amount as indicated by the negative infinity, and the optimal corner point does not change. This negative infinity is logical because currently there are no speakers being produced because the profit is too low. Any decrease in the profit on speakers would make them less attractive relative to the receivers, and we certainly would not produce any speakers because of this.

The profit on receivers has an upper bound of infinity (it may increase by any amount) and a lower bound of $100. If this profit equaled $100, then the corner points (0, 20) and (16, 12) would both be optimal. The profit at each of these would be $2,000.

In general, a change can be made to one (and only one) objective function coefficient, and the current optimal corner point remains optimal as long as the change is between the Upper and Lower Bounds. If two or more coefficients are changed simultaneously, then the problem should be solved with the new coefficients to determine whether or not this current solution remains optimal.

The upper and lower bounds relate to changing only one coefficient at a time.

Excel Solver and Changes in Objective Function Coefficients

Program 7.7A illustrates how the Excel 2013 spreadsheet for this example is set up for Solver. When *Solver* is selected from the *Data* tab, the appropriate inputs are made, and *Solve* is clicked in the Solver dialog box, the solution and the Solver Results window will appear as in Program 7.7B. Selecting *Sensitivity* from the reports area of this window will provide a Sensitivity Report on a new worksheet, with results as shown in Program 7.7C. Note how the cells are named based on the text from Program 7.7A. Notice that Excel does not provide lower bounds and upper bounds for the objective function coefficients. Instead, it gives the allowable increases

PROGRAM 7.7A

Excel 2013 Spreadsheet for High Note Sound Company

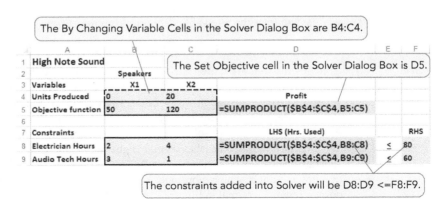

PROGRAM 7.7B   Excel 2013 Solution and Solver Results Window for High Note Sound Company

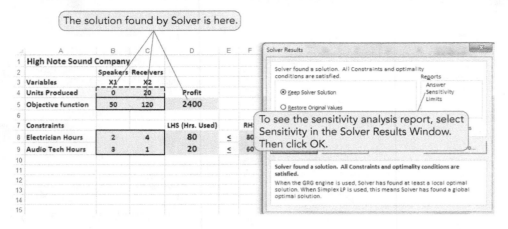

PROGRAM 7.7C

Excel 2013 Sensitivity Report for High Note Sound Company

The names presented in the Sensitivity Report combine the text in column A and the text above the data, unless the cells have been named using the Name Manager from the Formulas tab.

The profit on speakers may change by these amounts and the current corner point will remain optimal.

A B		C	D	E	F	G	H
6	Variable Cells						
7			Final	Reduced	Objective	Allowable	Allowable
8	Cell	Name	Value	Cost	Coefficient	Increase	Decrease
9	$B$4	Units Produced X1	0	-10	50	10	1E+30
10	$C$4	Units Produced X2	20	0	120	1E+30	20
11							
12	Constraints						
13			Final	Shadow	Constraint	Allowable	Allowable
14	Cell	Name	Value	Price	R.H. Side	Increase	Decrease
15	$D$8	Electrician Hours LHS (Hrs. Used)	80	30	80	160	80
16	$D$9	Audio Tech Hours LHS (Hrs. Used)	20	0	60	1E+30	40

The resources used are here. The RHS can change by these amounts, and the shadow price will still be relevant.

Excel solver gives allowable increases and decreases rather than upper and lower bounds.

and decreases for these. By adding the allowable increase to the current value, we may obtain the upper bound. For example, the allowable increase on the profit (objective coefficient) for speakers is 10, which means that the upper bound on this profit is $50 + $10 = $60. Similarly, we may subtract the allowable decrease from the current value to obtain the lower bound.

Changes in the Technological Coefficients

Changes in technological coefficients affect the shape of the feasible solution region.

Changes in what are called the **technological coefficients** often reflect changes in the state of technology. If fewer or more resources are needed to produce a product such as a speaker or stereo receiver, coefficients in the constraint equations will change. These changes will have no effect on the objective function of an LP problem, but they can produce a significant change in the shape of the feasible solution region, and hence in the optimal profit or cost.

Figure 7.18 illustrates the original High Note Sound Company graphical solution as well as two separate changes in technological coefficients. In Figure 7.18, Part (a), we see that the optimal solution lies at point a, which represents $X_1 = 0$, $X_2 = 20$. You should be able to prove to yourself that point a remains optimal in Figure 7.18, Part (b) despite a constraint change from $3X_1 + 1X_2 \le 60$ to $2X_1 + 1X_2 \le 60$. Such a change might take place when the firm discovers that it no longer demands three hours of audio technicians' time to produce a speaker, but only two hours.

FIGURE 7.18 Change in the Technological Coefficients for the High Note Sound Company

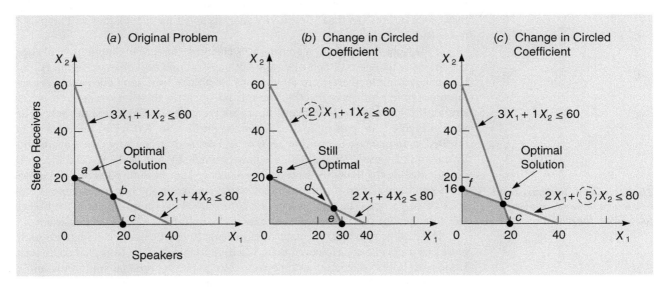

In Figure 7.18, Part (c), however, a change in the other constraint changes the shape of the feasible region enough to cause a new corner point (*g*) to become optimal. Before moving on, see if you reach an objective function value of $1,954 profit at point *g* (versus a profit of $1,920 at point *f*).*

Changes in the Resources or Right-Hand-Side Values

The right-hand-side values of the constraints often represent resources available to the firm. The resources could be labor hours or machine time or perhaps money or production materials available. In the High Note Sound Company example, the two resources are hours available of electricians' time and hours of audio technicians' time. If additional hours were available, a higher

IN ACTION **Swift & Company Uses LP to Schedule Production**

Based in Greeley, Colorado, Swift & Company has annual sales over $8 billion, with beef and related products making up the vast majority of this. Swift has five processing plants, which handle over 6 billion pounds of beef each year. Each head of beef is cut into two sides, which yield the chuck, the brisket, the loins, the ribs, the round, the plate, and the flank. With some cuts in greater demand than others, the customer service representatives (CSRs) try to meet the demand for customers while providing discounts when necessary to clear out some cuts that might be in excess supply. It is important that the CSRs have accurate information on product availability in close to real time so they can react quickly to changing demand.

With the cost of raw material being as high as 85%, and with a very thin profit margin, it is essential that the company operate efficiently. Swift started a project in March 2001 to develop a mathematical programming model that would optimize the

supply chain. Ten full-time employees worked with four operations research consultants from Aspen Technology on what was called Project Phoenix. At the heart of the final model are 45 integrated LP models that enable the company to dynamically schedule its operations in real time as orders are received.

With Project Phoenix, not only did profit margins increase, but the improvements in forecasting, cattle procurement, and manufacturing improved relations with customers and enhanced the reputation of Swift & Company in the marketplace. The company is better able to deliver products according to customer specification. While the model cost over $6 million to develop, in the first year of operation, it generated a benefit of $12.7 million.

Source: Based on Ann Bixby, Brian Downs, and Mike Self. "A Scheduling and Capable-to-Promise Application for Swift & Company," *Interfaces* 36, 1 (January–February 2006): 69–86.

---

*Note that the values of X_1 and X_2 at point *g* are fractions. Although the High Note Sound Company cannot produce 0.67, 0.75, or 0.90 of a speaker or stereo, we can assume that the firm can *begin* a unit one week and complete it the next. As long as the production process is fairly stable from week to week, this raises no major problems. If solutions *must* be whole numbers each period, refer to our discussion of integer programming in Chapter 10 to handle the situation.

total profit could be realized. How much should the company be willing to pay for additional hours? Is it profitable to have some electricians work overtime? Should we be willing to pay for more audio technician time? Sensitivity analysis about these resources will help us answer these questions.

If the right-hand side of a constraint is changed, the feasible region will change (unless the constraint is redundant), and often the optimal solution will change. In the High Note Sound Company example, there were 80 hours of electrician time available each week and the maximum possible profit was $2,400. There is no slack for this constraint, so it is a binding constraint. If the available electricians' hours are increased to 100 hours, the new optimal solution seen in Figure 7.19, part (a) is (0, 25) and the profit is $3,000. Thus, the extra 20 hours of time resulted in an increase in profit of $600 or $30 per hour. If the hours were decreased to 60 hours as shown in Figure 7.19, part (b), the new optimal solution is (0, 15) and the profit is $1,800. Thus, reducing the hours by 20 results in a decrease in profit of $600 or $30 per hour. This $30 per hour change in profit that resulted from a change in the hours available is called the dual price or dual value. The **dual price** for a constraint is the improvement in the objective function value that results from a one-unit increase in the right-hand side of the constraint.

The value of one additional unit of a scarce resource may be found from the dual price.

The dual price of $30 per hour of electrician time tells us we can increase profit if we have more electrician hours. However, there is a limit to this as there is limited audio technician time. If the total hours of electrician time were 240 hours, the optimal solution would be (0, 60) as shown in Figure 7.19, part (c) and the profit would be $7,200. Again, this is an increase of $30 profit per hour (the dual price) for each of the 160 hours that were added to the original amount. If the number of hours increased beyond 240, then profit would no longer increase and the optimal solution would still be (0, 60) as shown in Figure 7.19, part (c). There would simply be excess (slack) hours of electrician time and all of the audio technician time would be used. Thus, the dual price is relevant only within limits. Both QM for Windows and Excel Solver provide these limits.

QM for Windows and Changes in Right-Hand-Side Values

The QM for Windows sensitivity analysis output was shown in Program 7.6B. The dual value for the electrician hours constraint is given as 30, and the lower bound is zero while the upper bound is 240. This means that each additional hour of electrician time, up to a total of 240 hours, will increase the maximum possible profit by $30. Similarly, if the available electrician time is decreased, the maximum possible profit will decrease by $30 per hour until the available time is decreased to the lower bound of 0. If the amount of electrician time (the right-hand-side value for this constraint) is outside this range (0 to 240), then the dual value is no longer relevant and the problem should be resolved with the new right-hand-side value.

Dual prices will change if the amount of the resource (the right-hand side of the constraint) goes above the upper bound or below the lower bound given in the Ranging section of the QM for Windows output.

In Program 7.6B, the dual value for audio technician hours is shown to be $0 and the slack is 40, so it is a nonbinding constraint. There are 40 hours of audio technician time that are not being used despite the fact that they are currently available. If additional hours were made available they would not increase profit but would simply increase the amount of slack. This dual value of zero is relevant as long as the right-hand side does not go below the lower bound of 20. The upper limit is infinity indicating that adding more hours would simply increase the amount of slack.

Excel Solver and Changes in Right-Hand-Side Values

The Sensitivity report from Excel Solver was shown in Program 7.7C. Notice that Solver gives the shadow price instead of the dual price. A **shadow price** is the change in the objective function value (e.g., profit or cost) that results from a one-unit increase in the right-hand-side of a constraint.

The shadow price is the same as the dual price in maximization problems.

Since an improvement in the objective function value in a maximization problem is the same as a positive change (increase), the dual price and the shadow price are exactly the same for maximization problems. For a minimization problem, an improvement in the objective function value is a decrease, which is a negative change. So for minimization problems, the shadow price will be the negative of the dual price.

FIGURE 7.19

Changes in the Electricians' Time Resource for the High Note Sound Company

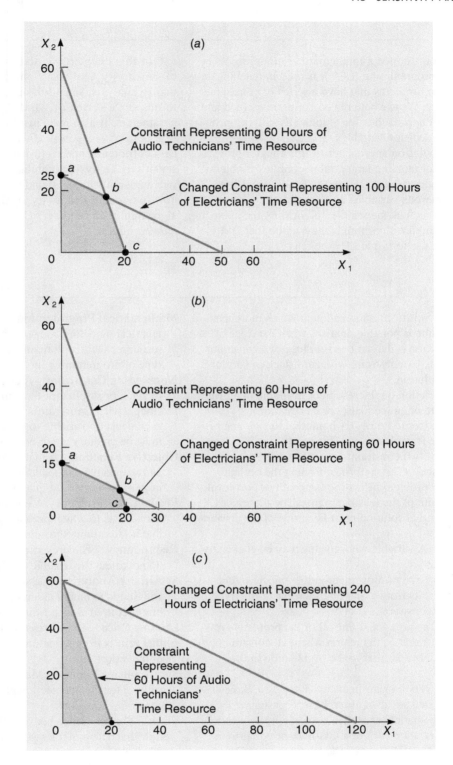

(a)

Constraint Representing 60 Hours of Audio Technicians' Time Resource

Changed Constraint Representing 100 Hours of Electricians' Time Resource

(b)

Constraint Representing 60 Hours of Audio Technicians' Time Resource

Changed Constraint Representing 60 Hours of Electricians' Time Resource

(c)

Changed Constraint Representing 240 Hours of Electricians' Time Resource

Constraint Representing 60 Hours of Audio Technicians' Time Resource

The Allowable Increase and Allowable Decrease for the right-hand side of each constraint is provided, and the shadow price is relevant for changes within these limits. For the electrician hours, the right-hand-side value of 80 may be increased by 160 (for a total of 240) or decreased by 80 (for a total of 0) and the shadow price remains relevant. If a change is made that exceeds these limits, then the problem should be resolved to find the impact of the change.

Summary

In this chapter, we introduce a mathematical modeling technique called linear programming (LP). It is used in reaching an optimum solution to problems that have a series of constraints binding the objective. We use both the corner point method and the isoprofit/isocost approaches for graphically solving problems with only two decision variables.

The graphical solution approaches of this chapter provide a conceptual basis for tackling larger, more complex problems, some of which are addressed in Chapter 8. To solve real-life LP problems with numerous variables and constraints, we need a solution procedure such as the simplex algorithm, the subject of Module 7. The simplex algorithm is the method that QM for Windows and Excel use to tackle LP problems.

In this chapter, we also present the important concept of sensitivity analysis. Sometimes referred to as postoptimality analysis, sensitivity analysis is used by management to answer a series of what-if? questions about LP model parameters. It also tests just how sensitive the optimal solution is to changes in profit or cost coefficients, technological coefficients, and right-hand-side resources. We explored sensitivity analysis graphically (i.e., for problems with only two decision variables) and with computer output, but to see how to conduct sensitivity algebraically through the simplex algorithm, read Module 7 (located at **www.pearsonhighered.com/render**).

Glossary

Alternate Optimal Solution   A situation in which more than one optimal solution is possible. It arises when the slope of the objective function is the same as the slope of a constraint.

Binding Constraint   A constraint with zero slack or surplus for the optimal solution.

Constraint   A restriction on the resources available to a firm (stated in the form of an inequality or an equation).

Corner Point, or Extreme Point   A point that lies on one of the corners of the feasible region. This means that it falls at the intersection of two constraint lines.

Corner Point Method   The method of finding the optimal solution to an LP problem by testing the profit or cost level at each corner point of the feasible region. The theory of LP states that the optimal solution must lie at one of the corner points.

Decision Variable   A variable whose value may be chosen by the decision maker.

Dual Price (value)   The improvement in the objective function value that results from a one-unit increase in the right-hand side of that constraint.

Feasible Region   The area satisfying all of the problem's resource restrictions; that is, the region where all constraints overlap. All possible solutions to the problem lie in the feasible region.

Feasible Solution   A point lying in the feasible region. Basically, it is any point that satisfies all of the problem's constraints.

Inequality   A mathematical expression containing a greater-than-or-equal-to relation ($\geq$) or a less-than-or-equal-to relation ($\leq$) used to indicate that the total consumption of a resource must be $\geq$ or $\leq$ some limiting value.

Infeasible Solution   Any point lying outside the feasible region. It violates one or more of the stated constraints.

Isocost Line   A straight line representing all combinations of X_1 and X_2 for a particular cost level.

Isoprofit Line   A straight line representing all nonnegative combinations of X_1 and X_2 for a particular profit level.

Linear Programming (LP)   A mathematical technique used to help management decide how to make the most effective use of an organization's resources.

Mathematical Programming   The general category of mathematical modeling and solution techniques used to allocate resources while optimizing a measurable goal. LP is one type of programming model.

Nonbinding Constraint   A constraint with a positive amount of slack or surplus for the optimal solution.

Nonnegativity Constraints   A set of constraints that requires each decision variable to be nonnegative; that is, each X_i must be greater than or equal to 0.

Objective Function   A mathematical statement of the goal of an organization, stated as an intent to maximize or to minimize some important quantity such as profits or costs.

Product Mix Problem   A common LP problem involving a decision as to which products a firm should produce given that it faces limited resources.

Redundancy   The presence of one or more constraints that do not affect the feasible solution region.

Sensitivity Analysis   The study of how sensitive an optimal solution is to model assumptions and to data changes. It is often referred to as postoptimality analysis.

Shadow Price   The increase in the objective function value that results from a one-unit increase in the right-hand side of that constraint.

Simultaneous Equation Method   The algebraic means of solving for the intersection point of two or more linear constraint equations.

Slack   The difference between the left-hand side and the right-hand side of a less-than-or-equal-to constraint. Often this is the amount of a resource that is not being used.

Surplus   The difference between the left-hand side and the right-hand side of a greater-than-or-equal-to constraint. Often this represents the amount by which a minimum quantity is exceeded.

Technological Coefficients   Coefficients of the variables in the constraint equations. The coefficients represent the amount of resources needed to produce one unit of the variable.

Unboundedness   A condition that exists when a solution variable and the profit can be made infinitely large without violating any of the problem's constraints in a maximization process.

Solved Problems

Solved Problem 7-1

Personal Mini Warehouses is planning to expand its successful Orlando business into Tampa. In doing so, the company must determine how many storage rooms of each size to build. Its objective and constraints follow:

Maximize monthly earnings $= 50X_1 + 20X_2$

subject to

$$20X_1 + 40X_2 \leq 4{,}000 \qquad \text{(advertising budget available)}$$
$$100X_1 + 50X_2 \leq 8{,}000 \qquad \text{(square footage required)}$$
$$X_1 \qquad\qquad \leq 60 \qquad \text{(rental limit expected)}$$
$$X_1, X_2 \geq 0$$

where

$X_1 =$ number of large spaces developed

$X_2 =$ number of small spaces developed

Solution

An evaluation of the five corner points of the accompanying graph indicates that corner point *C* produces the greatest earnings. Refer to the graph and table.

CORNER POINT	VALUES OF X_1, X_2	OBJECTIVE FUNCTION VALUE ($)
A	(0, 0)	0
B	(60, 0)	3,000
C	(60, 40)	3,800
D	(40, 80)	3,600
E	(0, 100)	2,000

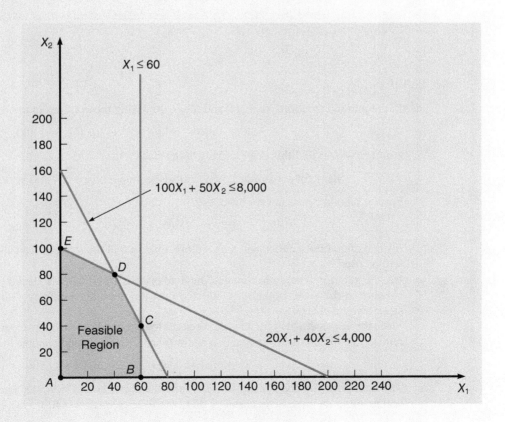

Solved Problem 7-2

The solution obtained with QM for Windows for Solved Problem 7-1 is given in the following program. Use this to answer the following questions.

a. For the optimal solution, how much of the advertising budget is spent?
b. For the optimal solution, how much square footage will be used?
c. Would the solution change if the budget were only $3,000 instead of $4,000?
d. What would the optimal solution be if the profit on the large spaces were reduced from $50 to $45?
e. How much would earnings increase if the square footage requirement were increased from 8,000 to 9,000?

Linear Programming Results

	X1	X2		RHS	Dual
	Solved Problem 7-2 Solution				
Maximize	50	20			
Constraint 1	20	40	<=	4,000	0
Constraint 2	100	50	<=	8,000	0.4
Constraint 3	1	0	<=	60	10
Solution->	60	40		3,800	

Ranging

Solved Problem 7-2 Solution

Variable	Value	Reduced	Original Val	Lower Bound	Upper Bound
X1	60	0	50	40	Infinity
X2	40	0	20	0	25
Constraint	Dual Value	Slack/Surplus	Original Val	Lower Bound	Upper Bound
Constraint 1	0	1,200	4,000	2,800	Infinity
Constraint 2	0.4	0	8,000	6,000	9,500
Constraint 3	10	0	60	40	80

Solution

a. In the optimal solution, $X_1 = 60$ and $X_2 = 40$. Using these values in the first constraint gives us

$$20X_1 + 40X_2 = 20(60) + 40(40) = 2,800$$

Another way to find this is by looking at the slack:

Slack for constraint 1 = 1,200 so the amount used is $4,000 - 1,200 = 2,800$

b. For the second constraint we have

$$100X_1 + 50X_2 = 100(60) + 50(40) = 8,000 \text{ square feet}$$

Instead of computing this, you may simply observe that the slack is 0, so all of the 8,000 square feet will be used.

c. No, the solution would not change. The dual price is 0 and there is slack available. The value 3,000 is between the lower bound of 2,800 and the upper bound of infinity. Only the slack for this constraint would change.

d. Since the new coefficient for X_1 is between the lower bound (40) and the upper bound (infinity), the current corner point remains optimal. So $X_1 = 60$ and $X_2 = 40$, and only the monthly earnings change.

$$\text{Earnings} = 45(60) + 20(40) = \$3,500$$

e. The dual price for this constraint is 0.4, and the upper bound is 9,500. The increase of 1,000 units will result in an increase in earnings of $1,000(0.4 \text{ per unit}) = \$400$.

Solved Problem 7-3

Solve the following LP formulation graphically, using the isocost line approach:

$$\text{Minimize costs} = 24X_1 + 28X_2$$

$$\begin{aligned}
\text{subject to} \quad 5X_1 + 4X_2 &\leq 2{,}000 \\
X_1 &\geq 80 \\
X_1 + X_2 &\geq 300 \\
X_2 &\geq 100 \\
X_1, X_2 &\geq 0
\end{aligned}$$

Solution

A graph of the four constraints follows. The arrows indicate the direction of feasibility for each constraint. The next graph illustrates the feasible solution region and plots of two possible objective function cost lines. The first, $10,000, was selected arbitrarily as a starting point. To find the optimal corner point, we need to move the cost line in the direction of lower cost, that is, down and to the left. The last point where a cost line touches the feasible region as it moves toward the origin is corner point D. Thus D, which represents $X_1 = 200$, $X_2 = 100$, and a cost of $7,600, is optimal.

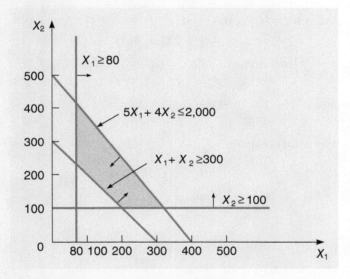

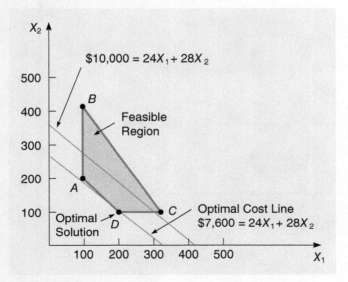

Solved Problem 7-4

Solve the following problem, using the corner point method. For the optimal solution, how much slack or surplus is there for each constraint?

$$\text{Maximize profit} = 30X_1 + 40X_2$$
$$\text{subject to} \quad 4X_1 + 2X_2 \leq 16$$
$$2X_1 - X_2 \geq 2$$
$$X_2 \leq 2$$
$$X_1, X_2 \geq 0$$

Solution

The graph appears next with the feasible region shaded.

CORNER POINT	COORDINATES	PROFIT ($)
A	$X_1 = 1, X_2 = 0$	30
B	$X_1 = 4, X_2 = 0$	120
C	$X_1 = 3, X_2 = 2$	170
D	$X_1 = 2, X_2 = 2$	140

The optimal solution is (3, 2). For this point,

$$4X_1 + 2X_2 = 4(3) + 2(2) = 16$$

Therefore, slack = 0 for constraint 1. Also,

$$2X_1 - 1X_2 = 2(3) - 1(2) = 4 > 2$$

Therefore, surplus = 4 − 2 = 2 for constraint 2. Also,

$$X_2 = 2$$

Therefore, slack = 0 for constraint 3.

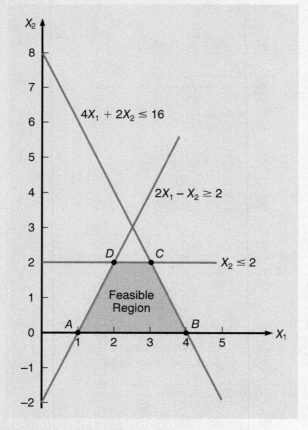

The optimal profit of $170 is at corner point C.

Self-Test

- Before taking the self-test, refer to the learning objectives at the beginning of the chapter, the notes in the margins, and the glossary at the end of the chapter.
- Use the key at the back of the book to correct your answers.
- Restudy pages that correspond to any questions that you answered incorrectly or material you feel uncertain about.

1. When using a graphical solution procedure, the region bounded by the set of constraints is called the
   a. solution.
   b. feasible region.
   c. infeasible region.
   d. maximum profit region.
   e. none of the above.

2. In an LP problem, at least one corner point must be an optimal solution if an optimal solution exists.
   a. True
   b. False

3. An LP problem has a bounded feasible region. If this problem has an equality ($=$) constraint, then
   a. this must be a minimization problem.
   b. the feasible region must consist of a line segment.
   c. the problem must be degenerate.
   d. the problem must have more than one optimal solution.

4. Which of the following would cause a change in the feasible region?
   a. Increasing an objective function coefficient in a maximization problem
   b. Adding a redundant constraint
   c. Changing the right-hand side of a nonredundant constraint
   d. Increasing an objective function coefficient in a minimization problem

5. If a nonredundant constraint is removed from an LP problem, then
   a. the feasible region will get larger.
   b. the feasible region will get smaller.
   c. the problem would become nonlinear.
   d. the problem would become infeasible.

6. In the optimal solution to a linear program, there are 20 units of slack for a constraint. From this we know that
   a. the dual price for this constraint is 20.
   b. the dual price for this constraint is 0.
   c. this constraint must be redundant.
   d. the problem must be a maximization problem.

7. A linear program has been solved and sensitivity analysis has been performed. The ranges for the objective function coefficients have been found. For the profit on X_1, the upper bound is 80, the lower bound is 60, and the current value is 75. Which of the following must be true if the profit on this variable is lowered to 70 and the optimal solution is found?
   a. A new corner point will become optimal.
   b. The maximum possible total profit may increase.
   c. The values for all the decision variables will remain the same.
   d. All of the above are possible.

8. A graphical method should only be used to solve an LP problem when
   a. there are only two constraints.
   b. there are more than two constraints.
   c. there are only two variables.
   d. there are more than two variables.

9. In LP, variables do not have to be integer valued and may take on any fractional value. This assumption is called
   a. proportionality.
   b. divisibility.
   c. additivity.
   d. certainty.

10. In solving a linear program, no feasible solution exists. To resolve this problem we might
   a. add another variable.
   b. add another constraint.
   c. remove or relax a constraint.
   d. try a different computer program.

11. If the feasible region gets larger due to a change in one of the constraints, the optimal value of the objective function
   a. must increase or remain the same for a maximization problem.
   b. must decrease or remain the same for a maximization problem.
   c. must increase or remain the same for a minimization problem.
   d. cannot change.

12. When alternate optimal solutions exist in an LP problem, then
   a. the objective function will be parallel to one of the constraints.
   b. one of the constraints will be redundant.
   c. two constraints will be parallel.
   d. the problem will also be unbounded.

13. If a linear program is unbounded, the problem probably has not been formulated correctly. Which of the following would most likely cause this?
   a. A constraint was inadvertently omitted.
   b. An unnecessary constraint was added to the problem.
   c. The objective function coefficients are too large.
   d. The objective function coefficients are too small.

14. A feasible solution to an LP problem
   a. must satisfy all of the problem's constraints simultaneously.
   b. need not satisfy all of the constraints, only some of them.
   c. must be a corner point of the feasible region.
   d. must give the maximum possible profit.

Discussion Questions and Problems

Discussion Questions

7-1 Discuss the similarities and differences between minimization and maximization problems using the graphical solution approaches of LP.

7-2 It is important to understand the assumptions underlying the use of any quantitative analysis model. What are the assumptions and requirements for an LP model to be formulated and used?

7-3 It has been said that each LP problem that has a feasible region has an infinite number of solutions. Explain.

7-4 You have just formulated a maximization LP problem and are preparing to solve it graphically. What criteria should you consider in deciding whether it would be easier to solve the problem by the corner point method or the isoprofit line approach?

7-5 Under what condition is it possible for an LP problem to have more than one optimal solution?

7-6 Develop your own set of constraint equations and inequalities and use them to illustrate graphically each of the following conditions:
   (a) an unbounded problem
   (b) an infeasible problem
   (c) a problem containing redundant constraints

7-7 The production manager of a large Cincinnati manufacturing firm once made the statement, "I would like to use LP, but it's a technique that operates under conditions of certainty. My plant doesn't have that certainty; it's a world of uncertainty. So LP can't be used here." Do you think this statement has any merit? Explain why the manager may have said it.

7-8 The mathematical relationships that follow were formulated by an operations research analyst at the Smith–Lawton Chemical Company. Which ones are invalid for use in an LP problem, and why?

$$\text{Maximize profit} = 4X_1 + 3X_1X_2 + 8X_2 + 5X_3$$
$$\text{subject to} \quad 2X_1 \qquad + X_2 + 2X_3 \leq 50$$
$$X_1 \qquad - 4X_2 \qquad \geq 6$$
$$1.5X_1^2 + 6X_2 + 3X_3 \geq 21$$
$$19X_2 - 0.35X_3 = 17$$
$$5X_1 \qquad + 4X_2 + 3\sqrt{X_3} \leq 80$$
$$-X_1 \qquad - X_2 + X_3 = 5$$

7-9 Discuss the role of sensitivity analysis in LP. Under what circumstances is it needed, and under what conditions do you think it is not necessary?

7-10 A linear program has the objective of maximizing profit $= 12X + 8Y$. The maximum profit is $8,000. Using a computer we find the upper bound for profit on X is 20 and the lower bound is 9. Discuss the changes to the optimal solution (the values of the variables and the profit) that would occur if the profit on X were increased to $15. How would the optimal solution change if the profit on X were increased to $25?

7-11 A linear program has a maximum profit of $600. One constraint in this problem is $4X + 2Y \leq 80$. Using a computer we find the dual price for this constraint is 3, and there is a lower bound of 75 and an upper bound of 100. Explain what this means.

7-12 Develop your own original LP problem with two constraints and two real variables.
   (a) Explain the meaning of the numbers on the right-hand side of each of your constraints.
   (b) Explain the significance of the technological coefficients.
   (c) Solve your problem graphically to find the optimal solution.
   (d) Illustrate graphically the effect of increasing the contribution rate of your first variable (X_1) by 50% over the value you first assigned it. Does this change the optimal solution?

7-13 Explain how a change in a technological coefficient can affect a problem's optimal solution. How can a change in resource availability affect a solution?

Problems

7-14 The Electrocomp Corporation manufactures two electrical products: air conditioners and large fans. The assembly process for each is similar in that both require a certain amount of wiring and drilling. Each air conditioner takes 3 hours of wiring and 2 hours of drilling. Each fan must go through 2 hours of wiring and 1 hour of drilling. During the next production period, 240 hours of wiring time are available and up to 140 hours of drilling time may be used. Each air conditioner sold yields a profit of $25. Each fan assembled may be sold for a $15 profit. Formulate and solve this LP production mix situation to find the best combination of air conditioners and fans that yields the highest profit. Use the corner point graphical approach.

7-15 Electrocomp's management realizes that it forgot to include two critical constraints (see Problem 7-14). In particular, management decides that there should be a minimum number of air conditioners produced

---

in order to fulfill a contract. Also, due to an oversupply of fans in the preceding period, a limit should be placed on the total number of fans produced.

(a) If Electrocomp decides that at least 20 air conditioners should be produced but no more than 80 fans should be produced, what would be the optimal solution? How much slack or surplus is there for each of the four constraints?

(b) If Electrocomp decides that at least 30 air conditioners should be produced but no more than 50 fans should be produced, what would be the optimal solution? How much slack or surplus is there for each of the four constraints at the optimal solution?

7-16 A candidate for mayor in a small town has allocated $40,000 for last-minute advertising in the days preceding the election. Two types of ads will be used: radio and television. Each radio ad costs $200 and reaches an estimated 3,000 people. Each television ad costs $500 and reaches an estimated 7,000 people. In planning the advertising campaign, the campaign manager would like to reach as many people as possible, but she has stipulated that at least 10 ads of each type must be used. Also, the number of radio ads must be at least as great as the number of television ads. How many ads of each type should be used? How many people will this reach?

7-17 The Outdoor Furniture Corporation manufactures two products, benches and picnic tables, for use in yards and parks. The firm has two main resources: its carpenters (labor force) and a supply of redwood for use in the furniture. During the next production cycle, 1,200 hours of labor are available under a union agreement. The firm also has a stock of 3,500 board feet of good-quality redwood. Each bench that Outdoor Furniture produces requires 4 labor hours and 10 board feet of redwood; each picnic table takes 6 labor hours and 35 board feet of redwood. Completed benches will yield a profit of $9 each, and tables will result in a profit of $20 each. How many benches and tables should Outdoor Furniture produce to obtain the largest possible profit? Use the graphical LP approach.

7-18 The dean of the Western College of Business must plan the school's course offerings for the fall semester. Student demands make it necessary to offer at least 30 undergraduate and 20 graduate courses in the term. Faculty contracts also dictate that at least 60 courses be offered in total. Each undergraduate course taught costs the college an average of $2,500 in faculty wages, and each graduate course costs $3,000. How many undergraduate and graduate courses should be taught in the fall so that total faculty salaries are kept to a minimum?

7-19 MSA Computer Corporation manufactures two models of minicomputers, the Alpha 4 and the

Beta 5. The firm employs five technicians, working 160 hours each per month, on its assembly line. Management insists that full employment (i.e., *all* 160 hours of time) be maintained for each worker during next month's operations. It requires 20 labor hours to assemble each Alpha 4 computer and 25 labor hours to assemble each Beta 5 model. MSA wants to see at least 10 Alpha 4s and at least 15 Beta 5s produced during the production period. Alpha 4s generate $1,200 profit per unit, and Beta 5s yield $1,800 each. Determine the most profitable number of each model of minicomputer to produce during the coming month.

7-20 A winner of the Texas Lotto has decided to invest $50,000 per year in the stock market. Under consideration are stocks for a petrochemical firm and a public utility. Although a long-range goal is to get the highest possible return, some consideration is given to the risk involved with the stocks. A risk index on a scale of 1–10 (with 10 being the most risky) is assigned to each of the two stocks. The total risk of the portfolio is found by multiplying the risk of each stock by the dollars invested in that stock.

The following table provides a summary of the return and risk:

STOCK	ESTIMATED RETURN	RISK INDEX
Petrochemical	12%	9
Utility	6%	4

The investor would like to maximize the return on the investment, but the average risk index of the investment should not be higher than 6. How much should be invested in each stock? What is the average risk for this investment? What is the estimated return for this investment?

7-21 Referring to the Texas Lotto situation in Problem 7-20, suppose the investor has changed his attitude about the investment and wishes to give greater emphasis to the risk of the investment. Now the investor wishes to minimize the risk of the investment as long as a return of at least 8% is generated. Formulate this as an LP problem and find the optimal solution. How much should be invested in each stock? What is the average risk for this investment? What is the estimated return for this investment?

7-22 Solve the following LP problem using the corner point graphical method. At the optimal solution, calculate the slack for each constraint:

Maximize profit $= 4X + 4Y$

subject to
$$3X + 5Y \le 150$$
$$X - 2Y \le 10$$
$$5X + 3Y \le 150$$
$$X, Y \ge 0$$

7-23 Consider this LP formulation:

$$\text{Minimize cost} = \$X + 2Y$$

$$\text{subject to} \quad X + 3Y \geq 90$$
$$8X + 2Y \geq 160$$
$$3X + 2Y \geq 120$$
$$Y \leq 70$$
$$X, Y \geq 0$$

Graphically illustrate the feasible region and apply the isocost line procedure to indicate which corner point produces the optimal solution. What is the cost of this solution?

7-24 The stock brokerage firm of Blank, Leibowitz, and Weinberger has analyzed and recommended two stocks to an investors' club of college professors. The professors were interested in factors such as short-term growth, intermediate growth, and dividend rates. These data on each stock are as follows:

	STOCK ($)	
FACTOR	LOUISIANA GAS AND POWER	TRIMEX INSULATION COMPANY
Short-term growth potential, per dollar invested	0.36	0.24
Intermediate growth potential (over next three years), per dollar invested	1.67	1.50
Dividend rate potential	4%	8%

Each member of the club has an investment goal of (1) an appreciation of no less than $720 in the short term, (2) an appreciation of at least $5,000 in the next three years, and (3) a dividend income of at least $200 per year. What is the smallest investment that a professor can make to meet these three goals?

7-25 Woofer Pet Foods produces a low-calorie dog food for overweight dogs. This product is made from beef products and grain. Each pound of beef costs $0.90, and each pound of grain costs $0.60. A pound of the dog food must contain at least 9 units of Vitamin 1 and 10 units of Vitamin 2. A pound of beef contains 10 units of Vitamin 1 and 12 units of Vitamin 2. A pound of grain contains 6 units of Vitamin 1 and 9 units of Vitamin 2. Formulate this as an LP problem to minimize the cost of the dog food. How many pounds of beef and grain should be included in each pound of dog food? What is the cost and vitamin content of the final product?

7-26 The seasonal yield of olives in a Piraeus, Greece, vineyard is greatly influenced by a process of branch pruning. If olive trees are pruned every two weeks, output is increased. The pruning process, however, requires considerably more labor than permitting the olives to grow on their own and results in a smaller size olive. It also, though, permits olive trees to be spaced closer together. The yield of 1 barrel of olives by pruning requires 5 hours of labor and 1 acre of land. The production of a barrel of olives by the normal process requires only 2 labor hours but takes 2 acres of land. An olive grower has 250 hours of labor available and a total of 150 acres for growing. Because of the olive size difference, a barrel of olives produced on pruned trees sells for $20, whereas a barrel of regular olives has a market price of $30. The grower has determined that because of uncertain demand, no more than 40 barrels of pruned olives should be produced. Use graphical LP to find

(a) the maximum possible profit.
(b) the best combination of barrels of pruned and regular olives.
(c) the number of acres that the olive grower should devote to each growing process.

7-27 Consider the following four LP formulations. Using a graphical approach, determine

(a) which formulation has more than one optimal solution.
(b) which formulation is unbounded.
(c) which formulation has no feasible solution.
(d) which formulation is correct as is.

Formulation 1

$$\text{Maximize } 10X_1 + 10X_2$$
$$\text{subject to} \quad 2X_1 \qquad\quad \leq 10$$
$$2X_1 + 4X_2 \leq 16$$
$$4X_2 \leq 8$$
$$X_1 \qquad\quad = 6$$

Formulation 2

$$\text{Maximize } X_1 + 2X_2$$
$$\text{subject to } X_1 \qquad\quad \leq 1$$
$$2X_2 \leq 2$$
$$X_1 + 2X_2 \leq 2$$

Formulation 3

$$\text{Maximize } 3X_1 + 2X_2$$
$$\text{subject to} \quad X_1 + X_2 \geq 5$$
$$X_1 \qquad\quad \geq 2$$
$$2X_2 \geq 8$$

Formulation 4

$$\text{Maximize } 3X_1 + 3X_2$$
$$\text{subject to } 4X_1 + 6X_2 \leq 48$$
$$4X_1 + 2X_2 \leq 12$$
$$3X_2 \geq 3$$
$$2X_1 \qquad\quad \geq 2$$

7-28 Graph the following LP problem and indicate the optimal solution point:

$$\text{Maximize profit} = \$3X + \$2Y$$
$$\text{subject to} \quad 2X + Y \leq 150$$
$$2X + 3Y \leq 300$$

(a) Does the optimal solution change if the profit per unit of X changes to $4.50?
(b) What happens if the profit function should have been $3X + $3Y?

7-29 Graphically analyze the following problem:

Maximize profit $= \$4X + \$6Y$

subject to

$$X + 2Y \leq 8 \text{ hours}$$
$$6X + 4Y \leq 24 \text{ hours}$$

(a) What is the optimal solution?

(b) If the first constraint is altered to $X + 3Y \leq 8$, does the feasible region or optimal solution change?

7-30 Examine the LP formulation in Problem 7-29. The problem's second constraint reads

$$6X + 4Y \leq 24 \text{ hours} \quad \text{(time available on machine 2)}$$

If the firm decides that 36 hours of time can be made available on machine 2 (namely, an additional 12 hours) at an additional cost of $10, should it add the hours?

7-31 Consider the following LP problem:

Maximize profit $= 5X + 6Y$

subject to

$$2X + Y \leq 120$$
$$2X + 3Y \leq 240$$
$$X, Y \geq 0$$

(a) What is the optimal solution to this problem? Solve it graphically.

(b) If a technical breakthrough occurred that raised the profit per unit of X to $8, would this affect the optimal solution?

(c) Instead of an increase in the profit coefficient X to $8, suppose that profit was overestimated and should only have been $3. Does this change the optimal solution?

7-32 Consider the LP formulation given in Problem 7-31. If the second constraint is changed from $2X + 3Y \leq 240$ to $2X + 4Y \leq 240$, what effect will this have on the optimal solution?

7-33 The computer output given below is for Problem 7-31. Use this to answer the following questions.

(a) How much could the profit on X increase or decrease without changing the values of X and Y in the optimal solution?

(b) If the right-hand side of constraint 1 were increased by 1 unit, how much would the profit increase?

(c) If the right-hand side of constraint 1 were increased by 10 units, how much would the profit increase?

7-34 The computer output on the next page is for a product mix problem in which there are two products and three resource constraints. Use the output to help you answer the following questions. Assume that you wish to maximize profit in each case.

(a) How many units of product 1 and product 2 should be produced?

(b) How much of each of the three resources is being used? How much slack is there for each constraint? Which of the constraints are binding, and which are nonbinding?

(c) What are the dual prices for each resource?

(d) If you could obtain more of one of the resources, which one should you obtain? How much should you be willing to pay for this?

(e) What would happen to profit if, with the original output, management decided to produce one more unit of product 2?

7-35 Graphically solve the following problem:

Maximize profit $= 8X_1 + 5X_2$

subject to

$$X_1 + X_2 \leq 10$$
$$X_1 \leq 6$$
$$X_1, X_2 \geq 0$$

(a) What is the optimal solution?

(b) Change the right-hand side of constraint 1 to 11 (instead of 10) and resolve the problem. How much did the profit increase as a result of this?

Linear Programming Results

Problem 33 Solution

	X	Y		RHS	Dual
Maximize	5	6			
const 1	2	1	<=	120	0.75
const 2	2	3	<=	240	1.75
Solution->	30	60		510	

Ranging

Problem 33 Solution

Variable	Value	Reduced Cost	Original Val	Lower Bound	Upper Bound
X	30	0	5	4	12
Y	60	0	6	2.5	7.5
Constraint	Dual Value	Slack/Surplus	Original Val	Lower Bound	Upper Bound
const 1	0.75	0	120	80	240
const 2	1.75	0	240	120	360

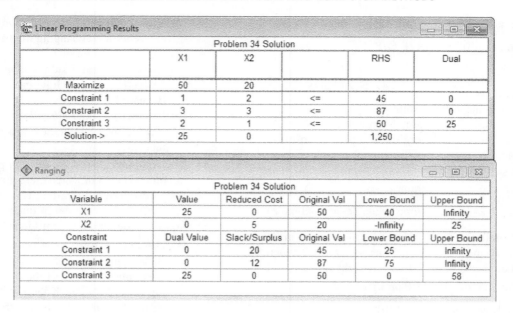

Linear Programming Results

Problem 34 Solution

	X1	X2		RHS	Dual
Maximize	50	20			
Constraint 1	1	2	<=	45	0
Constraint 2	3	3	<=	87	0
Constraint 3	2	1	<=	50	25
Solution->	25	0		1,250	

Ranging

Problem 34 Solution

Variable	Value	Reduced Cost	Original Val	Lower Bound	Upper Bound
X1	25	0	50	40	Infinity
X2	0	5	20	-Infinity	25
Constraint	Dual Value	Slack/Surplus	Original Val	Lower Bound	Upper Bound
Constraint 1	0	20	45	25	Infinity
Constraint 2	0	12	87	75	Infinity
Constraint 3	25	0	50	0	58

Linear Programming Results

Problem 35 Solution

	X1	X2		RHS	Dual
Maximize	8	5			
Constraint 1	1	1	<=	10	5
Constraint 2	1	0	<=	6	3
Solution->	6	4		68	

Ranging

Problem 35 Solution

Variable	Value	Reduced	Original Val	Lower Bound	Upper Bound
X1	6	0	8	5	Infinity
X2	4	0	5	0	8
Constraint	Dual Value	Slack/Surplus	Original Val	Lower Bound	Upper Bound
Constraint 1	5	0	10	6	Infinity
Constraint 2	3	0	6	0	10

(c) Change the right-hand side of constraint 1 to 6 (instead of 10) and resolve the problem. How much did the profit decrease as a result of this? Looking at the graph, what would happen if the right-hand-side value were to go below 6?

(d) Change the right-hand-side value of constraint 1 to 5 (instead of 10) and resolve the problem. How much did the profit decrease from the original profit as a result of this?

(e) Using the computer output on this page, what is the dual price of constraint 1? What is the lower bound on this?

(f) What conclusions can you draw from this regarding the bounds of the right-hand-side values and the dual price?

7-36 **Serendipity***

The three princes of Serendip
Went on a little trip.
They could not carry too much weight;
More than 300 pounds made them hesitate.
They planned to the ounce. When they returned to Ceylon
They discovered that their supplies were just about gone
When, what to their joy, Prince William found
A pile of coconuts on the ground.
"Each will bring 60 rupees," said Prince Richard with a grin

*The word *serendipity* was coined by the English writer Horace Walpole after a fairy tale titled *The Three Princes of Serendip*. Source of problem is unknown.

As he almost tripped over a lion skin.

"Look out!" cried Prince Robert with glee

As he spied some more lion skins under a tree.

"These are worth even more—300 rupees each

If we can just carry them all down to the beach."

Each skin weighed fifteen pounds and each coconut, five,

But they carried them all and made it alive.

The boat back to the island was very small

15 cubic feet baggage capacity—that was all.

Each lion skin took up one cubic foot

While eight coconuts the same space took.

With everything stowed they headed to sea

And on the way calculated what their new wealth might be.

"Eureka!" cried Prince Robert, "Our worth is so great

That there's no other way we could return in this state.

Any other skins or nut that we might have brought

Would now have us poorer. And now I know what—

I'll write my friend Horace in England, for surely

Only he can appreciate our serendipity."

Formulate and solve **Serendipity** by graphical LP in order to calculate "what their new wealth might be."

7-37 Bhavika Investments, a group of financial advisors and retirement planners, has been requested to provide advice on how to invest $200,000 for one of its clients. The client has stipulated that the money must be put into either a stock fund or a money market fund, and the annual return should be at least $14,000. Other conditions related to risk have also

been specified, and the following linear program was developed to help with this investment decision:

Minimize risk $= 12S + 5M$

subject to

$S + M = 200,000$		total investment is $200,000
$0.10S + 0.05M \geq 14,000$		return must be at least $14,000
$M \geq 40,000$		at least $40,000 must be in money market fund
$S, M \geq 0$		

where

$S =$ dollars invested in stock fund

$M =$ dollars invested in money market fund

The QM for Windows output is shown below.

(a) How much money should be invested in the money market fund and the stock fund? What is the total risk?

(b) What is the total return? What rate of return is this?

(c) Would the solution change if risk measure for each dollar in the stock fund were 14 instead of 12?

(d) For each additional dollar that is available, how much does the risk change?

(e) Would the solution change if the amount that must be invested in the money market fund were changed from $40,000 to $50,000?

7-38 Refer to the Bhavika Investments (Problem 7-37) situation once again. It has been decided that, rather than minimize risk, the objective should be to maximize return while placing restriction on the amount

Linear Programming Results

Problem 37 Solution

	S	M		RHS	Dual
Minimize	12	5			
Constraint 1	1	1	=	200,000	2
Constraint 2	0.1	0.05	>=	14,000	-140
Constraint 3	0	1	>=	40,000	0
Solution->	80,000	120,000.0		1,560,000	

Ranging

Problem 37 Solution

Variable	Value	Reduced Cost	Original Val	Lower Bound	Upper Bound
S	80,000	0	12	5	Infinity
M	120,000.0	0	5	-Infinity	12
Constraint	Dual Value	Slack/Surplus	Original Val	Lower Bound	Upper Bound
Constraint 1	2	0	200,000	160,000	280,000
Constraint 2	-140	0	14,000	10,000	18,000
Constraint 3	0	80,000.01	40,000	-Infinity	120,000.0

Linear Programming Results

Problem 38 Solution

	S	M		RHS	Dual
Maximize	0.1	0.05			
Constraint 1	1	1	=	200,000	0.1
Constraint 2	12	5	<=	2,200,000	0
Constraint 3	0	1	>=	40,000	-0.05
Solution->	160,000	40,000		18,000	

Ranging

Problem 38 Solution

Variable	Value	Reduced Cost	Original Val	Lower Bound	Upper Bound
S	160,000	0	0.1	0.05	Infinity
M	40,000	0	0.05	-Infinity	0.1
Constraint	Dual Value	Slack/Surplus	Original Val	Lower Bound	Upper Bound
Constraint 1	0.1	0	200,000	40,000	206,666.7
Constraint 2	0	80,000	2,200,000	2,120,000	Infinity
Constraint 3	-0.05	0	40,000	28,571.43	200,000

of risk. The average risk should be no more than 11 (with a total risk of 2,200,000 for the $200,000 invested). The linear program was reformulated, and the QM for Windows output is shown above.

(a) How much money should be invested in the money market fund and the stock fund? What is the total return? What rate of return is this?

(b) What is the total risk? What is the average risk?

(c) Would the solution change if return for each dollar in the stock fund were 0.09 instead of 0.10?

(d) For each additional dollar that is available, what is the marginal rate of return?

(e) How much would the total return change if the amount that must be invested in the money market fund were changed from $40,000 to $50,000?

Problems 7-39 to 7-44 test your ability to formulate LP problems that have more than two variables. They cannot be solved graphically but will give you a chance to set up a larger problem.

7-39 The Feed 'N Ship Ranch fattens cattle for local farmers and ships them to meat markets in Kansas City and Omaha. The owners of the ranch seek to determine the amounts of cattle feed to buy so that minimum nutritional standards are satisfied, and at the same time total feed costs are minimized. The feed mix can be made up of the three grains that contain the following ingredients per pound of feed:

	FEED (OZ.)		
INGREDIENT	STOCK X	STOCK Y	STOCK Z
A	3	2	4
B	2	3	1
C	1	0	2
D	6	8	4

The cost per pound of stocks X, Y, and Z are $2, $4, and $2.50, respectively. The minimum requirement per cow per month is 4 pounds of ingredient A, 5 pounds of ingredient B, 1 pound of ingredient C, and 8 pounds of ingredient D.

The ranch faces one additional restriction: it can only obtain 500 pounds of stock Z per month from the feed supplier regardless of its need. Because there are usually 100 cows at the Feed 'N Ship Ranch at any given time, this means that no more than 5 pounds of stock Z can be counted on for use in the feed of each cow per month.

(a) Formulate this as an LP problem.
(b) Solve using LP software.

7-40 The Weinberger Electronics Corporation manufactures four highly technical products that it supplies to aerospace firms that hold NASA contracts. Each of the products must pass through the following departments before they are shipped: wiring, drilling, assembly, and inspection. The time requirement in hours for each unit produced and its corresponding profit value are summarized in the following table:

	DEPARTMENT				UNIT PROFIT
PRODUCT	WIRING	DRILLING	ASSEMBLY	INSPECTION	($)
XJ201	0.5	0.3	0.2	0.5	9
XM897	1.5	1	4	1	12
TR29	1.5	2	1	0.5	15
BR788	1	3	2	0.5	11

The production available in each department each month, and the minimum monthly production requirement to fulfill contracts, are as follows:

DEPARTMENT	CAPACITY (HOURS)	PRODUCT	MINIMUM PRODUCTION LEVEL
Wiring	15,000	XJ201	150
Drilling	17,000	XM897	100
Assembly	26,000	TR29	300
Inspection	12,000	BR788	400

The production manager has the responsibility of specifying production levels for each product for the coming month. Help him by formulating (that is, setting up the constraints and objective function) Weinberger's problem using LP.

7-41 Outdoor Inn, a camping equipment manufacturer in southern Utah, is developing a production schedule for a popular type of tent, the Double Inn. Orders have been received for 180 of these to be delivered at the end of this month, 220 to be delivered at the end of next month, and 240 to be delivered at the end of the month after that. This tent may be produced at a cost of $120, and the maximum number of tents that can be produced in a month is 230. The company may produce some extra tents in one month and keep them in storage until the next month. The cost for keeping these in inventory for 1 month is estimated to be $6 per tent for each tent left at the end of the month. Formulate this as an LP problem to minimize cost while meeting demand and not exceeding the monthly production capacity. Solve it using any computer software. (*Hint:* Define variables to represent the number of tents left over at the end of each month.)

7-42 Outdoors Inn (see Problem 7-41) expanded its tent-making operations later in the year. While still making the Double Inn tent, it is also making a larger tent, the Family Rolls, which has four rooms. The company can produce up to a combined total of 280 tents per month. The following table provides the demand that must be met and the production costs for the next 3 months. Note that the costs will increase in month 2. The holding cost for keeping a tent in inventory at the end of the month for use in the next month is estimated to be $6 per tent for the Double Inn and $8 per tent for the Family Rolls. Develop a linear program to minimize the total cost. Solve it using any computer software.

MONTH	DEMAND FOR DOUBLE INN	COST TO PRODUCE DOUBLE INN	DEMAND FOR FAMILY ROLLS	COST TO PRODUCE FAMILY ROLLS
1	185	$120	60	$150
2	205	$130	70	$160
3	225	$130	65	$160

7-43 Modem Corporation of America (MCA) is the world's largest producer of modem communication devices for microcomputers. MCA sold 9,000 of the regular model and 10,400 of the smart ("intelligent") model this September. Its income statement for the month is shown in the Table for Problem 7-43. Costs presented are typical of prior months and are expected to remain at the same levels in the near future.

The firm is facing several constraints as it prepares its November production plan. First, it has experienced a tremendous demand and has been unable to keep any significant inventory in stock. This situation is not expected to change. Second, the firm is located in a small Iowa town from which additional labor is not readily available. Workers can be shifted from production of one modem to another, however. To produce the 9,000 regular modems in September required 5,000 direct labor hours. The 10,400 intelligent modems absorbed 10,400 direct labor hours.

Third, MCA is experiencing a problem affecting the intelligent modems model. Its component supplier is able to guarantee only 8,000 microprocessors for November delivery. Each intelligent modem requires one of these specially made microprocessors. Alternative suppliers are not available on short notice.

TABLE FOR PROBLEM 7-43

MCA Income Statement Month Ended September 30

	REGULAR MODEMS	INTELLIGENT MODEMS
Sales	$450,000	$640,000
Less: Discounts	10,000	15,000
Returns	12,000	9,500
Warranty replacements	4,000	2,500
Net sales	$424,000	$613,000
Sales costs		
Direct labor	60,000	76,800
Indirect labor	9,000	11,520
Materials cost	90,000	128,000
Depreciation	40,000	50,800
Cost of sales	$199,000	$267,120
Gross profit	$225,000	$345,880
Selling and general expenses		
General expenses—variable	30,000	35,000
General expenses—fixed	36,000	40,000
Advertising	28,000	25,000
Sales commissions	31,000	60,000
Total operating cost	$125,000	$160,000
Pretax income	$100,000	$185,880
Income taxes (25%)	25,000	46,470
Net income	$ 75,000	$139,410

MCA wants to plan the optimal mix of the two modem models to produce in November to maximize profits for MCA.

(a) Formulate, using September's data, MCA's problem as a linear program.
(b) Solve the problem graphically.
(c) Discuss the implications of your recommended solution.

 7-44 Working with chemists at Virginia Tech and George Washington Universities, landscape contractor Kenneth Golding blended his own fertilizer, called "Golding-Grow." It consists of four chemical compounds, C-30, C-92, D-21, and E-11. The cost per pound for each compound is indicated as follows:

CHEMICAL COMPOUND	COST PER POUND ($)
C-30	0.12
C-92	0.09
D-21	0.11
E-11	0.04

The specifications for Golding-Grow are as follows: (1) E-11 must constitute at least 15% of the blend; (2) C-92 and C-30 must together constitute at least 45% of the blend; (3) D-21 and C-92 can together constitute no more than 30% of the blend; and (4) Golding-Grow is packaged and sold in 50-pound bags.

(a) Formulate an LP problem to determine what blend of the four chemicals will allow Golding to minimize the cost of a 50-pound bag of the fertilizer.
(b) Solve using a computer to find the best solution.

7-45 Raptor Fuels produces three grades of gasoline—Regular, Premium, and Super. All of these are produced by blending two types of crude oil—Crude A and Crude B. The two types of crude contain specific ingredients which help in determining the octane rating of gasoline. The important ingredients and the costs are contained in the following table:

	CRUDE A	CRUDE B
Cost per gallon	$0.42	$0.47
Ingredient 1	40%	52%
Other ingredients	60%	48%

In order to achieve the desired octane ratings, at least 41% of Regular gasoline should be Ingredient 1; at least 44% of Premium gasoline must be Ingredient 1, and at least 48% of Super gasoline must be Ingredient 1. Due to current contract commitments, Raptor Fuels must produce as least 20,000 gallons of Regular, at least 15,000 gallons of Premium, and at least 10,000 gallons of Super. Formulate a linear program that could be used to determine how much of Crude A and Crude B should be used in each of the gasolines to meet the demands at the minimum cost. What is the minimum cost? How much of Crude A and Crude B are used in each gallon of the different types of gasoline?

Internet Homework Problems

See our Internet home page, at **www.pearsonhighered.com/render**, for additional homework problems, Problems 7-46 to 7-50.

Case Study

Mexicana Wire Works

Ron Garcia felt good about his first week as a management trainee at Mexicana Wire Winding, Inc. He had not yet developed any technical knowledge about the manufacturing process, but he had toured the entire facility, located in the suburbs of Mexico City, and had met many people in various areas of the operation.

Mexicana, a subsidiary of Westover Wire Works, a Texas firm, is a medium-sized producer of wire windings used in making electrical transformers. José Arroyo, the production control manager, described the windings to Garcia as being of standardized design. Garcia's tour of the plant, laid out by process type (see Figure 7.20), followed the manufacturing sequence for the windings: drawing, extrusion, winding, inspection, and packaging. After inspection, good product is packaged and sent to finished product storage; defective product is stored separately until it can be reworked.

On March 8, Vivian Espania, Mexicana's general manager, stopped by Garcia's office and asked him to attend a staff meeting at 1:00 P.M.

"Let's get started with the business at hand," Vivian said, opening the meeting. "You all have met Ron Garcia, our new management trainee. Ron studied operations management in his MBA program in southern California, so I think he is competent to help us with a problem we have been discussing for a long time without resolution. I'm sure that each of you on my staff will give Ron your full cooperation."

FIGURE 7.20
Mexicana Wire Winding, Inc.

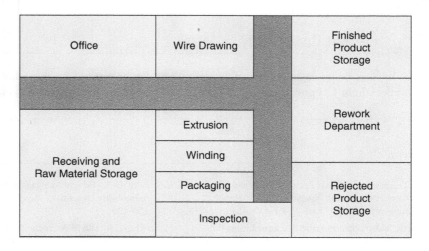

Vivian turned to José Arroyo, production manager. "José, why don't you describe the problem we are facing?"

"Well," José said, "business is very good right now. We are booking more orders than we can fill. We will have some new equipment on line within the next several months, which will take care of our capacity problems, but that won't help us in April. I have located some retired employees who used to work in the drawing department, and I am planning to bring them in as temporary employees in April to increase capacity there. Because we are planning to refinance some of our long-term debt, Vivian wants our profits to look as good as possible in April. I'm having a hard time figuring out which orders to run and which to back order so that I can make the bottom line look as good as possible. Can you help me with this?"

Garcia was surprised and apprehensive to receive such an important, high-profile assignment so early in his career. Recovering quickly, he said, "Give me your data and let me work with it for a day or two."

April Orders

Product W0075C	1,400 units
Product W0033C	250 units
Product W0005X	1,510 units
Product W0007X	1,116 units

Note: Vivian Espania has given her word to a key customer that we will manufacture 600 units of product W0007X and 150 units of product W0075C for him during April

Standard Cost

PRODUCT	MATERIAL	LABOR	OVERHEAD	SELLING PRICE
W0075C	$33.00	$ 9.90	$23.10	$100.00
W0033C	25.00	7.50	17.50	80.00
W0005X	35.00	10.50	24.50	130.00
W0007X	75.00	11.25	63.75	175.00

Selected Operating Data

Average output per month = 2,400 units

Average machine utilization = 63%

Average percentage of production set to rework department = 5% (mostly from Winding Department)

Average no. of rejected units awaiting rework = 850 (mostly from Winding Department)

Plant Capacity (Hours)

DRAWING	EXTRUSION	WINDING	PACKAGING
4,000	4,200	2,000	2,300

Note: Inspection capacity is not a problem; we can work overtime, as necessary, to accommodate any schedule.

Bill of Labor (Hours/Unit)

PRODUCT	DRAWING	EXTRUSION	WINDING	PACKAGING
W0075C	1.0	1.0	1.0	1.0
W0033C	2.0	1.0	3.0	0.0
W0005X	0.0	4.0	0.0	3.0
W0007X	1.0	1.0	0.0	2.0

Discussion Questions

1. What recommendations should Ron Garcia make, with what justification? Provide a detailed analysis with charts, graphs, and computer printouts included.
2. Discuss the need for temporary workers in the drawing department.
3. Discuss the plant layout.

Source: Professor Victor E. Sower, Sam Houston State University. This case material is based on an actual situation, with names and data altered for confidentiality.

Internet Case Study

See our Internet home page, at **www.pearsonhighered.com/render**, for this additional case study: **Agri Chem Corporation**. This case involves a company's response to an energy shortage.

Bibliography

Bassamboo, Achal, J. Michael Harrison, and Assaf Zeevi. "Design and Control of a Large Call Center: Asymptotic Analysis of an LP-Based Method," *Operations Research* 54, 3 (May–June 2006): 419–435.

Behjat, Laleh, Anthony Vannelli, and William Rosehart. "Integer Linear Programming Model for Global Routing," *INFORMS Journal on Computing* 18, 2 (Spring 2006): 137–150.

Bixby, Robert E. "Solving Real-World Linear Programs: A Decade and More of Progress," *Operations Research* 50, 1 (January–February 2002): 3–15.

Bodington, C. E., and T. E. Baker. "A History of Mathematical Programming in the Petroleum Industry," *Interfaces* 20, 4 (July–August 1990): 117–132.

Boros, E., L. Fedzhora, P. B. Kantor, K. Saeger, and P. Stroud. "A Large-Scale Linear Programming Model For Finding Optimal Container Inspection Strategies," *Naval Research Logistics* 56, 5 (August 2009): 404–420.

Chakravarti, N. "Tea Company Steeped in OR," *OR/MS Today* 27, 2 (April 2000): 32–34.

Ching, Wai-Ki, Wai-On Yuen, Michael K. Ng, and Shu-Qin Zhang. "A Linear Programming Approach for Determining Optimal Advertising Policy," *IMA Journal of Management Mathematics* 17, 1 (2006): 83–96.

Dantzig, George B. "Linear Programming Under Uncertainty," *Management Science* 50, 12 (December 2004): 1764–1769.

Degbotse, Alfred, Brian T. Denton, Kenneth Fordyce, R. John Milne, Robert Orzell, and Chi-Tai Wang. "IBM Blends Heuristics and Optimization to Plan Its Semiconductor Supply Chain," *Interfaces* 43 (March/April 2013): 130–141.

Gass, Saul I. "The First Linear-Programming Shoppe," *Operations Research* 50, 1 (January–February 2002): 61–68.

Greenberg, H. J. "How to Analyze the Results of Linear Programs—Part 1: Preliminaries," *Interfaces* 23, 4 (July–August 1993): 56–68.

Greenberg, H. J. "How to Analyze the Results of Linear Programs—Part 3: Infeasibility Diagnosis," *Interfaces* 23, 6 (November–December 1993): 120–139.

Hafizoğlu, A. B., and M Azizoğlu. "Linear Programming Based Approaches for the Discrete Time/Cost Trade-off Problem in Project Networks," *Journal of the Operational Research Society* 61 (April 2010): 676–685.

Higle, Julia L., and Stein W. Wallace. "Sensitivity Analysis and Uncertainty in Linear Programming," *Interfaces* 33, 4 (July–August 2003): 53–60.

Marszalkowski, Jakub and Drozdowski Maciej. "Optimization of Column Width in Website Layout for Advertisement Fit," *European Journal of Operational Research* 226, 3 (May 2013): 592–601.

Murphy, Frederic H. "ASP, the Art and Science of Practice: Elements of a Theory of the Practice of Operations Research: Expertise in Practice," *Interfaces* 35, 4 (July–August 2005): 313–322.

Orden, A. "LP from the '40s to the '90s," *Interfaces* 23, 5 (September–October 1993): 2–12.

Pazour, Jennifer A. and Lucas C. Neubert. "Routing and Scheduling of Cross-Town Drayage Operations at J.B. Hunt Transport," *Interfaces* 43, (March/April 2013): 117–129.

Romeijn, H. Edwin, Ravindra K. Ahuja, James F. Dempsey, and Arvind Kumar. "A New Linear Programming Approach to Radiation Therapy Treatment Planning Problems," *Operations Research* 54, 2 (March–April 2006): 201–216.

Rubin, D. S., and H. M. Wagner. "Shadow Prices: Tips and Traps for Managers and Instructors," *Interfaces* 20, 4 (July–August 1990): 150–157.

Wendell, Richard E. "Tolerance Sensitivity and Optimality Bounds in Linear Programming," *Management Science* 50, 6 (June 2004) 797–803.

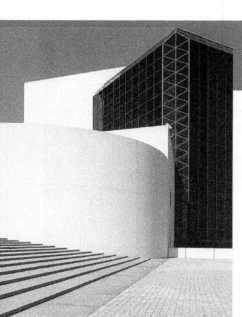

CHAPTER 8

Linear Programming Applications

LEARNING OBJECTIVES

After completing this chapter, students will be able to:

1. Model a wide variety of medium to large LP problems.
2. Understand major application areas, including marketing, production, labor scheduling, fuel blending, and finance.

3. Gain experience in solving LP problems with Excel Solver software.

CHAPTER OUTLINE

8.1 Introduction
8.2 Marketing Applications
8.3 Manufacturing Applications
8.4 Employee Scheduling Applications

8.5 Financial Applications
8.6 Ingredient Blending Applications
8.7 Other Linear Programming Applications

Summary • Self-Test • Problems • Internet Homework Problems • Case Study: Cable & Moore • Bibliography

8.1   Introduction

The graphical method of linear programming (LP) discussed in Chapter 7 is useful for understanding how to formulate and solve small LP problems. The purpose of this chapter is to go one step further and show how a large number of real-life problems can be modeled using LP. We do this by presenting examples of models in the areas of marketing research, media selection, production mix, labor scheduling, production scheduling, ingredient mix, and financial portfolio selection. We will solve many of these LP problems using Excel's Solver and QM for Windows.

Although some of these models are relatively small numerically, the principles developed here are definitely applicable to larger problems. Moreover, this practice in "paraphrasing" LP model formulations should help develop your skills in applying the technique to other, less common applications.

8.2   Marketing Applications

Media Selection

Media selection problems can be approached with LP from two perspectives. The objective can be to maximize audience exposure or to minimize advertising costs.

Linear programming models have been used in the advertising field as a decision aid in selecting an effective media mix. Sometimes the technique is employed in allocating a fixed or limited budget across various media, which might include radio or television commercials, newspaper ads, direct mailings, magazine ads, and so on. In other applications, the objective is the maximization of audience exposure. Restrictions on the allowable media mix might arise through contract requirements, limited media availability, or company policy. An example follows.

The Win Big Gambling Club promotes gambling junkets from a large Midwestern city to casinos in the Bahamas. The club has budgeted up to $8,000 per week for local advertising. The money is to be allocated among four promotional media: TV spots, newspaper ads, and two types of radio advertisements. Win Big's goal is to reach the largest possible high-potential audience through the various media. The following table presents the number of potential gamblers reached by making use of an advertisement in each of the four media. It also provides the cost per advertisement placed and the maximum number of ads that can be purchased per week.

MEDIUM	AUDIENCE REACHED PER AD	COST PER AD ($)	MAXIMUM ADS PER WEEK
TV spot (1 minute)	5,000	800	12
Daily newspaper (full-page ad)	8,500	925	5
Radio spot (30 seconds, prime time)	2,400	290	25
Radio spot (1 minute, afternoon)	2,800	380	20

Win Big's contractual arrangements require that at least five radio spots be placed each week. To ensure a broad-scoped promotional campaign, management also insists that no more than $1,800 be spent on radio advertising every week.

In formulating this as an LP, the first step is to completely understand the problem. Sometimes asking "what if" questions will help understand the situation. In this example, what would happen if exactly five ads of each type were used? What would this cost? How many people would it reach? Certainly the use of a spreadsheet for the calculations can help with this since formulas can be written to calculate the cost and the number of people reached. Once the situation is understood, the objective and the constraints are stated:

Objective:

Maximize number of people (audience) reached

Constraints:

(1) No more than 12 TV ads can be used. (2) No more than 5 newspaper ads can be used. (3) No more than 25 of the 30-second radio ads can be used. (4) No more than 20 of the 1-minute radio ads can be used. (5) Total amount spent cannot exceed $8,000. (6) Total number of radio ads must be at least 5. (7) Total amount spent on radio ads must not exceed $1,800.

Next, define the decision variables. The decisions being made here are the number of ads of each type to use. Once these are known, they can be used to calculate the amount spent and the number of people reached. Let

$$X_1 = \text{number of 1-minute TV spots taken each week}$$
$$X_2 = \text{number of full-page daily newspaper ads taken each week}$$
$$X_3 = \text{number of 30-second prime-time radio spots taken each week}$$
$$X_4 = \text{number of 1-minute afternoon radio spots taken each week}$$

Next, using these variables, write the mathematical expression for the objective and the constraint that were identified. The nonnegativity constraints are also explicitly stated.

Objective:

$$\text{Maximize audience coverage} = 5{,}000X_1 + 8{,}500X_2 + 2{,}400X_3 + 2{,}800X_4$$

subject to		
	$X_1 \le 12$	(maximum TV spots/week)
	$X_2 \le 5$	(maximum newspaper ads/week)
	$X_3 \le 25$	(maximum 30-second radio spots/week)
	$X_4 \le 20$	(maximum 1-minute radio spots/week)
$800X_1 + 925X_2 + 290X_3 + 380X_4 \le \$8{,}000$		(weekly advertising budget)
	$X_3 + X_4 \ge 5$	(minimum radio spots contracted)
$290X_3 + 380X_4 \le \$1{,}800$		(maximum dollars spent on radio)
	$X_1, X_2, X_3, X_4 \ge 0$	

The solution to this can be found using Excel's Solver. Program 8.1 gives the inputs to the Solver Parameter dialog box, the formula that must be written in the cell for the objective function value, and the cells where this formula should be copied. The results are shown in the spreadsheet. This solution is

$X_1 = 1.97$	TV spots
$X_2 = 5$	newspaper ads
$X_3 = 6.2$	30-second radio spots
$X_4 = 0$	one-minute radio spots

This produces an audience exposure of 67,240 contacts. Because X_1 and X_3 are fractional, Win Big would probably round them to 2 and 6, respectively. Problems that demand all-integer solutions are discussed in detail in Chapter 10.

Marketing Research

Linear programming has also been applied to marketing research problems and the area of consumer research. The next example illustrates how statistical pollsters can reach strategy decisions with LP.

Management Sciences Associates (MSA) is a marketing and computer research firm based in Washington, D.C., that handles consumer surveys. One of its clients is a national press service that periodically conducts political polls on issues of widespread interest. In a survey for the press service, MSA determines that it must fulfill several requirements in order to draw statistically valid conclusions on the sensitive issue of new U.S. immigration laws:

1. Survey at least 2,300 U.S. households in total.
2. Survey at least 1,000 households whose heads are 30 years of age or younger.

PROGRAM 8.1

Win Big Solution in Excel 2013

	A	B	C	D	E	F	G	H
1	Win Big Gambling Club							
2				Radio	Radio			
3		TV	Newspaper	30 sec.	1 min.			
4	Variables	X1	X2	X3	X4			
5	Solution	1.9688	5	6.2069	0	Total Audience		
6	Audience per ad	5000	8500	2400	2800	67240.3017		
7								
8	Constraints					LHS		RHS
9	Max. TV	1				1.9688	≤	12
10	Max. Newspaper		1			5	≤	5
11	Max. 30-sec. radio			1		6.2069	≤	25
12	Max. 1 min. radio				1	0	≤	20
13	Cost	800	925	290	380	8000	≤	8000
14	Radio dollars			290	380	1800	≤	1800
15	Radio spots			1	1	6.2069	≥	5

Solver Parameter Inputs and Selections

Set Objective: F6

By Changing cells: B5:E5

To: Max

Subject to the Constraints:

F9:F14 <= H9:H14

F15 >= H15

Solving Method: Simplex LP

☑ Make Variables Non-Negative

Key Formulas

	F
5	Total Audience
6	=SUMPRODUCT($B$5:$E$5,B6:E6)

Copy F6 to F9:F15

3. Survey at least 600 households whose heads are between 31 and 50 years of age.
4. Ensure that at least 15% of those surveyed live in a state that borders on Mexico.
5. Ensure that no more than 20% of those surveyed who are 51 years of age or over live in a state that borders on Mexico.

MSA decides that all surveys should be conducted in person. It estimates that the costs of reaching people in each age and region category are as follows:

	COST PER PERSON SURVEYED ($)		
REGION	AGE ≤ 30	AGE 31–50	AGE ≥ 51
State bordering Mexico	$7.50	$6.80	$5.50
State not bordering Mexico	$6.90	$7.25	$6.10

MSA would like to meet the five sampling requirements at the least possible cost.

In formulating this as an LP, the objective is to minimize cost. The five requirements about the number of people to be sampled with specific characteristics result in five constraints. The decision variables come from the decisions that must be made, which are the number of people sampled from each of the two regions in each of the three age categories. Thus, the six variables are

X_1 = number surveyed who are 30 or younger and live in a border state

X_2 = number surveyed who are 31–50 and live in a border state

X_3 = number surveyed who are 51 or older and live in a border state

X_4 = number surveyed who are 30 or younger and do not live in a border state

X_5 = number surveyed who are 31–50 and do not live in a border state

X_6 = number surveyed who are 51 or older and do not live in a border state

Objective function:

$$\text{Minimize total interview costs} = \$7.50X_1 + \$6.80X_2 + \$5.50X_3$$
$$+ \$6.90X_4 + \$7.25X_5 + \$6.10X_6$$

subject to

$$X_1 + X_2 + X_3 + X_4 + X_5 + X_6 \geq 2{,}300 \quad \text{(total households)}$$
$$X_1 + \qquad\qquad X_4 \qquad\qquad \geq 1{,}000 \quad \text{(households 30 or younger)}$$
$$X_2 + \qquad\qquad X_5 \qquad \geq 600 \quad \text{(households 31--50 in age)}$$
$$X_1 + X_2 + X_3 \geq 0.15(X_1 + X_2 + X_3 + X_4 + X_5 + X_6) \quad \text{(border states)}$$
$$X_3 \leq 0.2(X_3 + X_6) \quad \text{(limit on age group 51+ who live in border state)}$$
$$X_1, X_2, X_3, X_4, X_5, X_6 \geq 0$$

The computer solution to MSA's problem costs \$15,166 and is presented in the following table and in Program 8.2, which presents the input and output from Excel 2013. Note that the variables in the constraints are moved to the left-hand side of the inequality.

REGION	AGE $\leq$ 30	AGE 31–50	AGE $\geq$ 51
State bordering Mexico	0	600	140
State not bordering Mexico	1,000	0	560

PROGRAM 8.2

MSA Solution in Excel 2013

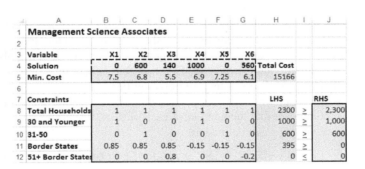

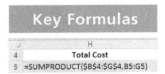

Solver Parameter Inputs and Selections

Set Objective: H5

By Changing cells: B4:G4

To: Min

Subject to the Constraints:

  H8:H11 <= J8:J11

  H12 >= J12

Solving Method: Simplex LP

☑ **Make Variables Non-Negative**

Key Formulas

	H
4	Total Cost
5	=SUMPRODUCT($B$4:$G$4,B5:G5)

Copy H5 to H8:H12

8.3 Manufacturing Applications

Production Mix

A fertile field for the use of LP is in planning for the optimal mix of products to manufacture. A company must meet a myriad of constraints, ranging from financial concerns to sales demand to material contracts to union labor demands. Its primary goal is to generate the largest profit possible.

Fifth Avenue Industries, a nationally known manufacturer of menswear, produces four varieties of ties. One is an expensive, all-silk tie; one is an all-polyester tie; one is a blend of polyester and cotton; and one is a blend of silk and cotton. The following table illustrates the cost and availability (per monthly production planning period) of the three materials used in the production process:

MATERIAL	COST PER YARD ($)	MATERIAL AVAILABLE PER MONTH (YARDS)
Silk	24	1,200
Polyester	6	3,000
Cotton	9	1,600

The firm has fixed contracts with several major department store chains to supply ties. The contracts require that Fifth Avenue Industries supply a minimum quantity of each tie but allow for a larger demand if Fifth Avenue chooses to meet that demand. (Most of the ties are not shipped with the name Fifth Avenue on their label, incidentally, but with "private stock" labels supplied by the stores.) Table 8.1 summarizes the contract demand for each of the four styles of ties, the selling price per tie, and the fabric requirements of each variety. Fifth Avenue's goal is to maximize its monthly profit. It must decide upon a policy for product mix.

In formulating this problem, the objective is to maximize profit. There are three constraints (one for each material) indicating that the amount of silk, polyester, and cotton cannot exceed the amount that is available. There are four constraints (one for each type of tie) that specify that the number of all silk ties, all polyester ties, poly–silk ties, and silk–cotton ties produced must be at least the minimum contract amount. There are four more constraints (one for each type of tie) that indicate that the number of each of these ties produced cannot exceed the monthly demand. The variables are defined as

$$X_1 = \text{number of all-silk ties produced per month}$$
$$X_2 = \text{number of polyester ties}$$
$$X_3 = \text{number of blend 1 poly–cotton ties}$$
$$X_4 = \text{number of blend 2 silk–cotton ties}$$

TABLE 8.1 Data for Fifth Avenue Industries

VARIETY OF TIE	SELLING PRICE PER TIE ($)	MONTHLY CONTRACT MINIMUM	MONTHLY DEMAND	MATERIAL REQUIRED PER TIE (YARDS)	MATERIAL REQUIREMENTS
All silk	19.24	5,000	7,000	0.125	100% silk
All polyester	8.70	10,000	14,000	0.08	100% polyester
Poly–cotton blend 1	9.52	13,000	16,000	0.10	50% polyester–50% cotton
Silk–cotton blend 2	10.64	5,000	8,500	0.11	60% silk–40% cotton

But first the firm must establish the profit per tie:

1. Each all-silk tie (X_1) requires 0.125 yard of silk, at a cost of $24.00 per yard. Therefore, the material cost per tie is $3.00. The selling price is $19.24, leaving a net profit of $16.24 per silk tie.
2. Each all-polyester tie (X_2) requires 0.08 yard of polyester, at a cost of $6 per yard. Therefore, the material cost per tie is $0.48. The selling price is $8.70, leaving a net profit of $8.22 per polyester tie.
3. Each poly–cotton (blend 1) tie (X_3) requires 0.05 yard of polyester, at a cost of $6 per yard, and 0.05 yard of cotton, at $9 per yard, for a cost of $0.30 + $0.45 = $0.75 per tie. The selling price is $9.52, leaving a net profit of $8.77 per poly–cotton tie.
4. Performing similar calculations will show that each silk–cotton (blend 2) tie (X_4) has a material cost per tie of $1.98 and a profit of $8.66.

The objective function may now be stated as

$$\text{Maximize profit} = \$16.24X_1 + \$8.22X_2 + \$8.77X_3 + \$8.66X_4$$

subject to		
$0.125X_1 + 0.066X_4 \leq 1,200$	(yards of silk)
$0.08X_2 + 0.05X_3 \leq 3,000$	(yards of polyester)
$0.05X_3 + 0.044X_4 \leq 1,600$	(yards of cotton)
$X_1 \geq 5,000$	(contract minimum for all silk)
$X_1 \leq 7,000$	(contract maximum)
$X_2 \geq 10,000$	(contract minimum for all polyester)
$X_2 \leq 14,000$	(contract maximum)
$X_3 \geq 13,000$	(contract minimum for blend 1)
$X_3 \leq 16,000$	(contract maximum)
$X_4 \geq 5,000$	(contract minimum for blend 2)
$X_4 \leq 8,500$	(contract maximum)
$X_1, X_2, X_3, X_4 \geq 0$	

Using Excel and its Solver command, the computer-generated solution is to produce 5,112 all-silk ties each month; 14,000 all-polyester ties; 16,000 poly–cotton blend 1 ties; and 8,500 silk–cotton blend 2 ties. This produces a profit of $412,028 per production period. See Program 8.3 for details.

Production Scheduling

Setting a low-cost production schedule over a period of weeks or months is a difficult and important management problem in most plants. The production manager has to consider many factors: labor capacity, inventory and storage costs, space limitations, product demand, and labor relations. Because most companies produce more than one product, the scheduling process is often quite complex.

Basically, the problem resembles the product mix model for each period in the future. The objective is either to maximize profit or to minimize the total cost (production plus inventory) of carrying out the task.

Production scheduling is amenable to solution by LP because it is a problem that must be solved on a regular basis. When the objective function and constraints for a firm are established, the inputs can easily be changed each month to provide an updated schedule.

An example of production scheduling: Greenberg Motors

Greenberg Motors, Inc., manufactures two different electrical motors for sale under contract to Drexel Corp., a well-known producer of small kitchen appliances. Its model GM3A is found in many Drexel food processors, and its model GM3B is used in the assembly of blenders.

Three times each year, the procurement officer at Drexel contacts Irwin Greenberg, the founder of Greenberg Motors, to place a monthly order for each of the coming four months. Drexel's demand for motors varies each month based on its own sales forecasts, production capacity, and financial position. Greenberg has just received the January–April order and must begin his own four-month production plan. The demand for motors is shown in Table 8.2.

PROGRAM 8.3

Fifth Avenue Solution in Excel 2013

	A	B	C	D	E	F	G	H
1	Fifth Avenue Industries							
2								
3		All silk	All poly.	Blend 1	Blend 2			
4	Variables	X1	X2	X3	X4			
5	Values	5112	14000	16000	8500	Total Profit		
6	Profit	16.24	8.22	8.77	8.66	412028.88		
7								
8	Constraints					LHS		RHS
9	Silk available	0.125			0.066	1200	≤	1200
10	Polyester available		0.08	0.05		1920	≤	3000
11	Cotton available			0.05	0.044	1174	≤	1600
12	Maximum silk	1				5112	≤	7000
13	Maximum polyester		1			14000	≤	14000
14	Maximum blend 1			1		16000	≤	16000
15	Maximum blend 2				1	8500	≤	8500
16	Minimum silk	1				5112	≥	5000
17	Minimum polyester		1			14000	≥	10000
18	Minimum blend 1			1		16000	≥	13000
19	Minimum blend 2				1	8500	≥	5000

Solver Parameter Inputs and Selections

Set Objective: F6

By Changing cells: B5:E5

To: Max

Subject to the Constraints:

    F9:F15 <= H9:H15

    F16:F19 >= H16:H19

Solving Method: Simplex LP

☑ Make Variables Non-Negative

Key Formulas

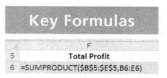

	F
5	Total Profit
6	=SUMPRODUCT($B$5:$E$5,B6:E6)

Copy F6 to F9:F19

TABLE 8.2

Four-Month Order Schedule for Electrical Motors

MODEL	JANUARY	FEBRUARY	MARCH	APRIL
GM3A	800	700	1,000	1,100
GM3B	1,000	1,200	1,400	1,400

Production planning at Greenberg Motors must consider several factors:

1. The company must meet the demand for each of the two products in each of the four months (see Table 8.2). Also, the company would like to have 450 units of the GM3A and 300 units of the GM3B in inventory at the end of April, as demand in May is expected to be somewhat higher than demand in the previous months.
2. There is a carrying, or holding, cost for any inventory left at the end of the month. So producing too many extra units of either product may not be desirable. The carrying cost assigned to the GM3A is $0.36 per unit per month, while the carrying cost for the GM3B is $0.26 per unit per month.
3. The company has been able to maintain a no-layoff policy, and it would like to continue with this. This is easier if the labor hours used do not fluctuate too much from month to month. Maintaining a production schedule that would require from 2,240 to 2,560 labor hours per month is desired. The GM3A requires 1.3 labor hours per unit, while the GM3B requires only 0.9 labor hours.

4. Warehouse limitations cannot be exceeded without great additional costs. There is room at the end of the month for only 3,300 units of the GM3A and GM3B combined.

Although these factors sometimes conflict, Greenberg has found that linear programming is an effective tool in setting up a production schedule that will minimize total cost. Production costs are currently $20 per unit for the GM3A and $15 per unit for the GM3B. However, each of these is due to increase by 10% on March 1 as a new labor agreement goes into effect.

In formulating this as a linear program, it is important to understand how all the important factors are related, how the costs are calculated, how the labor hours per month are calculated, and how demand is met with both production and inventory on hand. To help with understanding this, try to determine the number of labor hours used, the number of units left in inventory at the end of each month for each product, and the total cost if exactly 1,000 of the GM3A and exactly 1,200 of the GM3B were produced each month.

To begin formulating the linear program for the Greenberg production problem, the objective and the constraints are:

Objective:

$$\text{Minimize total cost (production cost plus carrying cost)}$$

Constraints:

> 4 demand constraints (1 constraint for each of 4 months) for GM3A
>
> 4 demand constraints (1 constraint for each of 4 months) for GM3B
>
> 2 constraints (1 for GM3A and 1 for GM3B) for the inventory at the end of April
>
> 4 constraints for minimum labor hours (1 constraint for each month)
>
> 4 constraints for maximum labor hours (1 constraint for each month)
>
> 4 constraints for inventory storage capacity each month

The decisions involve determining how many units of each of 2 products to produce in each of 4 months, so there will be 8 variables. But, since the objective is to minimize cost, and there are costs associated not only with the units produced each month but also with the number of units of each left in inventory, it would be best to define variables for these also. Let

A_i = number of units of GM3A produced in month i ($i = 1, 2, 3, 4$ for January–April)

B_i = number of units of GM3B produced in month i ($i = 1, 2, 3, 4$ for January–April)

IA_i = units of GM3A left in inventory at end of month i ($i = 1, 2, 3, 4$ for January–April)

IB_i = units of GM3B left in inventory at end of month i ($i = 1, 2, 3, 4$ for January–April)

The objective function in the LP model is

$$\text{Minimize cost} = 20A_1 + 20A_2 + 22A_3 + 22A_4 + 15B_1 + 15B_2 + 16.50B_3$$
$$+ 16.50B_4 + 0.36IA_1 + 0.36IA_2 + 0.36IA_3 + 0.36IA_4$$
$$+ 0.26IB_1 + 0.26IB_2 + 0.26IB_3 + 0.26IB_4$$

Inventory constraints set the relationship between closing inventory this month, closing inventory last month, this month's production, and sales this month.

In setting up the constraints, we must recognize the relationship between last month's ending inventory, the current month's production, and the sales to Drexel this month. The inventory at the end of a month is

$$\begin{pmatrix} \text{Inventory} \\ \text{at the} \\ \text{end of} \\ \text{this month} \end{pmatrix} = \begin{pmatrix} \text{Inventory} \\ \text{at the} \\ \text{end of} \\ \text{last month} \end{pmatrix} + \begin{pmatrix} \text{Current} \\ \text{month's} \\ \text{production} \end{pmatrix} - \begin{pmatrix} \text{Sales} \\ \text{to Drexel} \\ \text{this month} \end{pmatrix}$$

While the constraints could be written in this form, inputting the problem into the computer requires all variables to be on the left-hand side of the constraint. Rearranging the terms to do this results in

$$\begin{pmatrix} \text{Inventory} \\ \text{at the} \\ \text{end of} \\ \text{last month} \end{pmatrix} + \begin{pmatrix} \text{Current} \\ \text{month's} \\ \text{production} \end{pmatrix} - \begin{pmatrix} \text{Inventory} \\ \text{at the} \\ \text{end of} \\ \text{this month} \end{pmatrix} = \begin{pmatrix} \text{Sales} \\ \text{to Drexel} \\ \text{this month} \end{pmatrix}$$

Using this, the demand constraints are:

$$A_1 - IA_1 = 800 \qquad \text{(demand for GM3A in January)}$$
$$IA_1 + A_2 - IA_2 = 700 \qquad \text{(demand for GM3A in February)}$$
$$IA_2 + A_3 - IA_3 = 1{,}000 \qquad \text{(demand for GM3A in March)}$$
$$IA_3 + A_4 - IA_4 = 1{,}100 \qquad \text{(demand for GM3A in April)}$$
$$B_1 - IB_1 = 1{,}000 \qquad \text{(demand for GM3B in January)}$$
$$IB_1 + B_2 - IB_2 = 1{,}200 \qquad \text{(demand for GM3B in February)}$$
$$IB_2 + B_3 - IB_3 = 1{,}400 \qquad \text{(demand for GM3B in March)}$$
$$IB_3 + B_4 - IB_4 = 1{,}400 \qquad \text{(demand for GM3B in April)}$$
$$IA_4 = 450 \qquad \text{(inventory of GM3A at end of April)}$$
$$IB_4 = 300 \qquad \text{(inventory of GM3B at end of April)}$$

Employment constraints are set for each month.

The constraints for the minimum and maximum number of labor hours each month are:

$$1.3A_1 + 0.9B_1 \geq 2{,}240 \qquad \text{(minimum labor hours in January)}$$
$$1.3A_2 + 0.9B_2 \geq 2{,}240 \qquad \text{(minimum labor hours in February)}$$
$$1.3A_3 + 0.9B_3 \geq 2{,}240 \qquad \text{(minimum labor hours in March)}$$
$$1.3A_4 + 0.9B_4 \geq 2{,}240 \qquad \text{(minimum labor hours in April)}$$
$$1.3A_1 + 0.9B_1 \leq 2{,}560 \qquad \text{(maximum labor hours in January)}$$
$$1.3A_2 + 0.9B_2 \leq 2{,}560 \qquad \text{(maximum labor hours in February)}$$
$$1.3A_3 + 0.9B_3 \leq 2{,}560 \qquad \text{(maximum labor hours in March)}$$
$$1.3A_4 + 0.9B_4 \leq 2{,}560 \qquad \text{(maximum labor hours in April)}$$

The storage capacity constraints are:

$$IA_1 + IB_1 \leq 3{,}300 \qquad \text{(storage capacity in January)}$$
$$IA_2 + IB_2 \leq 3{,}300 \qquad \text{(storage capacity in February)}$$
$$IA_3 + IB_3 \leq 3{,}300 \qquad \text{(storage capacity in March)}$$
$$IA_4 + IB_4 \leq 3{,}300 \qquad \text{(storage capacity in April)}$$
$$\text{All variables} \geq 0 \qquad \text{(nonnegativity constraints)}$$

The solution was obtained using Solver in Excel 2013, as shown in Program 8.4. Some of the variables are not integers, but this is not a problem because work in process can be carried over from one month to the next. Table 8.3 summarizes the solution with the values rounded. The total cost is about \$169,295. Greenberg can use this model to develop production schedules again in the future by letting the subscripts on the variables represent new months and making minor changes to the problem. The only things in the model that would have to be changed are the RHS values for the demand constraints (and inventory desired at the end of the fourth month) and the objective function coefficients (costs) if they should change.

PROGRAM 8.4

Greenberg Motors Solution in Excel 2013

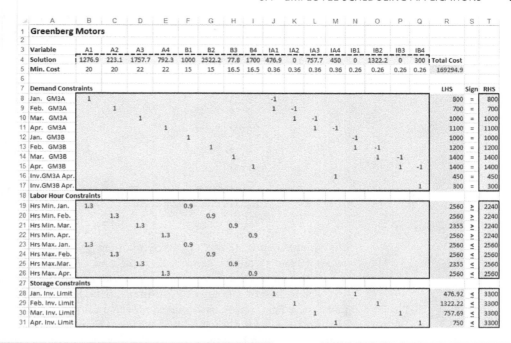

Solver Parameter Inputs and Selections

Set Objective: F5

By Changing cells: B4:Q4

To: Min

Subject to the Constraints:

R19:R22 >= T19:T22

R23:R26 <= T23:T26

R28:R31 <= T28:T31

R8:R17 = T8:T17

Solving Method: Simplex LP

☑ Make Variables Non-Negative

Key Formulas

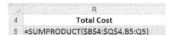

Copy formula in R5 to R8:R17
Copy formula in R5 to R19:R26
Copy formula in R5 to R28:R31

TABLE 8.3

Solution to Greenberg Motors Problem

PRODUCTION SCHEDULE	JANUARY	FEBRUARY	MARCH	APRIL
Units of GM3A produced	1,277	223	1,758	792
Units of GM3B produced	1,000	2,522	78	1,700
Inventory of GM3A carried	477	0	758	450
Inventory of GM3B carried	0	1,322	0	300
Labor hours required	2,560	2,560	2,355	2,560

8.4 Employee Scheduling Applications

Labor Planning

Labor planning problems address staffing needs over a specific time period. They are especially useful when managers have some flexibility in assigning workers to jobs that require overlapping or interchangeable talents. Large banks frequently use LP to tackle their labor scheduling.

TABLE 8.4

Hong Kong Bank of Commerce and Industry

TIME PERIOD	NUMBER OF TELLERS REQUIRED
9 A.M.–10 A.M.	10
10 A.M.–11 A.M.	12
11 A.M.–Noon	14
Noon–1 P.M.	16
1 P.M.–2 P.M.	18
2 P.M.–3 P.M.	17
3 P.M.–4 P.M.	15
4 P.M.–5 P.M.	10

Hong Kong Bank of Commerce and Industry is a busy bank that has requirements for between 10 and 18 tellers, depending on the time of day. The lunch time, from noon to 2 P.M., is usually heaviest. Table 8.4 indicates the workers needed at various hours that the bank is open.

The bank now employs 12 full-time tellers, but many people are on its roster of available part-time employees. A part-time employee must put in exactly four hours per day but can start anytime between 9 A.M. and 1 P.M. Part-timers are a fairly inexpensive labor pool, since no retirement or lunch benefits are provided for them. Full-timers, on the other hand, work from 9 A.M. to 5 P.M. but are allowed 1 hour for lunch. (Half of the full-timers eat at 11 A.M., the other half at noon.) Full-timers thus provide 35 hours per week of productive labor time.

By corporate policy, the bank limits part-time hours to a maximum of 50% of the day's total requirement. Part-timers earn $8 per hour (or $32 per day) on average, and full-timers earn $100 per day in salary and benefits, on average. The bank would like to set a schedule that would minimize its total personnel costs. It will release one or more of its full-time tellers if it is profitable to do so.

In formulating this as an LP, the objective is to minimize cost. There is a constraint for each hour of the day, stating that the number of people working at the bank during that hour should be at least the minimum number shown in Table 8.4, so there are eight of these constraints. Another constraint will limit the total number of full-time workers to be no more than 12. The last constraint will specify that the number of part-time hours must not exceed 50% of the total hours.

The bank must decide how many full-time tellers to use, so there will be one decision variable for that. Similarly, the bank must decide about using part-time tellers, but this is more complex as the part-time workers can start at different times of the day while all full-time workers start at the beginning of the day. Thus, there must be a variable indicating the number of part-time workers starting at each hour of the day from 9 A.M. until 1 P.M. Any worker who starts at 1 P.M. will work until closing, so there is no need to consider having any part-time workers start after that. Let

$$F = \text{full-time tellers}$$
$$P_1 = \text{part-timers starting at 9 A.M (leaving at 1 P.M.)}$$
$$P_2 = \text{part-timers starting at 10 A.M (leaving at 2 P.M.)}$$
$$P_3 = \text{part-timers starting at 11 A.M (leaving at 3 P.M.)}$$
$$P_4 = \text{part-timers starting at noon (leaving at 4 P.M.)}$$
$$P_5 = \text{part-timers starting at 1 P.M (leaving at 5 P.M.)}$$

Objective function:

$$\text{Minimize total daily personnel cost} = \$100F + \$32(P_1 + P_2 + P_3 + P_4 + P_5)$$

Constraints:

For each hour, the available labor hours must be at least equal to the required labor hours.

$$
\begin{aligned}
F + P_1 &\geq 10 && \text{(9 A.M.–10 A.M. needs)} \\
F + P_1 + P_2 &\geq 12 && \text{(10 A.M.–11 A.M. needs)} \\
0.5F + P_1 + P_2 + P_3 &\geq 14 && \text{(11 A.M.–noon needs)} \\
0.5F + P_1 + P_2 + P_3 + P_4 &\geq 16 && \text{(noon–1 P.M. needs)} \\
F + P_2 + P_3 + P_4 + P_5 &\geq 18 && \text{(1 P.M.–2 P.M. needs)} \\
F + P_3 + P_4 + P_5 &\geq 17 && \text{(2 P.M.–3 P.M. needs)} \\
F + P_4 + P_5 &\geq 15 && \text{(3 P.M.–4 P.M. needs)} \\
F + P_5 &\geq 10 && \text{(4 P.M.–5 P.M. needs)}
\end{aligned}
$$

Only 12 full-time tellers are available, so

$$F \leq 12$$

Part-time worker hours cannot exceed 50% of total hours required each day, which is the sum of the tellers needed each hour:

$$4(P_1 + P_2 + P_3 + P_4 + P_5) \leq 0.50(10 + 12 + 14 + 16 + 18 + 17 + 15 + 10)$$

or

$$4P_1 + 4P_2 + 4P_3 + 4P_4 + 4P_5 \leq 0.50(112)$$
$$F, P_1, P_2, P_3, P_4, P_5 \geq 0$$

Alternate optimal solutions are common in many LP problems. The sequence in which you enter the constraints into QM for Windows can affect the solution found.

Program 8.5 gives the solution to this, found using Solver in Excel 2013. There are several alternate optimal schedules that Hong Kong Bank can follow. The first is to employ only 10 full-time tellers $(F = 10)$ and to start 7 part-timers at 10 A.M. $(P_2 = 7)$, 2 part-timers at 11 A.M. $(P_3 = 2)$, and 5 part-timers at noon $(P_4 = 5)$. No part-timers would begin at 9 A.M. or 1 P.M.

A second solution also employs 10 full-time tellers, but starts 6 part-timers at 9 A.M. $(P_1 = 6)$, 1 part-timer at 10 A.M. $(P_2 = 1)$, 2 part-timers at 11 A.M. and 5 at noon $(P_3 = 2 \text{ and } P_4 = 5)$, and 0 part-timers at 1 P.M. $(P_5 = 0)$. The cost of either of these two policies is $1,448 per day.

8.5 Financial Applications

Portfolio Selection

Maximizing return on investment subject to a set of risk constraints is a popular financial application of LP.

A problem frequently encountered by managers of banks, mutual funds, investment services, and insurance companies is the selection of specific investments from among a wide variety of alternatives. The manager's overall objective is usually to maximize expected return on investment, given a set of legal, policy, or risk restraints.

For example, the International City Trust (ICT) invests in short-term trade credits, corporate bonds, gold stocks, and construction loans. To encourage a diversified portfolio, the board of directors has placed limits on the amount that can be committed to any one type of investment. ICT has $5 million available for immediate investment and wishes to do two things: (1) maximize the return on the investments made over the next six months and (2) satisfy the diversification requirements as set by the board of directors.

PROGRAM 8.5

Labor Planning Solution in Excel 2013

	A	B	C	D	E	F	G	H	I	J
1	Labor Planning Example									
2										
3										
4	Variables	F	P1	P2	P3	P4	P5			
5	Values	10	0	7	2	5	0	Total Cost		
6	Cost	100	32	32	32	32	32	1448		
7										
8	Constraints							LHS	Sign	RHS
9	9 a.m. - 10 a.m.	1	1					10	≥	10
10	10 a.m. - 11 a.m.	1	1	1				17	≥	12
11	11 a.m. - noon	0.5	1	1	1			14	≥	14
12	noon - 1 p.m.	0.5	1	1	1	1		19	≥	16
13	1 p.m. - 2 p.m.	1		1	1	1	1	24	≥	18
14	2 p.m. - 3 p.m.	1			1	1	1	17	≥	17
15	3 p.m. - 4 p.m.	1				1	1	15	≥	15
16	4 p.m. - 5 p.m.	1					1	10	≥	10
17	Max. Full time	1						10	≤	12
18	Total PT hours		4	4	4	4	4	56	≤	56

Solver Parameter Inputs and Selections

Set Objective: H6

By Changing cells: B5:G5

To: Min

Subject to the Constraints:

H9:H16 >= J9:J16

H17:H18 <= J17:J18

Solving Method: Simplex LP

☑ Make Variables Non-Negative

Key Formulas

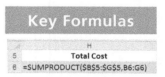

	H
5	Total Cost
6	=SUMPRODUCT($B$5:$G$5,B6:G6)

Copy H6 to H9:H18

The specifics of the investment possibilities are as follows:

INVESTMENT	INTEREST RETURN	MAXIMUM INVESTMENT ($ MILLIONs)
Trade credit	7%	1.0
Corporate bonds	11%	2.5
Gold stocks	19%	1.5
Construction loans	15%	1.8

In addition, the board specifies that at least 55% of the funds invested must be in gold stocks and construction loans, and that no less than 15% be invested in trade credit.

In formulating this as an LP, the objective is to maximize the return. There are four separate constraints limiting the maximum amount in each investment option to the maximum given in the table. The fifth constraint specifies that the total amount in gold stocks and construction loans must be at least 55% of the total amount invested, and the next constraint specifies that the total amount in trade credit must be at least 15% of the total amount invested. The final constraint stipulates that the total amount invested cannot exceed $5 million (it could be less). Define the variables as

$$X_1 = \text{dollars invested in trade credit}$$
$$X_2 = \text{dollars invested in corporate bonds}$$
$$X_3 = \text{dollars invested in gold stocks}$$
$$X_4 = \text{dollars invested in construction loans}$$

The total amount invested is $X_1 + X_2 + X_3 + X_4$, which may be less than $5 million. This is important when calculating 55% of the total amount invested and 15% of the total amount invested in two of the constraints.

Objective:

$$\text{Maximize dollars of interest earned} = 0.07X_1 + 0.11X_2 + 0.19X_3 + 0.15X_4$$

$$\begin{aligned}
\text{subject to} \quad X_1 & \leq 1{,}000{,}000 \\
X_2 & \leq 2{,}500{,}000 \\
X_3 & \leq 1{,}500{,}000 \\
X_4 & \leq 1{,}800{,}000 \\
X_3 + X_4 & \geq 0.55(X_1 + X_2 + X_3 + X_4) \\
X_1 & \geq 0.15(X_1 + X_2 + X_3 + X_4) \\
X_1 + X_2 + X_3 + X_4 & \leq 5{,}000{,}000 \\
X_1, X_2, X_3, X_4 & \geq 0
\end{aligned}$$

 IN ACTION Optimization at UPS

On an average day, UPS delivers 13 million packages to almost 8 million customers in 200 countries and territories. Deliveries are classified as same-day air, next-day air, and second-day air. The next-day air operations average more than 1.1 million packages per day and generate annual revenue of over $5 billion. The company has 256 aircraft and many more on order. During the busiest time of year, between Thanksgiving and New Year's Day, the company leases additional aircraft to meet the demand. The size of its fleet makes UPS the 9th-largest commercial airline in the United States and the 11th-largest commercial airline in the world.

In the next-day delivery operation, the pickup and delivery of packages by UPS involves several stages. Packages are carried by truck to ground centers. From there, the packages are taken to the airport, and then they are flown to one of the airport hubs with at most one stop at another airport to pick up more packages. At the hub, the packages are sorted and loaded onto planes and flown to the destination. Packages are then loaded on large trucks and taken to ground centers. At the ground centers, additional sorting is done, packages are put on smaller trucks, and the packages are delivered to their final destinations before 10:30 A.M. The same aircraft are used in the second-day

deliveries as well, so these two types of operations must be coordinated.

A team from UPS and Massachusetts Institute of Technology worked together to develop an optimization-based planning system called VOLCANO (Volume, Location, and Aircraft Network Optimizer) that is used for planning and managing operations. This group developed optimization methods to minimize overall cost (ownership and operating) while meeting capacity and service standard constraints. Mathematical models are used to determine the minimum cost set of routes, fleet assignments, and package flows. Constraints include the number of aircraft, landing restrictions at airports, and aircraft operating characteristics (such as speed, capacity, and range).

The VOLCANO system is credited with saving over $87 million from late in 2000 to the end of 2002. It is expected that $189 million will be saved over the next decade. This optimizer is also used to identify the needed fleet composition and recommend future aircraft acquisitions.

Source: Based on Andrew P. Armacost, Cynthia Barnhart, Keith A. Ware, and Alysia M. Wilson. "UPS Optimizes Its Air Network," *Interfaces* 34, 1 (January–February 2004): 15–25.

PROGRAM 8.6

ICT Portfolio Solution in Excel 2013

	A	B	C	D	E	F	G	H
1	ICT Portfolio Selection							
2								
3	Variable	X1	X2	X3	X4			
4	Solution	750000	950000	1500000	1800000	Total Return		
5	Max. Return	0.07	0.11	0.19	0.15	712000		
6								
7						LHS		RHS
8	Trade	1				750000	≤	1,000,000
9	Bonds		1			950000	≤	2,500,000
10	Gold			1		1500000	≤	1,500,000
11	Construction				1	1800000	≤	1,800,000
12	Min. Gold+Const	-0.55	-0.55	0.45	0.45	550000	≥	0
13	Min. Trade	0.85	-0.15	-0.15	-0.15	0	≥	0
14	Total Invested	1	1	1	1	5000000	≤	5000000

Solver Parameter Inputs and Selections

Set Objective: F5

By Changing cells: B4:E4

To: Min

Subject to the Constraints:

    F8:F11 <= H8:H11

    F12:F13 >= H12:H13

    F14 <= H14

Solving Method: Simplex LP

☑ **Make Variables Non-Negative**

Key Formulas

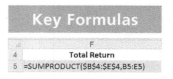

	F
4	Total Return
5	=SUMPRODUCT($B$4:$E$4,B5:E5)

Copy F5 to F8:F14

Program 8.6 shows the solution found using Solver in Excel. ICT maximizes its interest earned by making the following investment: $X_1 = \$750,000$, $X_2 = \$950,000$, $X_3 = \$1,500,000$, and $X_4 = \$1,800,000$, and the total interest earned is \$712,000.

Truck Loading Problem

The truck loading problem involves deciding which items to load on a truck so as to maximize the value of a load shipped. As an example, we consider Goodman Shipping, an Orlando firm owned by Steven Goodman. One of his trucks, with a capacity of 10,000 pounds, is about to be loaded.* Awaiting shipment are the following items:

ITEM	VALUE ($)	WEIGHT (POUNDS)
1	22,500	7,500
2	24,000	7,500
3	8,000	3,000
4	9,500	3,500
5	11,500	4,000
6	9,750	3,500

---

*Adapted from an example in S. L. Savage. *What's Best!* Oakland, CA: General Optimization, Inc., and Holden-Day, 1985.

Each of these six items, we see, has an associated dollar value and weight.

The objective is to maximize the total value of the items loaded onto the truck without exceeding the truck's weight capacity. We let X_i be the proportion of each item i loaded on the truck:

$$\text{Maximize load value} = \$22{,}500X_1 + \$24{,}000X_2 + \$8{,}000X_3 + \$9{,}500X_4 \\ + \$11{,}500X_5 + \$9{,}750X_6$$

$$\text{subject to} \quad 7{,}500X_1 + 7{,}500X_2 + 3{,}000X_3 + 3{,}500X_4 + 4{,}000X_5 \\ + 3{,}500X_6 \leq 10{,}000 \text{ lb capacity}$$

$$X_1 \leq 1$$
$$X_2 \leq 1$$
$$X_3 \leq 1$$
$$X_4 \leq 1$$
$$X_5 \leq 1$$
$$X_6 \leq 1$$
$$X_1, X_2, X_3, X_4, X_5, X_6 \geq 0$$

These final six constraints reflect the fact that at most one "unit" of an item can be loaded onto the truck. In effect, if Goodman can load a *portion* of an item (say, item 1 is a batch of 1,000 folding chairs, not all of which need be shipped together), the X_is will all be proportions ranging from 0 (nothing) to 1 (all of that item loaded).

To solve this LP problem, we turn to Excel's Solver. Program 8.7 shows Goodman's Excel formulation, input data, and the solution, which yields a total load value of $31,500.

The answer leads us to an interesting issue that we deal with in detail in Chapter 10. What does Goodman do if fractional values of items cannot be loaded? For example, if luxury cars were the items being loaded, we clearly cannot ship one-third of a Maserati.

PROGRAM 8.7
Goodman Truck Loading Solution in Excel

	A	B	C	D	E	F	G	H	I	J
1	Goodman Shipping									
2										
3	Variables	X1	X2	X3	X4	X5	X6			
4	Values	0.3333	1	0	0	0	0	Total Value		
5	Load Value $	22500	24000	8000	9500	11500	9750	31500		
6										
7	Constraints							LHS	Sign	RHS
8	Total weight	7500	7500	3000	3500	4000	3500	10000	≤	10000
9	% Item 1	1						0.3333333	≤	1
10	% Item 2		1					1	≤	1
11	% Item 3			1				0	≤	1
12	% Item 4				1			0	≤	1
13	% Item 5					1		0	≤	1
14	% Item 6						1	0	≤	1

Solver Parameter Inputs and Selections

Set Objective: H5

By Changing cells: B4:G4

To: Min

Subject to the Constraints:

  H8:H14 <= J8:J14

Solving Method: Simplex LP

☑ **Make Variables Non-Negative**

Key Formulas

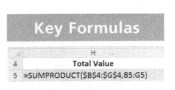

Copy H5 to H8:H14

If the proportion of item 1 was rounded up to 1.00, the weight of the load would increase to 15,000 pounds. This would violate the 10,000 pounds maximum weight constraint. Therefore, the fraction of item 1 must be rounded down to zero. This would drop the value of the load to 7,500 pounds, leaving 2,500 pounds of the load capacity unused. Because no other item weighs less than 2,500 pounds, the truck cannot be filled up further.

Thus, we see that by using regular LP and rounding the fractional weights, the truck would carry only item 2, for a load weight of 7,500 pounds and a load value of $24,000.

QM for Windows and spreadsheet optimizers such as Excel's Solver are capable of dealing with *integer programming* problems as well; that is, LP problems requiring integer solutions. Using Excel, the integer solution to Goodman's problem is to load items 3, 4, and 6, for a total weight of 10,000 pounds and load value of $27,250.

8.6   Ingredient Blending Applications

Diet Problems

The diet problem, one of the earliest applications of LP, was originally used by hospitals to determine the most economical diet for patients. Known in agricultural applications as the feed mix problem, the diet problem involves specifying a food or feed ingredient combination that satisfies stated nutritional requirements at a minimum cost level.

The Whole Food Nutrition Center uses three bulk grains to blend a natural cereal that it sells by the pound. The cost of each bulk grain and the protein, riboflavin, phosphorus, and magnesium units per pound of each are shown in Table 8.5.

On the packaging for each of its products, Whole Food indicates the nutritional content in each bowl of cereal when eaten with 0.5 cup of milk. The USRDA (U.S. Recommended Dietary Allowance) and the more recent DRI (Dietary Reference Intake) were consulted to establish recommended amounts of certain vitamins and minerals for an average adult. Based on these figures and the desired amounts for labeling on the package, Whole Food has determined that each 2-ounce serving of the cereal should contain 3 units of protein, 2 units of riboflavin, 1 unit of phosphorous, and 0.425 unit of magnesium.

In modeling this as an LP, the objective is to minimize cost. There will be four constraints (one each for protein, riboflavin, phosphorous, and magnesium) stipulating that the number of units must be at least the minimum amount specified. Since these requirements are for each 2 ounce serving, the last constraint must say that the total amount of the grains used will be 2 ounces, or 0.125 pound.

In defining the variables, notice that the cost is expressed per pound of the three grains. Thus, in order to calculate the total cost, we must know the number of pounds of the grains used in one serving of the cereal. Also, the numbers in Table 8.5 are expressed in units per pound of grain, so defining variables as the number of pounds of the grains makes it easier to calculate the amounts of protein, riboflavin, phosphorous, and magnesium. We let

$$X_A = \text{pounds of grain A in one 2-ounce serving of cereal}$$
$$X_B = \text{pounds of grain B in one 2-ounce serving of cereal}$$
$$X_C = \text{pounds of grain C in one 2-ounce serving of cereal}$$

TABLE 8.5   Whole Food's Natural Cereal Requirements

GRAIN	COST PER POUND (CENTS)	PROTEIN (UNITS/LB)	RIBOFLAVIN (UNITS/LB)	PHOSPHORUS (UNITS/LB)	MAGNESIUM (UNITS/LB)
A	33	22	16	8	5
B	47	28	14	7	0
C	38	21	25	9	6

Objective function:

Minimize total cost of mixing a 2-ounce serving $= \$0.33X_A + \$0.47X_B + \$0.38X_C$
subject to

$$22X_A + 28X_B + 21X_C \geq 3 \quad \text{(protein units)}$$
$$16X_A + 14X_B + 25X_C \geq 2 \quad \text{(riboflavin units)}$$
$$8X_A + 7X_B + 9X_C \geq 1 \quad \text{(phosphorus units)}$$
$$5X_A + 0X_B + 6X_C \geq 0.425 \quad \text{(magnesium units)}$$
$$X_A + X_B + X_C = 0.125 \quad \text{(total mix is 2 ounces or 0.125 pound)}$$
$$X_A, X_B, X_C \geq 0$$

The solution to this problem requires mixing together 0.025 lb of grain A, 0.050 lb of grain B, and 0.050 lb of grain C. Another way of stating the solution is in terms of the proportion of the 2-ounce serving of each grain, namely, 0.4 ounce of grain A, 0.8 ounce of grain B, and 0.8 ounce of grain C in each serving. The cost per serving is $0.05. Program 8.8 illustrates this solution using Solver in Excel 2013.

Ingredient Mix and Blending Problems

Diet and feed mix problems are actually special cases of a more general class of LP problems known as *ingredient* or *blending problems*. Blending problems arise when a decision must be made regarding the blending of two or more resources to produce one or more products. Resources, in this case, contain one or more essential ingredients that must be blended so that each final product contains specific percentages of each ingredient. The following example deals with an application frequently seen in the petroleum industry, the blending of crude oils to produce refinable gasoline.

PROGRAM 8.8
Whole Food Diet Solution in Excel 2013

	A	B	C	D	E	F	G
1	Whole Foods Nutrition Problem						
3		Grain A	Grain B	Grain C			
4	Variable	Xa	Xb	Xc			
5	Solution	0.025	0.05	0.05	Total Cost		
6	Minimize	0.33	0.47	0.38	0.05075		
8	Constraints				LHS	Sign	RHS
9	Protein	22	28	21	3	≥	3
10	Riboflavin	16	14	25	2.35	≥	2
11	Phosphorus	8	7	9	1	≥	1
12	Magnesium	5	0	6	0.425	≥	0.425
13	Total Weight	1	1	1	0.125	=	0.125

Solver Parameter Inputs and Selections

Set Objective: E6
By Changing cells: B5:D5
To: Min
Subject to the Constraints:
E9:E12 <= G9:G12
E13 = G13
Solving Method: Simplex LP
☑ Make Variables Non-Negative

Key Formulas

	E
5	Total Cost
6	=SUMPRODUCT($B$5:$D$5,B6:D6)

Copy E6 to E9:E13

Major oil refineries all use LP for blending crude oils to produce gasoline grades.

The Low Knock Oil Company produces two grades of cut-rate gasoline for industrial distribution. The grades, regular and economy, are produced by refining a blend of two types of crude oil, type X100 and type X220. Each crude oil differs not only in cost per barrel, but in composition as well. The following table indicates the percentage of crucial ingredients found in each of the crude oils and the cost per barrel for each:

CRUDE OIL TYPE	INGREDIENT A (%)	INGREDIENT B (%)	COST/BARREL ($)
X100	35	55	30.00
X220	60	25	34.80

Weekly demand for the regular grade of Low Knock gasoline is at least 25,000 barrels, and demand for the economy is at least 32,000 barrels per week. *At least* 45% of each barrel of regular must be ingredient A. *At most* 50% of each barrel of economy should contain ingredient B. While the gasoline yield from one barrel of crude depends on the type of crude and the type of processing used, we will assume for the sake of this example that one barrel of crude oil will yield one barrel of gasoline.

The Low Knock management must decide how many barrels of each type of crude oil to buy each week for blending to satisfy demand at minimum cost. In modeling this as an LP, the objective is to minimize cost. Each of the two types of gasoline has a demand constraint, and each of the two types of gasoline has a constraint restricting the amount of the ingredients. Thus, there are four constraints. The decisions involve the amount of each type of crude to use in each type of gasoline, so these will be the decision variables. Let

$$X_1 = \text{barrels of crude X100 blended to produce the refined regular}$$
$$X_2 = \text{barrels of crude X100 blended to produce the refined economy}$$
$$X_3 = \text{barrels of crude X220 blended to produce the refined regular}$$
$$X_4 = \text{barrels of crude X220 blended to produce the refined economy}$$

This problem can be formulated as follows:

Objective:

$$\text{Minimize cost} = \$30X_1 + \$30X_2 + \$34.80X_3 + \$34.80X_4$$

subject to

$$X_1 + X_3 \geq 25{,}000 \quad \text{(demand for regular)}$$
$$X_2 + X_4 \geq 32{,}000 \quad \text{(demand for economy)}$$

At least 45% of each barrel of regular must be ingredient A:

$$(X_1 + X_3) = \text{total amount of crude blended to produce the refined regular gasoline demand}$$

Thus,

$$0.45(X_1 + X_3) = \text{minimum amount of ingredient A required}$$

But

$$0.35X_1 + 0.60X_3 = \text{amount of ingredient A in refined regular gas}$$

So

$$0.35X_1 + 0.60X_3 \geq 0.45X_1 + 0.45X_3$$

or

$$-0.10X_1 + 0.15X_3 \geq 0 \quad \text{(ingredient A in regular constraint)}$$

Similarly, at most 50% of each barrel of economy should be ingredient B:

$$X_2 + X_4 = \text{total amount of crude blended to produce the refined economy gasoline demanded}$$

Thus,

$$0.50(X_2 + X_4) = \text{maximum amount of ingredient B allowed}$$

But

$$0.55X_2 + 0.25X_4 = \text{amount of ingredient B in refined economy gas}$$

So

$$0.55X_2 + 0.25X_4 \leq 0.50X_2 + 0.50X_4$$

or

$$0.05X_2 - 0.25X_4 \leq 0 \ (\text{ingredient B in economy constraint})$$

Here is the entire LP formulation:

$$\text{Minimize cost} = 30X_1 + 30X_2 + 34.80X_3 + 34.80X_4$$

$$
\begin{aligned}
\text{subject to} \quad X_1 \qquad\quad + \quad X_3 \qquad\qquad &\geq 25{,}000 \\
X_2 + \qquad\qquad\quad X_4 &\geq 32{,}000 \\
-0.10X_1 \qquad + \ 0.15X_3 \qquad\quad &\geq 0 \\
0.05X_2 \qquad\qquad - \ 0.25X_4 &\leq 0 \\
X_1, X_2, X_3, X_4 &\geq 0
\end{aligned}
$$

Using Excel, the solution to Low Knock Oil's formulation was found to be

$$X_1 = 15{,}000 \text{ barrels of X100 into regular}$$
$$X_2 = 26{,}666.67 \text{ barrels of X100 into economy}$$
$$X_3 = 10{,}000 \text{ barrels of X220 into regular}$$
$$X_4 = 5{,}333.33 \text{ barrels of X220 into economy}$$

The cost of this mix is $1,783,600. Refer to Program 8.9 for details.

8.7 Other Linear Programming Applications

There are many other types of linear programming applications. One particular application was first developed and used by American Airlines in the early 1990s, and it is called revenue management. This was designed to use differential pricing for seats so that additional revenue could be obtained. Some customers who were willing to book with certain restrictions, such as 14-day advance purchase or with a stay over a Saturday night, would receive lower fares. However, if all seats are sold at this reduced cost, then higher paying passengers, often business travelers who might try to book seats at the last minute, would not be able to do so. The extra revenue generated from these passengers is then lost. A revenue management system was developed to determine how many seats to make available to each type of passenger. Linear programs would have an objective of maximizing the total revenue, while constraints would be based on the number of total seats available on the plane and the number of seats allocated to each category. Companies have reported dramatic increases in revenues as a result of this.

Given the success of revenue management systems in the airlines industry, similar systems were also adopted by many hotel chains. The airline industry and the hotel industry have products with similar characteristics—a limited inventory of a very perishable

PROGRAM 8.9

Low Knock Oil Solution in Excel 2013

	A	B	C	D	E	F	G	H
1	Low Knock Oil Company							
2								
3		X100 Reg	X100 Econ	X220 Reg	X220 Econ			
4	Variable	X1	X2	X3	X4			
5	Solution	15000	26666.67	10000	5333.33	Total Cost		
6	Cost	30	30	34.8	34.8	1783600		
7								
8	Constraints					LHS	Sign	RHS
9	Demand Regular	1		1		25000	≥	25000
10	Demand Economy		1		1	32000	≥	32000
11	Ing. A in Regular	-0.1		0.15		0	≥	0
12	Ing. B in Economy		0.05		-0.25	0	≤	0

Solver Parameter Inputs and Selections

Set Objective: F6

By Changing cells: B5:E5

To: Min

Subject to the Constraints:

   F9:F11 >= H9:H11

   F12 <= H12

Solving Method: Simplex LP

☑ **Make Variables Non-Negative**

Key Formulas

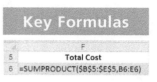

	F
5	Total Cost
6	=SUMPRODUCT($B$5:$E$5,B6:E6)

Copy F6 to F9:F12

product. A plane has a limited number of seats, and when the plane takes off, any empty seats can no longer be sold and the revenue is lost. A hotel has a limited number of rooms, and once a particular date has passed, an empty room on that date cannot be sold and the revenue is lost.

Another common type of application is data envelopment analysis (DEA). This is sometimes used to measure the efficiency of several similar operating units such as hospitals or schools. It is often used with nonprofit entities where measuring the success of a particular unit is difficult as there is no single objective, such as profit, that is to be optimized. In developing the LP, the inputs and outputs of the particular system must be identified. For a hospital system, the inputs might be the number of doctors working, the number of nurses working, the number of bed-day available per year, and the total payroll. The outputs might be the number of patient-days in the hospital, the number of nurses trained, the number of surgeries performed, the number of outpatient procedures performed, and the number of doctors trained. Constraints are developed for each of these inputs and outputs for each unit in the system. The objective is basically to minimize the resources needed to generate specific levels of output. The results indicate whether fewer resources could have been used to generate the same level of outputs when compared to a typical unit in the system. Efforts can then be made to identify specific areas that are deemed to be potentially inefficient, and improvements can be targeted for these areas.

Transportation problems, transshipment problems, and assignment problems are very widely used in business. These are so common that special purpose algorithms have been developed to solve these more quickly than the current procedures used for other type of linear programming problems. These applications will be presented in the next chapter.

IN ACTION Harrah's Cherokee Casino Uses Linear Programming for Revenue Management

Identifying the customers who would generate the most revenue is usually very difficult, but Harrah's Cherokee Casino has benefited from a unique way of placing customers into particular market segments based on spending habits. Harrah's encourages casino customers to join their Total Rewards club. Points in this club are earned each time the member plays a casino game or spends money in a restaurant, spa, gift shop, or hotel facility. Earning points entitles players to receive benefits such as free or discounted rooms, meals, show tickets, and other things. Tracking the size of the bets as well as the number of bets allows Harrah's to place the players in segments based on the amount that they typically play when visiting the casinos. The best revenue generators are guests who typically gamble more money during each day of their stay. When a player tries to reserve a room, a low-spending player might be told there are no rooms available, while a high-spending customer will get to reserve the room. To promote goodwill, the customer in the lower-spending segment might be offered a free room at a nearby hotel. The additional revenue that will be obtained by reserving the room for a high-roller will more than offset this cost.

An LP is used to maximize the revenue generated subject to the total number of rooms available and the total number of rooms that are allocated to each segment of customers. The variables include the number of rooms to make available for each segment. The shadow prices of the constraints indicate how much extra revenue will be generated if one additional room is made available to the different segments. The model is frequently updated based on the number of rooms still available, the number of days remaining until the date of the reservation, and other factors. Based on results from this model, marketing efforts are targeted for very specific Total Rewards members when it appears that hotel traffic might be light on a particular day.

While revenue management implementations typically increase revenue by 3–7%, Harrah's has experienced a 15% increase in revenues from the revenue management systems throughout its many hotels and casinos. At Harrah's Cherokee Casino, the hotel opened with the system already in place so there is no basis for comparison. However, the profit margin of this particular property is 60% on gross revenue, which is twice the industry average.

Source: Based on Metters, Richard, et al. "The 'Killer Application' of Revenue Management: Harrah's Cherokee Casino & Hotel," *Interfaces* 38, 3 (May–June 2008): 161–175.

Summary

In this chapter we continued our discussion of linear programming models. The basic steps for formulating a linear program were followed for a variety of problems. These included applications in marketing, production scheduling, finance, and ingredient blending. Attention was paid to understanding the problem, identifying the objective and the constraints, defining the decision variables, and developing the mathematical model from these.

In future chapters, additional applications of linear programming will be presented. The transportation problem will be discussed in Chapter 9, along with two other closely related applications: the assignment problem and the transshipment problem.

Self-Test

- Before taking the self-test, refer to the learning objectives at the beginning of the chapter, the notes in the margins, and the glossary at the end of the chapter.
- Use the key at the back of the book to correct your answers.
- Restudy pages that correspond to any questions that you answered incorrectly or material you feel uncertain about.

1. Linear programming can be used to select effective media mixes, allocate fixed or limited budgets across media, and maximize audience exposure.
   a. True
   b. False
2. Using LP to maximize audience exposure in an advertising campaign is an example of the type of LP application known as
   a. marketing research.
   b. media selection.
   c. portfolio assessment.

   d. media budgeting.
   e. all of the above.
3. Which of the following *does not* represent a factor manager might consider when employing LP for production scheduling:
   a. labor capacity
   b. space limitations
   c. product demand
   d. risk assessment
   e. inventory costs

4. When applying LP to diet problems, the objective function is usually designed to
   a. maximize profits from blends of nutrients.
   b. maximize ingredient blends.
   c. minimize production losses.
   d. maximize the number of products to be produced.
   e. minimize the costs of nutrient blends.
5. The diet problem is
   a. also called the feed mix problem in agriculture.
   b. a special case of the ingredient mix problem.

c. a special case of the blending problem.
d. all of the above.
6. The selection of specific investments from among a wide variety of alternatives is the type of LP problem known as
   a. the product mix problem.
   b. the investment banker problem.
   c. the portfolio selection problem.
   d. the Wall Street problem.
   e. none of the above.

Problems

8-1 *(Production problem)* Winkler Furniture manufactures two different types of china cabinets: a French Provincial model and a Danish Modern model. Each cabinet produced must go through three departments: carpentry, painting, and finishing. The table below contains all relevant information concerning production times per cabinet produced and production capacities for each operation per day, along with net revenue per unit produced. The firm has a contract with an Indiana distributor to produce a minimum of 300 of each cabinet per week (or 60 cabinets per day). Owner Bob Winkler would like to determine a product mix to maximize his daily revenue.
(a) Formulate as an LP problem.
(b) Solve using an LP software program or spreadsheet.

8-2 *(Investment decision problem)* The Heinlein and Krampf Brokerage firm has just been instructed by one of its clients to invest $250,000 of her money obtained recently through the sale of land holdings in Ohio. The client has a good deal of trust in the investment house, but she also has her own ideas about the distribution of the funds being invested. In particular, she requests that the firm select whatever stocks and bonds they believe are well rated, but within the following guidelines:

(a) Municipal bonds should constitute at least 20% of the investment.
(b) At least 40% of the funds should be placed in a combination of electronic firms, aerospace firms, and drug manufacturers.
(c) No more than 50% of the amount invested in municipal bonds should be placed in a high-risk, high-yield nursing home stock.

Subject to these restraints, the client's goal is to maximize projected return on investments. The analysts at Heinlein and Krampf, aware of these guidelines, prepare a list of high-quality stocks and bonds and their corresponding rates of return:

INVESTMENT	PROJECTED RATE OF RETURN (%)
Los Angeles municipal bonds	5.3
Thompson Electronics, Inc.	6.8
United Aerospace Corp.	4.9
Palmer Drugs	8.4
Happy Days Nursing Homes	11.8

(a) Formulate this portfolio selection problem using LP.
(b) Solve this problem.

Data for Problem 8-1

CABINET STYLE	CARPENTRY (HOURS/ CABINET)	PAINTING (HOURS/ CABINET)	FINISHING (HOURS/ CABINET)	NET REVENUE/ CABINET ($)
French Provincial	3	1.5	0.75	28
Danish Modern	2	1	0.75	25
Department capacity (hours)	360	200	125	

Note: means the problem may be solved with QM for Windows; means the problem may be solved with Excel; and means the problem may be solved with QM for Windows and/or Excel.

8-3 *(Restaurant work scheduling problem).* The famous Y. S. Chang Restaurant is open 24 hours a day. Waiters and busboys report for duty at 3 A.M., 7 A.M., 11 A.M., 3 P.M., 7 P.M., or 11 P.M., and each works an 8-hour shift. The following table shows the minimum number of workers needed during the six periods into which the day is divided. Chang's scheduling problem is to determine how many waiters and busboys should report for work at the start of each time period to minimize the total staff required for one day's operation. (*Hint:* Let X_i equal the number of waiters and busboys beginning work in time period i, where $i = 1, 2, 3, 4, 5, 6$.)

PERIOD	TIME	NUMBER OF WAITERS AND BUSBOYS REQUIRED
1	3 A.M.–7 A.M.	3
2	7 A.M.–11 A.M.	12
3	11 A.M.–3 P.M.	16
4	3 P.M.–7 P.M.	9
5	7 P.M.–11 P.M.	11
6	11 P.M.–3 A.M.	4

8-4 *(Animal feed mix problem)* The Battery Park Stable feeds and houses the horses used to pull tourist-filled carriages through the streets of Charleston's historic waterfront area. The stable owner, an ex-racehorse trainer, recognizes the need to set a nutritional diet for the horses in his care. At the same time, he would like to keep the overall daily cost of feed to a minimum.

The feed mixes available for the horses' diet are an oat product, a highly enriched grain, and a mineral product. Each of these mixes contains a certain amount of five ingredients needed daily to keep the average horse healthy. The table on this page shows these minimum requirements, units of each ingredient per pound of feed mix, and costs for the three mixes.

In addition, the stable owner is aware that an overfed horse is a sluggish worker. Consequently, he determines that 6 pounds of feed per day are the most that any horse needs to function properly. Formulate this problem and solve for the optimal daily mix of the three feeds.

8-5 The Kleenglass Corporation makes a dishwasher that has excellent cleaning power. This dishwasher uses less water than most competitors, and it is extremely quiet. Orders have been received from several retails stores for delivery at the end of each of the next 3 months, as shown below:

MONTH	NUMBER OF UNITS
June	195
July	215
August	205

Due to limited capacity, only 200 of these can be made each month on regular time, and the cost is $300 each. However, an extra 15 units per month can be produced if overtime is used, but the cost goes up to $325 each. Also, if there are any dishwashers produced in a month that are not sold in that month, there is a $20 cost to carry this item to the next month. Use linear programming to determine how many units to produce in each month on regular time and on overtime to minimize the total cost while meeting the demands.

8-6 Eddie Kelly is running for reelection as mayor of a small town in Alabama. Jessica Martinez, Kelly's campaign manager during this election, is planning the marketing campaign, and there is some stiff competition. Martinez has selected four ways to advertise: television ads, radio ads, billboards,

Data for Problem 8-4

	FEED MIX			
DIET REQUIREMENT (INGREDIENTS)	OAT PRODUCT (UNITS/LB)	ENRICHED GRAIN (UNITS/LB)	MINERAL PRODUCT (UNITS/LB)	MINIMUM DAILY REQUIREMENT (UNITS)
A	2	3	1	6
B	0.5	1	0.5	2
C	3	5	6	9
D	1	1.5	2	8
E	0.5	0.5	1.5	5
Cost/lb	$0.09	$0.14	$0.17	

and newspaper ads. The costs of these, the audience reached by each type of ad, and the maximum number available is shown in the following table:

TYPE OF AD	COST PER AD	AUDIENCE REACHED/AD	MAXIMUM NUMBER
TV	$800	30,000	10
Radio	$400	22,000	10
Billboards	$500	24,000	10
Newspapers	$100	8,000	10

In addition, Martinez has decided that there should be at least six ads on TV or radio or some combination of those two. The amount spent on billboards and newspapers together must not exceed the amount spent on TV ads. While fundraising is still continuing, the monthly budget for advertising has been set at $15,000. How many ads of each type should be placed to maximize the total number of people reached?

8-7 *(Media selection problem)* The advertising director for Diversey Paint and Supply, a chain of four retail stores on Chicago's North Side, is considering two media possibilities. One plan is for a series of half-page ads in the Sunday *Chicago Tribune* newspaper, and the other is for advertising time on Chicago TV. The stores are expanding their lines of do-it-yourself tools, and the advertising director is interested in an exposure level of at least 40% within the city's neighborhoods and 60% in northwest suburban areas.

The TV viewing time under consideration has an exposure rating per spot of 5% in city homes and 3% in the northwest suburbs. The Sunday newspaper has corresponding exposure rates of 4% and 3% per ad. The cost of a half-page *Tribune* advertisement is $925; a television spot costs $2,000.

Diversey Paint would like to select the least costly advertising strategy that would meet desired exposure levels.
(a) Formulate using LP.
(b) Solve the problem.

8-8 *(Automobile leasing problem)* Sundown Rent-a-Car, a large automobile rental agency operating in the Midwest, is preparing a leasing strategy for the next six months. Sundown leases cars from an automobile manufacturer and then rents them to the public on a daily basis. A forecast of the demand for Sundown's cars in the next six months follows:

MONTH	MARCH	APRIL	MAY	JUNE	JULY	AUGUST
Demand	420	400	430	460	470	440

Cars may be leased from the manufacturer for either three, four, or five months. These are leased on the first day of the month and are returned on the last day of the month. Every six months the automobile

manufacturer is notified by Sundown about the number of cars needed during the next six months. The automobile manufacturer has stipulated that at least 50% of the cars leased during a six-month period must be on the five-month lease. The cost per month on each of the three types of leases are $420 for the three-month lease, $400 for the four-month lease, and $370 for the five-month lease.

Currently, Sundown has 390 cars. The lease on 120 cars expires at the end of March. The lease on another 140 cars expires at the end of April, and the lease on the rest of these expires at the end of May.

Use LP to determine how many cars should be leased in each month on each type of lease to minimize the cost of leasing over the six-month period. How many cars are left at the end of August?

8-9 Management of Sundown Rent-a-Car (see Problem 8-8) has decided that perhaps the cost during the six-month period is not the appropriate cost to minimize because the agency may still be obligated to additional months on some leases after that time. For example, if Sundown had some cars delivered at the beginning of the sixth month, Sundown would still be obligated for two additional months on a three-month lease. Use LP to determine how many cars should be leased in each month on each type of lease to minimize the cost of leasing over the entire life of these leases.

8-10 *(High school busing problem)* The Arden County, Maryland, superintendent of education is responsible for assigning students to the *three* high schools in his county. He recognizes the need to bus a certain number of students, for several sectors of the county are beyond walking distance to a school. The superintendent partitions the county into *five* geographic sectors as he attempts to establish a plan that will minimize the total number of student miles traveled by bus. He also recognizes that if a student happens to live in a certain sector and is assigned to the high school in that sector, there is no need to bus that student because he or she can walk to school. The three schools are located in sectors B, C, and E.

The following table reflects the number of high-school-age students living in each sector and the busing distance in miles from each sector to each school:

	DISTANCE TO SCHOOL			
SECTOR	SCHOOL IN SECTOR B	SCHOOL IN SECTOR C	SCHOOL IN SECTOR E	NUMBER OF STUDENTS
A	5	8	6	700
B	0	4	12	500
C	4	0	7	100
D	7	2	5	800
E	12	7	0	400
				2,500

Each high school has a capacity of 900 students. Set up the objective function and constraints of this problem using LP so that the total number of student miles traveled by bus is minimized. Then solve the problem.

☠: 8-11 *(Pricing and marketing strategy problem)* The I. Kruger Paint and Wallpaper Store is a large retail distributor of the Supertrex brand of vinyl wall-coverings. Kruger will enhance its citywide image in Miami if it can outsell other local stores in total number of rolls of Supertrex next year. It is able to estimate the demand function as follows:

Number of rolls of Supertrex sold = 20 × Dollars spent on advertising + 6.8 × Dollars spent on in-store displays + 12 × Dollars invested in on-hand wallpaper inventory − 65,000 × Percentage markup taken above wholesale cost of a roll

The store budgets a total of $17,000 for advertising, in-store displays, and on-hand inventory of Supertrex for next year. It decides it must spend at least $3,000 on advertising; in addition, at least 5% of the amount invested in on-hand inventory should be devoted to displays. Markups on Supertrex seen at other local stores range from 20% to 45%. Kruger decides that its markup had best be in this range as well.
(a) Formulate as an LP problem.
(b) Solve the problem.
(c) What is the difficulty with the answer?
(d) What constraint would you add?

☠: 8-12 *(College meal selection problem)* Kathy Roniger, campus dietitian for a small Idaho college, is responsible for formulating a nutritious meal plan for students. For an evening meal, she feels that the following five meal-content requirements should be met: (1) between 900 and 1,500 calories; (2) at least 4 milligrams of iron; (3) no more than 50 grams of fat; (4) at least 26 grams of protein; and (5) no more than 50 grams of carbohydrates. On a particular day, Roniger's food stock includes seven items that can be prepared and served for supper to meet these requirements. The cost per pound for each food item and the contribution to each of the five nutritional requirements are given in the table below.

What combination and amounts of food items will provide the nutrition Roniger requires at the least total food cost?
(a) Formulate as an LP problem.
(b) What is the cost per meal?
(c) Is this a well-balanced diet?

☠: 8-13 *(High-tech production problem)* Quitmeyer Electronics Incorporated manufactures the following six microcomputer peripheral devices: internal modems, external modems, graphics circuit boards, CD drives, hard disk drives, and memory expansion boards. Each of these technical products requires time, in minutes, on three types of electronic testing equipment, as shown in the table below.

The first two test devices are available 120 hours per week. The third (device 3) requires more preventive maintenance and may be used only

Data for Problem 8-12

TABLE OF FOOD VALUES AND COSTS

FOOD ITEM	CALORIES/ LB	IRON (MG/LB)	FAT (GM/LB)	PROTEIN (GM/LB)	CARBOHYDRATES (GM/LB)	COST/ LB ($)
Milk	295	0.2	16	16	22	0.60
Ground meat	1216	0.2	96	81	0	2.35
Chicken	394	4.3	9	74	0	1.15
Fish	358	3.2	0.5	83	0	2.25
Beans	128	3.2	0.8	7	28	0.58
Spinach	118	14.1	1.4	14	19	1.17
Potatoes	279	2.2	0.5	8	63	0.33

Source: Pennington, Jean A. T., and Judith S. Douglass. Bowes and Church's Food Values of Portions Commonly Used, 18th ed., Philadelphia: Lippincott Williams & Wilkins, 2004, pp. 100–130.

Data for Problem 8-13

	INTERNAL MODEM	EXTERNAL MODEM	CIRCUIT BOARD	CD DRIVES	HARD DRIVES	MEMORY BOARDS
Test device 1	7	3	12	6	18	17
Test device 2	2	5	3	2	15	17
Test device 3	5	1	3	2	9	2

100 hours each week. The market for all six computer components is vast, and Quitmeyer Electronics believes that it can sell as many units of each product as it can manufacture. The table that follows summarizes the revenues and material costs for each product:

DEVICE	REVENUE PER UNIT SOLD ($)	MATERIAL COST PER UNIT ($)
Internal modem	200	35
External modem	120	25
Graphics circuit board	180	40
CD drive	130	45
Hard disk drive	430	170
Memory expansion board	260	60

In addition, variable labor costs are $15 per hour for test device 1, $12 per hour for test device 2, and $18 per hour for test device 3. Quitmeyer Electronics wants to maximize its profits.

(a) Formulate this problem as an LP model.
(b) Solve the problem by computer. What is the best product mix?
(c) What is the value of an additional minute of time per week on test device 1? Test device 2? Test device 3? Should Quitmeyer Electronics add more test device time? If so, on which equipment?

8-14 (Nuclear plant staffing problem) South Central Utilities has just announced the August 1 opening of its second nuclear generator at its Baton Rouge, Louisiana, nuclear power plant. Its personnel department has been directed to determine how many nuclear technicians need to be hired and trained over the remainder of the year.

The plant currently employs 350 fully trained technicians and projects the following personnel needs:

MONTH	PERSONNEL HOURS NEEDED
August	40,000
September	45,000
October	35,000
November	50,000
December	45,000

By Louisiana law, a reactor employee can actually work no more than 130 hours per month. (Slightly over 1 hour per day is used for check-in and check-out, recordkeeping, and daily radiation health scans.) Policy at South Central Utilities also dictates that layoffs are not acceptable in those months when the nuclear plant is overstaffed. So, if more trained employees are available than are needed in any month, each worker is still fully paid, even though he or she is not required to work the 130 hours.

Training new employees is an important and costly procedure. It takes one month of one-on-one classroom instruction before a new technician is permitted to work alone in the reactor facility. Therefore, South Central must hire trainees one month before they are actually needed. Each trainee teams up with a skilled nuclear technician and requires 90 hours of that employee's time, meaning that 90 hours less of the technician's time are available that month for actual reactor work.

Personnel department records indicate a turnover rate of trained technicians at 5% per month. In other words, about 5% of the skilled employees at the start of any month resign by the end of that month. A trained technician earns an average monthly salary of $2,000 (regardless of the number of hours worked, as noted earlier). Trainees are paid $900 during their one month of instruction.

(a) Formulate this staffing problem using LP.
(b) Solve the problem. How many trainees must begin each month?

8-15 (Agricultural production planning problem) Margaret Black's family owns five parcels of farmland broken into a southeast sector, north sector, northwest sector, west sector, and southwest sector. Margaret is involved primarily in growing wheat, alfalfa, and barley crops and is currently preparing her production plan for next year. The Pennsylvania Water Authority has just announced its yearly water allotment, with the Black farm receiving 7,400 acre-feet. Each parcel can only tolerate a specified amount of irrigation per growing season, as specified in the following table:

PARCEL	AREA (ACRES)	WATER IRRIGATION LIMIT (ACRE-FEET)
Southeast	2,000	3,200
North	2,300	3,400
Northwest	600	800
West	1,100	500
Southwest	500	600

Each of Margaret's crops needs a minimum amount of water per acre, and there is a projected limit on sales of each crop. Crop data follow:

CROP	MAXIMUM SALES	WATER NEEDED PER ACRE (ACRE-FEET)
Wheat	110,000 bushels	1.6
Alfalfa	1,800 tons	2.9
Barley	2,200 tons	3.5

Margaret's best estimate is that she can sell wheat at a net profit of $2 per bushel, alfalfa at $40 per ton, and barley at $50 per ton. One acre of land yields an average of 1.5 tons of alfalfa and 2.2 tons of barley. The wheat yield is approximately 50 bushels per acre.

(a) Formulate Margaret's production plan.

(b) What should the crop plan be, and what profit will it yield?

(c) The Water Authority informs Margaret that for a special fee of $6,000 this year, her farm will qualify for an additional allotment of 600 acre-feet of water. How should she respond?

8-16 (Material blending problem) Amalgamated Products has just received a contract to construct steel body frames for automobiles that are to be produced at the new Japanese factory in Tennessee. The Japanese auto manufacturer has strict quality control standards for all of its component subcontractors and has informed Amalgamated that each frame must have the following steel content:

MATERIAL	MINIMUM PERCENTAGE	MAXIMUM PERCENTAGE
Manganese	2.1	2.3
Silicon	4.3	4.6
Carbon	5.05	5.35

Amalgamated mixes batches of eight different available materials to produce one ton of steel used in the body frames. The table on this page details these materials.

Formulate and solve the LP model that will indicate how much each of the eight materials should be blended into a 1-ton load of steel so that Amalgamated meets its requirements while minimizing costs.

8-17 Refer to Problem 8-16. Find the cause of the difficulty and recommend how to adjust it. Then solve the problem again.

8-18 (Hospital expansion problem) Mt. Sinai Hospital in New Orleans is a large, private, 600-bed facility, complete with laboratories, operating rooms, and x-ray equipment. In seeking to increase revenues, Mt. Sinai's administration has decided to make a 90-bed addition on a portion of adjacent land currently used for staff parking. The administrators feel that the labs, operating rooms, and x-ray department are not being fully utilized at present and do not need to be expanded to handle additional patients. The addition of 90 beds, however, involves deciding how many beds should be allocated to the medical staff for medical patients and how many to the surgical staff for surgical patients.

The hospital's accounting and medical records departments have provided the following pertinent information. The average hospital stay for a medical patient is 8 days, and the average medical patient generates $2,280 in revenues. The average surgical patient is in the hospital 5 days and receives a $1,515 bill. The laboratory is capable of handling 15,000 tests per year more than it was handling. The average medical patient requires 3.1 lab tests and the average surgical patient takes 2.6 lab tests. Furthermore, the average medical patient uses one x-ray, whereas the average surgical patient requires two x-rays. If the hospital was expanded by 90 beds, the x-ray department could handle up to 7,000 x-rays without significant additional cost. Finally, the administration estimates that up to 2,800 additional operations could be performed in existing operating room facilities. Medical patients, of course, do not require surgery, whereas each surgical patient generally has one surgery performed.

Formulate this problem so as to determine how many medical beds and how many surgical beds should be added to maximize revenues. Assume that the hospital is open 365 days a year. Then solve the problem.

8-19 Prepare a written report to the CEO of Mt. Sinai Hospital in Problem 8-18 on the expansion of the hospital. Round off your answers to the nearest *integer*. The format of presentation of results is important. The CEO is a busy person and wants to be able

Data for Problem 8-16

MATERIAL AVAILABLE	MANGANESE (%)	SILICON (%)	CARBON (%)	POUNDS AVAILABLE	COST PER POUND ($)
Alloy 1	70.0	15.0	3.0	No limit	0.12
Alloy 2	55.0	30.0	1.0	300	0.13
Alloy 3	12.0	26.0	0	No limit	0.15
Iron 1	1.0	10.0	3.0	No limit	0.09
Iron 2	5.0	2.5	0	No limit	0.07
Carbide 1	0	24.0	18.0	50	0.10
Carbide 2	0	25.0	20.0	200	0.12
Carbide 3	0	23.0	25.0	100	0.09

to find your optimal solution quickly in your report. Cover all the areas given in the following sections, but do not mention any variables or shadow prices.

(a) What is the maximum revenue per year, how many medical patients/year are there, and how many surgical patients/year are there? How many medical beds and how many surgical beds of the 90-bed addition should be added?

(b) Are there any empty beds with this optimal solution? If so, how many empty beds are there? Discuss the effect of acquiring more beds if needed.

(c) Are the laboratories being used to their capacity? Is it possible to perform more lab tests/year? If so, how many more? Discuss the effect of acquiring more lab space if needed.

(d) Is the x-ray facility being used to its maximum? Is it possible to do more x-rays/year? If so, how many more? Discuss the effect of acquiring more x-ray facilities if needed.

(e) Is the operating room being used to capacity? Is it possible to do more operations/year? If so, how many more? Discuss the effect of acquiring more operating room facilities if needed. (**Source:** Professor Chris Vertullo.)

8-20 In the Low Knock Oil Company blending problem, it was assumed that one barrel of crude would result in one barrel of gasoline as the final product. In processing one barrel of crude, a typical gasoline yield is about 0.46 barrels, although it could be higher or lower than this, depending on the particular crude and processing used. However, other products such as diesel, jet fuel, home fuel oil, and asphalt also come from that same barrel. Assuming that only 46% of the crude turns into gasoline, modify the Low Knock Oil Company linear programming example to account for this. Solve the resulting LP problem, using any computer software.

8-21 A paper mill produces rolls of paper that are 10 inches wide and 100 feet long. These rolls are used for creating narrower rolls of paper that are used in cash registers, automatic teller machines (ATMs), and other devices. The narrower widths (2, 2.5, and 3 inches) needed for these devices are obtained by cutting the 10-inch rolls using pre-specified cutting patterns. Cutting pattern #1 will cut the 10-inch roll into four rolls that are 2.5 inches each. Cutting pattern #2 results in three rolls that are each 3 inches wide (leaving 1 inch of waste on the end). Cutting pattern #3 results in one roll that is 3 inches wide and two rolls that are 3.5 inches wide. Cutting pattern #4 results in one of the 2.5-inch rolls, one of the 3-inch rolls, and one of the 3.5-inch rolls (leaving 1 inch of waste). Cutting pattern #5 results in 1 roll that is 2.5 inches wide and two rolls that are 3.5 inches wide (leaving 0.5 inches of waste on the end). An order has been received for 2,000 of the 2.5-inch rolls,

4,000 of the 3-inch rolls, and 5,000 of the 3.5 inch rolls. How many rolls should be cut on each pattern if the company wants to minimize the total number of 10-inch rolls used? How many rolls should be cut on each pattern if the company wants to minimize the total waste?

8-22 (*Portfolio selection problem*) Daniel Grady is the financial advisor for a number of professional athletes. An analysis of the long-term goals for many of these athletes has resulted in a recommendation to purchase stocks with some of their income that is set aside for investments. Five stocks have been identified as having very favorable expectations for future performance. Although the expected return is important in these investments, the risk, as measured by the beta of the stock, is also important. (A high value of beta indicates that the stock has a relatively high risk.) The expected return and the betas for five stocks are as follows:

STOCK	1	2	3	4	5
Expected return (%)	11.0	9.0	6.5	15.0	13.0
Beta	1.20	0.85	0.55	1.40	1.25

Daniel would like to minimize the beta of the stock portfolio (calculated using a weighted average of the amounts put into the different stocks) while maintaining an expected return of at least 11%. Since future conditions may change, Daniel has decided that no more than 35% of the portfolio should be invested in any one stock.

(a) Formulate this as a linear program. (*Hint*: Define the variables to be the proportion of the total investment that would be put in each stock. Include a constraint that restricts the sum of these variables to be 1.)

(b) Solve this problem. What are the expected return and beta for this portfolio?

8-23 (*Airline fuel problem*) Coast-to-Coast Airlines is investigating the possibility of reducing the cost of fuel purchases by taking advantage of lower fuel costs in certain cities. Since fuel purchases represent a substantial portion of operating expenses for an airline, it is important that these costs be carefully monitored. However, fuel adds weight to an airplane, and consequently, excess fuel raises the cost of getting from one city to another. In evaluating one particular flight rotation, a plane begins in Atlanta, flies from Atlanta to Los Angeles, from Los Angeles to Houston, from Houston to New Orleans, and from New Orleans to Atlanta. When the plane arrives in Atlanta, the flight rotation is said to have been completed, and then it starts again. Thus, the fuel on board when the flight arrived in Atlanta must be taken into consideration when the flight begins.

Data for Problem 8-23

LEG	MINIMUM FUEL REQUIRED (1,000 GAL.)	MAXIMUM FUEL ALLOWED (1,000 GAL.)	REGULAR FUEL CONSUMPTION (1,000 GAL.)	FUEL PRICE PER GALLON
Atlanta–Los Angeles	24	36	12	$4.15
Los Angeles–Houston	15	23	7	$4.25
Houston–New Orleans	9	17	3	$4.10
New Orleans–Atlanta	11	20	5	$4.18

Along each leg of this route, there is a minimum and a maximum amount of fuel that may be carried. This and additional information is provided in the table above.

The regular fuel consumption is based on the plane carrying the minimum amount of fuel. If more than this is carried, the amount of fuel consumed is higher. Specifically, for each 1,000 gallons of fuel above the minimum, 5% (or 50 gallons per 1,000 gallons of extra fuel) is lost due to excess fuel consumption. For example, if 25,000 gallons of fuel were on board when the plane takes off from Atlanta, the fuel consumed on this route would be $12 + 0.05 = 12.05$ thousand gallons. If 26 thousand gallons were on board, the fuel consumed would be increased by another 0.05 thousand, for a total of 12.1 thousand gallons.

Formulate this as an LP problem to minimize the cost. How many gallons should be purchased in each city? What is the total cost of this?

Internet Homework Problems

See our Internet home page, at **www.pearsonhighered.com/render**, for additional homework problems, Problems 8-24 to 8-26.

Case Study

Cable & Moore

With the company expanding into several new markets in the coming months, Cable & Moore was anticipating a large increase in sales revenue. The future looked bright for this provider of television, telephone, and Internet services. However, management of Cable & Moore was well aware of the importance of customer service in new markets. If the public had problems with new service and could not quickly and efficiently have their problems solved, demand would quickly erode and it might take years to recover from the bad publicity. Therefore, management was adamant that there would be enough well-trained customer service representatives to handle the calls from new customers and from potential customers.

Based on experience in other markets, the anticipated number of phone calls to customer service was projected. Given the average call-length, the number of hours of customer-service time from April to August was projected and is shown in the table below.

MONTH	APRIL	MAY	JUNE	JULY	AUGUST
Hours needed	21,600	24,600	27,200	28,200	29,700

Through experience, management knew that training a new employee well was essential. Each new employee was put through a 1-month training program, and was assigned to an existing employee for an entire month. Normally an existing employee would work 160 hours per month. However, when an employee was assigned to perform training of a new-hire, the productive work hours for that employee dropped to 80 hours per month.

During the training period, the trainee was paid $2,000 for the month. At the end of that time, the monthly salary increases to the standard salary for a regular customer service representative which is $3,000 per month. In the past, the company lost about 5% of the trained customer service representatives per month due to attrition. While the company is looking to improve upon this, for the next several months it is anticipated that this will continue. There will be 150 trained employees at the beginning of April. Management of the company would like to develop a schedule of hiring new employees so that there are sufficient customer service representatives to meet the demand, but this is to be done at the lowest possible cost.

Discussion Questions

1. Develop a schedule for hiring new employees. What is the total cost of this schedule?
2. Discuss any limitations that exist for this solution.
3. How would the schedule change if the attrition rate could be lowered to 3% per month instead of 5%? What would be the impact on the cost?

 Internet Case Study

See out Internet home page, at **www.pearsonhighered.com/render**, for this additional case study: **Chase Manhattan Bank**. This case is about scheduling employees at a bank.

Bibliography

See the Bibliography at the end of Chapter 7.

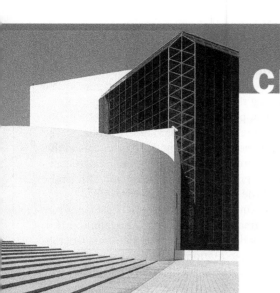

CHAPTER 9

Transportation, Assignment, and Network Models

LEARNING OBJECTIVES

After completing this chapter, students will be able to:

1. Structure LP problems for the transportation, transshipment, and assignment models.
2. Solve facility location and other application problems with transportation models.
3. Use LP to model shortest-route and maximal-flow problems.
4. Solve minimal-spanning tree problems.

CHAPTER OUTLINE

9.1 Introduction
9.2 The Transportation Problem
9.3 The Assignment Problem
9.4 The Transshipment Problem

9.5 Maximal-Flow Problem
9.6 Shortest-Route Problem
9.7 Minimal-Spanning Tree Problem

Summary • Glossary • Solved Problems • Self-Test • Discussion Questions and Problems • Internet Homework Problems • Case Study: Andrew–Carter, Inc. • Case Study: Northeastern Airlines • Case Study: Southwestern University Traffic Problems • Internet Case Studies • Bibliography

Appendix 9.1: Using QM for Windows

9.1 Introduction

Chapter 8 provided examples of a number of managerial problems that could be modeled using linear programming (LP), and this chapter will provide even more such examples. However, all of the problems in this chapter can be modeled as networks as well as linear programs. The use of networks helps in visualizing and understanding the managerial problem. These models include the transportation problem, the transshipment problem, the assignment problem, the maximal-flow problem, the shortest-route problem, and the minimal-spanning tree problem. The use of linear programming software will be the primary means of solving these problems in this chapter. However, to take advantage of the unique structure of some of these problems, specialized algorithms have been developed to solve very large problems more quickly and efficiently. These algorithms are presented on the Companion Website for this textbook in Module 8.

The basic transportation problem is concerned with finding the best (usually least cost) way to distribute goods from sources such as factories, to final destinations such as retail outlets. If there are intermediate points, such as regional distribution centers, where the items must go before being shipped to the final destination, then the transportation problem becomes a transshipment problem. The assignment problem involves finding the best (usually least cost) way to assign individuals or pieces of equipment to projects or jobs on a one-to-one basis. In other words, each person is assigned to only one job, and each job only needs one person assigned to it.

The maximal-flow technique finds the maximum flow of any quantity or substance through a network. This technique can determine, for example, the maximum number of vehicles (cars, trucks, and so forth) that can go through a network of roads from one location to another. The shortest-route technique can find the shortest path through a network. For example, this technique can find the shortest route from one city to another through a network of roads. The minimal-spanning tree technique determines the path through the network that connects all the points while minimizing total distance. When the points represent houses in a subdivision, the minimal-spanning tree technique can be used to determine how to connect all of the houses to electrical power, water systems, and so on, in a way that minimizes the total distance or length of power lines or water pipes.

The circles in the networks are called nodes. *The lines connecting them are called* arcs.

While there are many different types of examples in this chapter, some terminology is common to all of the network models. The points on the network are referred to as **nodes** and the lines on the network that connect these nodes are called **arcs**. Typically nodes are presented as circles, although sometimes squares or rectangles are used for the nodes.

IN ACTION Improving Package Delivery

TNT Express is one of the world's largest delivery companies. The 77,000 employees of the company handle over 4 million packages each week, using about 30,000 trucks and other road vehicles and about 50 aircraft. Trying to maintain a high level of customer service while keeping costs low through efficient operations is a daunting task. In 2005, the director of operations for TNT Express turned to the use of operations research models to improve the road network of deliveries in Italy. A decrease in costs of over 6% caused the company to incorporate the use of optimization models into every aspect of their supply chain.

Several initiatives were developed to improve their supply chain. The Global Optimization (GO) Academy was established to teach employees the principles of optimization. Communities of practice (CoPs) were developed and key employees met three times a year to discuss and share their best practices with

their suppliers and academia members. In addition to developing optimization models and improving efficiency, the company taught employees the basic concepts of operations management and management science so that everyone would recognize opportunities for improvement through the use of these techniques.

The result of TNT Express implementing these practices was a cost savings of 207 million Euros from 2008 to 2011. Other benefits include the reduction of CO_2 emissions from their vehicles by 283 million kilograms, improved networking with other employees of the company, and a feeling of empowerment as workers now feel they can obtain support from colleagues outside their own operating units or even outside their own country. Optimization models truly delivered for TNT Express.

Source: Based on H. Fleuren, C. Goossens, M. Hendricks, M.-L. Lombard, and J. Poppelaars. "Supply Chain Wide Optimization at TNT Express," *Interfaces* 43, 1 (January/February 2013): 5–20.

9.2 The Transportation Problem

The **transportation problem** deals with the distribution of goods from several points of supply (*origins* or **sources**) to a number of points of demand (**destinations**). Usually we are given a capacity (supply) of goods at each source, a requirement (demand) for goods at each destination, and the shipping cost per unit from each source to each destination. An example is shown in Figure 9.1. The objective of such a problem is to schedule shipments so that total transportation costs are minimized. At times, production costs are also included.

Transportation models can also be used when a firm is trying to decide where to locate a new facility. Before opening a new warehouse, factory, or sales office, it is good practice to consider a number of alternative sites. Good financial decisions concerning the facility location also attempt to minimize total transportation and production costs for the entire system.

Linear Program for the Transportation Example

The Executive Furniture Corporation is faced with the transportation problem shown in Figure 9.1. The company would like to minimize the transportation costs while meeting the demand at each destination and not exceeding the supply at each source. In formulating this as a linear program, there are three supply constraints (one for each source) and three demand constraints (one for each destination). The decisions to be made are the number of units to ship on each route, so there is one decision variable for each arc (arrow) in the network. Let

$$X_{ij} = \text{number of units shipped from source } i \text{ to destination } j$$

where

$$i = 1, 2, 3, \text{ with } 1 = \text{Des Moines}, 2 = \text{Evansville, and } 3 = \text{Fort Lauderdale}$$
$$j = 1, 2, 3, \text{ with } 1 = \text{Albuquerque}, 2 = \text{Boston, and } 3 = \text{Cleveland}$$

The LP formulation is

$$\text{Minimize total cost} = 5X_{11} + 4X_{12} + 3X_{13} + 8X_{21} + 4X_{22}$$
$$+ 3X_{23} + 9X_{31} + 7X_{32} + 5X_{33}$$

subject to

$$X_{11} + X_{12} + X_{13} \leq 100 \quad \text{(Des Moines supply)}$$
$$X_{21} + X_{22} + X_{23} \leq 300 \quad \text{(Evansville supply)}$$
$$X_{31} + X_{32} + X_{33} \leq 300 \quad \text{(Fort Lauderdale supply)}$$
$$X_{11} + X_{21} + X_{31} = 300 \quad \text{(Albuquerque demand)}$$
$$X_{12} + X_{22} + X_{32} = 200 \quad \text{(Boston demand)}$$
$$X_{13} + X_{23} + X_{33} = 200 \quad \text{(Cleveland demand)}$$
$$X_{ij} \geq 0 \text{ for all } i \text{ and } j$$

The solution is found using computer software, and the optimal shipping schedule is the following:

100 units from Des Moines to Albuquerque

200 units from Evansville to Boston

100 units from Evansville to Cleveland

200 units from Ft. Lauderdale to Albuquerque

100 units from Ft. Lauderdale to Cleveland

The total cost is $3,900. The following section will illustrate how this solution was found.

Solving Transportation Problems Using Computer Software

The solution to this transportation problem modeled as an LP problem could be found by using Solver in Excel 2013 as illustrated in Chapter 7, by using QM for Windows, or by using Excel QM in Excel 2013. When using Excel 2013 and Solver, the constraints could be entered in rows as discussed in Chapter 7. However, the special structure for this problem allows for an

FIGURE 9.1

Network Representation of a Transportation Problem, with Costs, Demands, and Supplies

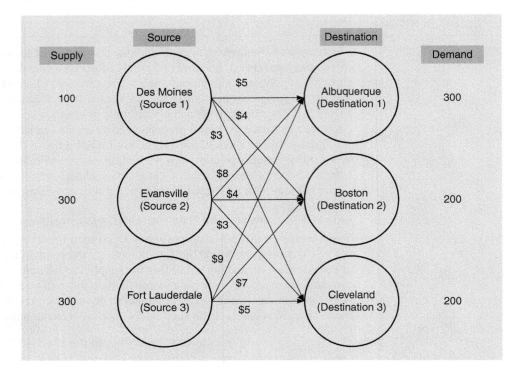

easier and more intuitive input in Excel 2013 with Solver, and Excel QM will be used for this example to illustrate this.

Program 9.1 provides the input data and the solution for this example. Click the *Excel QM* tab and select the *Alphabetical* Menu from the Excel QM ribbon. When the menu appears, scroll down and select *Transportation*. In the input window that opens, enter the number of Origins or sources (3 in this example), the number of Destinations (3 in this example), select *Minimize*, and click *OK*. A worksheet appears and you enter the costs, supplies, and demands shown in the data table. Then click the *Data* tab, select *Solver* from the Data ribbon, and click *Solve* in the Solver input window. You do not have to write any formulas or change any of the parameters.

A General LP Model for Transportation Problems

In this example, there were 3 sources and 3 destinations. The LP had $3 \times 3 = 9$ variables and $3 + 3 = 6$ constraints. In general, for a transportation problem with m sources and n destination, the number of variables is mn, and the number of constraints is $m + n$. For example, if

PROGRAM 9.1

Executive Furniture Corporation Solution in Excel 2013 Using Excel QM

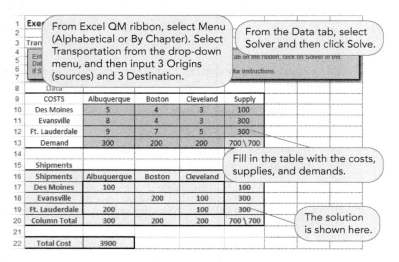

there are 5 (i.e., $m = 5$) constraints and 8 (i.e., $n = 8$) variables, the linear program would have $5(8) = 40$ variables and $5 + 8 = 13$ constraints.

The use of the double subscripts on the variables makes the general form of the linear program for a transportation problem with m sources and n destinations easy to express. Let

x_{ij} = number of units shipped from source i to destination j

c_{ij} = cost of one unit from source i to destination j

s_i = supply at source i

d_j = demand at destination j

The linear programming model is

$$\text{Minimize cost} = \sum_{j=1}^{n} \sum_{i=1}^{m} c_{ij} x_{ij}$$

subject to

$$\sum_{j=1}^{n} x_{ij} \leq s_i \qquad i = 1, 2, \ldots, m$$

$$\sum_{i=1}^{m} x_{ij} = d_j \qquad j = 1, 2, \ldots, n$$

$$x_{ij} \geq 0 \qquad \text{for all } i \text{ and } j$$

Facility Location Analysis

The transportation method has proved to be especially useful in helping a firm decide where to locate a new factory or warehouse. Since a new location is an issue of major financial importance to a company, several alternative locations must ordinarily be considered and evaluated. Even though a wide variety of subjective factors are considered, including quality of labor supply, presence of labor unions, community attitude and appearance, utilities, and recreational and educational facilities for employees, a final decision also involves minimizing total shipping and production costs. This means that each alternative facility location should be analyzed within the framework of one *overall* distribution system.

To determine which of two locations should be selected for a new production facility, linear programming models will be developed for two transportation problems—one for each location. If three or more locations were being considered, a transportation problem modeled as a linear programming model would be developed for each of these. The existing sources and destinations would be used in each of these, and one new source would be included as well. This will find the minimum cost for the distribution system if that one source is added to the system. This would be repeated for the second source, and the minimum costs for these two problems will be compared to find which one is better. This will be illustrated in the following example.

The Hardgrave Machine Company produces computer components at its plants in Cincinnati, Salt Lake City, and Pittsburgh. These plants have not been able to keep up with demand for orders at Hardgrave's four warehouses in Detroit, Dallas, New York, and Los Angeles. As a result, the firm has decided to build a new plant to expand its productive capacity. The two sites being considered are Seattle and Birmingham; both cities are attractive in terms of labor supply, municipal services, and ease of factory financing.

Table 9.1 presents the production costs and output requirements for each of the three existing plants, demand at each of the four warehouses, and estimated production costs of the new proposed plants. Transportation costs from each plant to each warehouse are summarized in Table 9.2.

The important question that Hardgrave now faces is this: Which of the new locations will yield the lowest cost for the firm in combination with the existing plants and warehouses? Note that the cost of each individual plant-to-warehouse route is found by adding the shipping costs (in the body of Table 9.2) to the respective unit production costs (from Table 9.1). Thus, the total production plus shipping cost of one computer component from Cincinnati to Detroit is $73 ($25 for shipping plus $48 for production).

To determine which new plant (Seattle or Birmingham) shows the lowest total systemwide cost of distribution and production, we solve two transportation problems—one for each of the

TABLE 9.1

Hardgrave's Demand and Supply Data

WAREHOUSE	MONTHLY DEMAND (UNITS)	PRODUCTION PLANT	MONTHLY SUPPLY	COST TO PRODUCE ONE UNIT ($)
Detroit	10,000	Cincinnati	15,000	48
Dallas	12,000	Salt Lake City	6,000	50
New York	15,000	Pittsburgh	14,000	52
Los Angeles	9,000		35,000	
	46,000			

Supply needed from new plant = 46,000 − 35,000 = 11,000 units per month

ESTIMATED PRODUCTION COST PER UNIT AT PROPOSED PLANTS	
Seattle	$53
Birmingham	$49

TABLE 9.2

Hardgrave's Shipping Costs

FROM \ TO	DETROIT	DALLAS	NEW YORK	LOS ANGELES
CINCINNATI	$25	$55	$40	$60
SALT LAKE CITY	35	30	50	40
PITTSBURGH	36	45	26	66
SEATTLE	60	38	65	27
BIRMINGHAM	35	30	41	50

two possible combinations. The first linear program will be for the Seattle location, and the second will be for Birmingham. To evaluate the Seattle location, the variables are defined as follows:

$$X_{ij} = \text{number of units shipped from source } i \text{ to destination } j$$

where

$i = 1, 2, 3, 4$ with $1 = $ Cincinnati, $2 = $ Salt Lake City, $3 = $ Pittsburgh, and $4 = $ Seattle

$j = 1, 2, 3, 4$ with $1 = $ Detroit, $2 = $ Dallas, $3 = $ New York, and $4 = $ Los Angeles

The linear program formulation has an objective of minimizing the total cost—transportation cost plus production cost.

Minimize total cost = $73X_{11} + 103X_{12} + 88X_{13} + 108X_{14} + 85X_{21} + 80X_{22} + 100X_{23}$
$+ 90X_{24} + 88X_{31} + 97X_{32} + 78X_{33} + 118X_{34} + 113X_{41} + 91X_{42} + 118X_{43} + 80X_{44}$

subject to

$$X_{11} + X_{21} + X_{31} + X_{41} = 10,000 \quad \text{Detroit Demand}$$
$$X_{12} + X_{22} + X_{32} + X_{42} = 12,000 \quad \text{Dallas Demand}$$
$$X_{13} + X_{23} + X_{33} + X_{43} = 15,000 \quad \text{New York Demand}$$
$$X_{14} + X_{24} + X_{34} + X_{44} = 9,000 \quad \text{Los Angeles Demand}$$
$$X_{11} + X_{12} + X_{13} + X_{14} \leq 15,000 \quad \text{Cincinnati Supply}$$
$$X_{21} + X_{22} + X_{23} + X_{24} \leq 6,000 \quad \text{Salt Lake City Supply}$$
$$X_{31} + X_{32} + X_{33} + X_{34} \leq 14,000 \quad \text{Pittsburgh Supply}$$
$$X_{41} + X_{42} + X_{43} + X_{44} \leq 11,000 \quad \text{Seattle Supply}$$

All variables ≥ 0

When this is solved, the total cost with the Seattle location is found to be $3,704,000.

For the second transportation model, the linear program is modified and the Birmingham location replaces the Seattle location. Now in the linear program, $i = 4$ represents Birmingham instead of Seattle, the last constraint is for Birmingham instead of Seattle, and the costs for these four variables in the objective function are now 84 for X_{41}, 79 for X_{42}, 90 for X_{43}, and 99 for X_{44}. Nothing else in the problem changes. When this is solved, the total cost with the Birmingham location is $3,741,000. Thus, the Seattle location results in an overall lower cost and would be the preferred location based on cost.

Excel QM will be used for this example, and Program 9.2 provides the solution for the problem with the Seattle location. To enter the problem, click the *Excel QM* tab, select the *Alphabetical* Menu from the Excel QM ribbon, and when the menu appears, scroll down to select *Transportation*. An input window opens and you simply enter the number of Origins (sources), the number of Destinations, select *Minimize*, and click *OK*. A worksheet is then developed and you enter the numbers for the costs, the supplies, and the demands shown in the Data table in Program 9.2. Once all inputs have been entered, click the *Data* tab, select *Solver*, and click *Solve* from the Solver input window. No other input for Solver is necessary. The shipments for the optimal solution are shown in the Shipments table. Program 9.3 provides the Excel QM results for the Birmingham location.

PROGRAM 9.2

Facility Location (Seattle) Solution in Excel 2013 Using Excel QM

From Excel QM ribbon, select Menu (Alphabetical or By Chapter). Select Transportation from the drop-down menu, and then input 4 Origins (sources) and 4 Destination.

After entering the costs, click the Data tab and select Solver. Then click Solve.

COSTS	Detroit	Dallas	New York	Los Angeles	Supply
Cincinnati	73	103	88	108	15000
Salt Lake City	85	80	100	90	6000
Pittsburgh	88	97	78	118	14000
Seattle	113	91	118	80	11000
Demand	10000	12000	15000	9000	46000 \ 46000

Fill in the table with the costs, supplies, and demands.

Shipments	Detroit	Dallas	New York	Los Angeles	
Cincinnati	10000	4000	1000		
Salt Lake City		6000			6000
Pittsburgh			14000		14000
Seattle		2000		9000	11000
Column Total	10000	12000		9000	46000 \ 46000

The cost is here.

Total Cost	3704000

PROGRAM 9.3

Facility Location (Birmingham) Solution in Excel 2013 Using Excel QM

	A	B	C	D	E	F	G	H
1	Hardgrave Machine							
2								
3	Transportation							
4								
5	Enter the transportation data in the shaded area. Then go to the DATA Tab on the ribbon, click on Solver in the Data							
6	Analysis Group and then click SOLVE. If SOLVER is not on the Data Tab then please see the Help file (Solver) for instructions							
7								
8	Data							
9	COSTS	Detroit	Dallas	New York	Los Angeles	Supply		
10	Cincinnati	73	103	88	108	15000		
11	Salt Lake City	85	80	100	90	6000		
12	Pittsburgh	88	97	78	118	14000		
13	Birmingham	84	79	90	99	11000		
14	Demand	10000	12000	15000	9000	46000 \ 46000		
15								
16	Shipments							
17	Shipments	Detroit	Dallas	New York	Los Angeles	Row Total		
18	Cincinnati	10000		1000	4000	15000		
19	Salt Lake City		1000		5000	6000		
20	Pittsburgh			14000		14000		
21	Birmingham		11000			11000		
22	Column Total	10000	12000		9000	46000 \ 46000		
23								
24	Total Cost	3741000						

The cost is here.

9.3 The Assignment Problem

The **assignment problem** refers to the class of LP problem that involves determining the most efficient assignment of people to projects, sales people to territories, auditors to companies for audits, contracts to bidders, jobs to machines, heavy equipment (such as cranes) to construction jobs, and so on. The objective is most often to minimize total costs or total time of performing the tasks at hand. One important characteristic of assignment problems is that only one job or worker is assigned to one machine or project.

An assignment problem is equivalent to a transportation problem with each supply and demand equal to 1.

Figure 9.2 provides a network representation of an assignment problem. Notice that this network is very similar to the network for the transportation problem. In fact, an assignment problem may be viewed as a special type of transportation problem in which the supply at each source and the demand at each destination must equal one. Each person may only be assigned to one job or project, and each job only needs one person.

Linear Program for Assignment Example

The network in Figure 9.2 represents a problem faced by the Fix-It Shop, which has just received three new repair projects that must be completed quickly: (1) a radio, (2) a toaster oven, and (3) a coffee table. Three repair persons, each with different talents, are available to do the jobs. The shop owner estimates the cost in wages if the workers are assigned to each of the three projects. The costs differ due to the talents of each worker on each of the jobs. The owner wishes

FIGURE 9.2

Example of an Assignment Problem in a Transportation Network Format

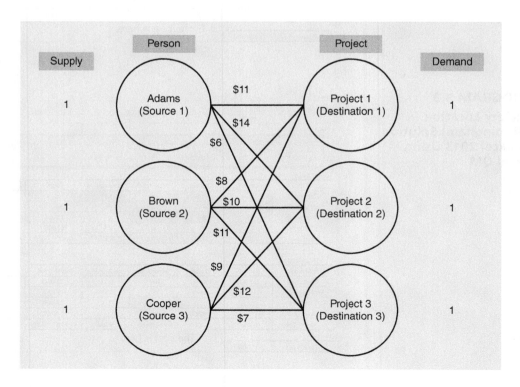

to assign the jobs so that total cost is minimized and each job must have one person assigned to it, and each person can only be assigned to one job.

In formulating this as a linear program, the general LP form of the transportation problem can be used. In defining the variables, let

Special variables 0-1 are used with the assignment model.

$$X_{ij} = \begin{cases} 1 \text{ if person } i \text{ is assigned to project } j \\ 0 \text{ otherwise} \end{cases}$$

where

$$i = 1, 2, 3, \text{ with } 1 = \text{Adams}, 2 = \text{Brown}, \text{ and } 3 = \text{Cooper}$$
$$j = 1, 2, 3, \text{ with } 1 = \text{Project 1}, 2 = \text{Project 2}, \text{ and } 3 = \text{Project 3}$$

The LP formulation is

$$\text{Minimize total cost} = 11X_{11} + 14X_{12} + 6X_{13} + 8X_{21} + 10X_{22}$$
$$+ 11X_{23} + 9X_{31} + 12X_{32} + 7X_{33}$$

subject to

$$X_{11} + X_{12} + X_{13} \leq 1$$
$$X_{21} + X_{22} + X_{23} \leq 1$$
$$X_{31} + X_{32} + X_{33} \leq 1$$
$$X_{11} + X_{21} + X_{31} = 1$$
$$X_{12} + X_{22} + X_{32} = 1$$
$$X_{13} + X_{23} + X_{33} = 1$$
$$x_{ij} = 0 \text{ or } 1 \text{ for all } i \text{ and } j$$

The solution is shown in Program 9.4. From this, $x_{13} = 1$, so Adams is assigned to project 3; $x_{22} = 1$, so Brown is assigned to project 2; and $x_{31} = 1$, so Cooper is assigned to project 1. All other variables are 0. The total cost is $25.

This problem could be input into Excel, Excel QM, or QM for Windows as a linear program, or it could be input as a transportation problem with all supplies and demands equal to 1. However, both Excel QM and QM for Windows have a module for this assignment problem. In Excel QM, from the *Alphabetical* Menu on the Excel QM ribbon, select *Assignment*. The initialization window opens and you enter the number of assignments and select *Minimization*. Click *OK* and a worksheet opens for you to enter the costs as shown in the data table in Program 9.4. Then select *Solver* from the *Data* ribbon, and click *Solve* in the Solver input window. The results are shown in Program 9.4.

PROGRAM 9.4

Mr. Fix-It Shop Assignment Solution in Excel 2013 Using Excel QM

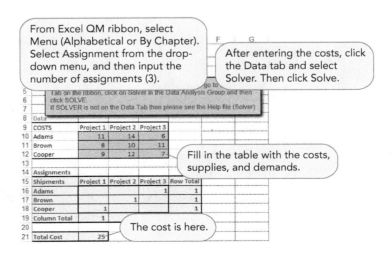

From Excel QM ribbon, select Menu (Alphabetical or By Chapter). Select Assignment from the drop-down menu, and then input the number of assignments (3).

After entering the costs, click the Data tab and select Solver. Then click Solve.

Fill in the table with the costs, supplies, and demands.

The cost is here.

	Project 1	Project 2	Project 3	Row Total
COSTS	Project 1	Project 2	Project 3	
Adams	11	14	6	
Brown	8	10	11	
Cooper	9	12	7	
Assignments				
Shipments	Project 1	Project 2	Project 3	Row Total
Adams			1	1
Brown		1		1
Cooper	1			1
Column Total	1			
Total Cost	25			

The software for the assignment problem assumes that the problem is balanced, which means that the number of sources (or people) is equal to the number of destinations (or jobs). If the problem is not balanced, a dummy source or a dummy destination is added to the problem to make it balanced. In some cases, more than one dummy source or destination is used. Because this dummy is not a real assignment and only indicates which source or destination will be lacking an assignment, all costs are zero. Solved Problem 9-2 at the end of the chapter will illustrate this.

In the assignment problem, the variables are required to be either 0 or 1. Due to the special structure of this problem with the constraint coefficients as 0 or 1 and all the right-hand-side values equal to 1, the problem can be solved as a linear program. The solution to such a problem (if one exists) will always have the variables equal to 0 or 1. There are other types of problems where the use of such 0–1 variables is desired, but the solution to such problems using normal linear programming methods will not necessarily have only zeros and ones. In such cases, special methods must be used to force the variables to be either 0 or 1, and this will be discussed as a special type of integer programming problem which will be seen in Chapter 10.

9.4   The Transshipment Problem

A transportation problem with intermediate points is a transshipment problem.

In a transportation problem, if the items being transported must go through an intermediate point (called a *transshipment point*) before reaching a final destination, the problem is called a *transshipment problem*. For example, a company might be manufacturing a product at several factories to be shipped to a set of regional distribution centers. From these centers, the items are shipped to retail outlets that are the final destinations. Figure 9.3 provides a network representation of a transshipment problem. In this example, there are two sources, two transshipment points, and three final destinations.

Linear Program for Transshipment Example

Frosty Machines manufactures snow blowers in factories located in Toronto and Detroit. These are shipped to regional distribution centers in Chicago and Buffalo, where they are delivered to the supply houses in New York, Philadelphia, and St. Louis, as illustrated in Figure 9.3.

The available supplies at the factories, the demands at the final destination, and shipping costs are shown in the Table 9.3. Notice that snow blowers may not be shipped directly from Toronto or Detroit to any of the final destinations but must first go to either Chicago or Buffalo. This is why Chicago and Buffalo are listed not only as destinations but also as sources.

Frosty would like to minimize the transportation costs associated with shipping sufficient snow blowers to meet the demands at the three destinations while not exceeding the supply at each factory. Thus, we have supply and demand constraints similar to the transportation problem, but we also have one constraint for each transshipment point indicating that anything

FIGURE 9.3

Network Representation of Transshipment Example

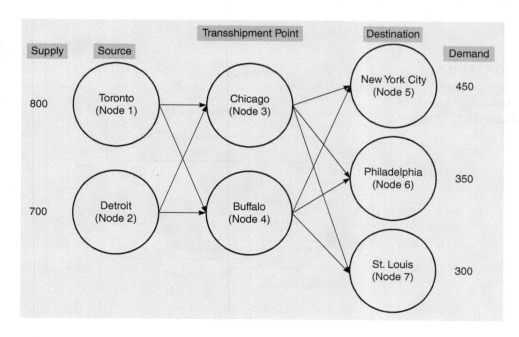

TABLE 9.3 Frosty Machine Transshipment Data

			TO			
FROM	CHICAGO	BUFFALO	NEW YORK CITY	PHILADELPHIA	ST. LOUIS	SUPPLY
Toronto	$4	$7	—	—	—	800
Detroit	$5	$7	—	—	—	700
Chicago	—	—	$6	$4	$5	—
Buffalo	—	—	$2	$3	$4	—
Demand	—	—	450	350	300	

shipped from these to a final destination must have been shipped into that transshipment point from one of the sources. The verbal statement of this problem would be as follows:

Minimize cost

subject to

1. The number of units shipped from Toronto is not more than 800
2. The number of units shipped from Detroit is not more than 700
3. The number of units shipped to New York is 450
4. The number of units shipped to Philadelphia is 350
5. The number of units shipped to St. Louis is 300
6. The number of units shipped out of Chicago is equal to the number of units shipped into Chicago
7. The number of units shipped out of Buffalo is equal to the number of units shipped into Buffalo

Special transshipment constraints are used in the linear program.

The decision variables should represent the number of units shipped from each source to each transshipment point and the number of units shipped from each transshipment point to each final destination, as these are the decisions management must make. The decision variables are

$$X_{ij} = \text{number of units shipped from location (node) } i \text{ to location (node) } j$$

where

$$i = 1, 2, 3, 4$$
$$j = 3, 4, 5, 6, 7$$

The numbers are the nodes shown in Figure 9.3, and there is one variable for each arc (route) in the figure.

The LP model is

$$\text{Minimize total cost} = 4X_{13} + 7X_{14} + 5X_{23} + 7X_{24} + 6X_{35} + 4X_{36} + 5X_{37} + 2X_{45} + 3X_{46} + 4X_{47}$$

subject to

$X_{13} + X_{14} \leq 800$	(Supply at Toronto [node 1])
$X_{23} + X_{24} \leq 700$	(Supply at Detroit [node 2])
$X_{35} + X_{45} = 450$	(Demand at New York City [node 5])
$X_{36} + X_{46} = 350$	(Demand at Philadelphia [node 6])
$X_{37} + X_{47} = 300$	(Demand at St. Louis [node 7])
$X_{13} + X_{23} = X_{35} + X_{36} + X_{37}$	(Shipping through Chicago [node 3])
$X_{14} + X_{24} = X_{45} + X_{46} + X_{47}$	(Shipping through Buffalo [node 4])

$$x_{ij} \geq 0 \text{ for all } i \text{ and } j$$

The solution found using Solver in Excel 2013 and Excel QM is shown in Program 9.5. The total cost is $9,550 by shipping 650 units from Toronto to Chicago, 150 units from Toronto to Buffalo, 300 units from Detroit to Buffalo, 350 units from Chicago to Philadelphia, 300 units from Chicago to St. Louis, and 450 units from Buffalo to New York City.

PROGRAM 9.5

Excel QM Solution to Frosty Machine Transshipment Problem in Excel 2013

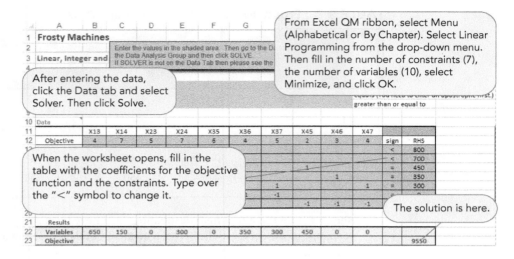

From Excel QM ribbon, select Menu (Alphabetical or By Chapter). Select Linear Programming from the drop-down menu. Then fill in the number of constraints (7), the number of variables (10), select Minimize, and click OK.

After entering the data, click the Data tab and select Solver. Then click Solve.

When the worksheet opens, fill in the table with the coefficients for the objective function and the constraints. Type over the "<" symbol to change it.

The solution is here.

	X13	X14	X23	X24	X35	X36	X37	X45	X46	X47	sign	RHS
Objective	4	7	5	7	6	4	5	2	3	4		
											<	800
											<	700
						1					=	450
							1				=	350
				1				1		1	=	300
		1	-1								=	
					-1	-1	-1					
Results												
Variables	650	150	0	300	0	350	300	450	0	0		
Objective												9550

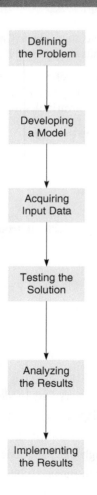

MODELING IN THE REAL WORLD Moving Sugar Cane in Cuba

Defining the Problem

The sugar market has been in a crisis for over a decade. Low sugar prices and decreasing demand have added to an already unstable market. Sugar producers needed to minimize costs. They targeted the largest unit cost in the manufacturing of raw sugar contributor—namely, sugar cane transportation costs.

Developing a Model

To solve this problem, researchers developed a linear program with some integer decision variables (e.g., number of trucks) and some continuous (linear) variables and linear decision variables (e.g., tons of sugar cane).

Acquiring Input Data

In developing the model, the inputs gathered were the operating demands of the sugar mills involved, the capacities of the intermediary storage facilities, the per-unit transportation costs per route, and the production capacities of the various sugar cane fields.

Testing the Solution

The researchers involved first tested a small version of their mathematical formulation using a spreadsheet. After noting encouraging results, they implemented the full version of their model on a large capacity computer. Results were obtained for this very large and complex model (on the order of 40,000 decision variables and 10,000 constraints) in just a few milliseconds.

Analyzing the Results

The solution obtained contained information on the quantity of cane delivered to each sugar mill, the field where cane should be collected, and the means of transportation (by truck, by train, etc.), and several other vital operational attributes.

Implementing the Results

While solving such large problems with some integer variables might have been impossible only a decade ago, solving these problems now is certainly possible. To implement these results, the researchers worked to develop a more user-friendly interface so that managers would have no problem using this model to help make decisions.

Source: Based on E. L. Milan, S. M. Fernandez, and L. M. Pla Aragones. "Sugar Cane Transportation in Cuba: A Case Study," *European Journal of Operational Research*, 174, 1 (2006): 374–386.

9.5 Maximal-Flow Problem

The **maximal-flow problem** involves determining the maximum amount of material that can flow from one point (the **source**) to another (the **sink**) in a network. Examples of this type of problem include determining the maximum number of cars that can flow through a highway system, the maximum amount of a liquid that can flow through a series of pipes, the maximum number of cell-phone calls that can pass through a series of cell towers, and the maximum amount of data that can flow through a computer network.

To find the maximal flow from the source or start of a network to the sink or finish of that network, two common methods are used: linear programming and the maximal-flow technique. We will begin by presenting an example and demonstrating the use of linear programming for this type of problem.

Example

Waukesha, a small town in Wisconsin, is in the process of developing a road system for the downtown area. Bill Blackstone, one of the city planners, would like to determine the maximum number of cars that can flow through the town from west to east. The road network is shown in Figure 9.4. The streets are indicated by their respective arcs. For example, the arc from node 1 to node 2 is arc 1–2. The arc in the reverse direction (from node 2 to node 1) is arc 2–1. The numbers by the nodes indicate the maximum number of cars (in hundreds of cars per hour) that can flow from the various nodes along the respective arcs. The maximum flow along arc 1–2 is 3, while the flow along arc 1–3 is 10. The city planners would like to know the capacity of the current road system in the west to east direction.

The maximal-flow problem can be modeled as a linear program. This type of problem may be viewed as a special type of transshipment problem with one source, one destination, and a number of transshipment points. The number shipped through the network would be called the flow. The objective is to maximize the flow through the network. There are two types of constraints. The first set of constraints restricts the amount of flow on any arc to the capacity of that arc. The second set of constraints indicates that the amount of flow out of a node will equal the amount of flow into that node. These are the same as the transshipment constraints in the transshipment problem.

The variables are defined as:

$$X_{ij} = \text{flow from node } i \text{ to node } j$$

One additional arc will be added to the network, and this arc will go from the sink (node 6) back to the source (node 1). The flow along this arc represents the total flow in the network. The first set of constraints in the linear program are the maximum flows along each arc in each direction. They are grouped together based on the node from which the flow originates. The last six

FIGURE 9.4

Road Network for Waukesha Maximal-Flow Example

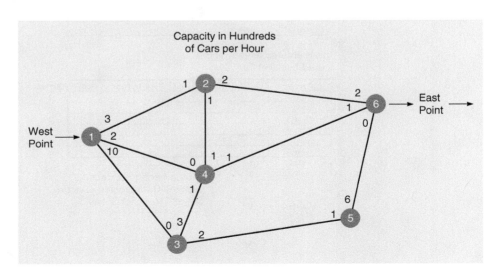

constraints are restricting the flow out of a node to equal the flow into a node (i.e., the flow into a node minus the flow out of that node must equal zero). The linear program is

Maximize flow $= X_{61}$

subject to

$X_{12} \le 3$	$X_{13} \le 10$	$X_{14} \le 2$	Capacities for arcs from node 1
$X_{21} \le 1$	$X_{24} \le 1$	$X_{26} \le 2$	Capacities for arcs from node 2
$X_{34} \le 3$	$X_{35} \le 2$		Capacities for arcs from node 3
$X_{42} \le 1$	$X_{43} \le 1$	$X_{46} \le 1$	Capacities for arcs from node 4
$X_{53} \le 1$	$X_{56} \le 1$		Capacities for arcs from node 5
$X_{62} \le 2$	$X_{64} \le 1$		Capacities for arcs from node 6

$$(X_{21} + X_{61}) - (X_{12} + X_{13} + X_{14}) = 0 \qquad \text{Flows into} = \text{flows out of node 1}$$
$$(X_{12} + X_{42} + X_{62}) - (X_{21} + X_{24} + X_{26}) = 0 \qquad \text{Flows into} = \text{flows out of node 2}$$
$$(X_{13} + X_{43} + X_{53}) - (X_{34} + X_{35}) = 0 \qquad \text{Flows into} = \text{flows out of node 3}$$
$$(X_{14} + X_{24} + X_{34} + X_{64}) - (X_{42} + X_{43} + X_{46}) = 0 \qquad \text{Flows into} = \text{flows out of node 4}$$
$$(X_{35}) - (X_{56} + X_{53}) = 0 \qquad \text{Flows into} = \text{flows out of node 5}$$
$$(X_{26} + X_{46} + X_{56}) - (X_{61} + X_{62} + X_{64}) = 0 \qquad \text{Flows into} = \text{flows out of node 6}$$
$$X_{ij} \ge 0$$

The problem is now ready to solve using the linear programming module QM for Windows or using Solver in Excel 2013. However, Program 9.6 illustrates the solution found using Excel QM. To obtain this, from the Excel QM ribbon, select *Network Analysis as LP* and then choose *Maximal Flow*. In the initialization window that opens, you enter the number of nodes (6) and click *OK*. A worksheet is developed as seen in Program 9.6. Enter the data for the arc capacities, and then click *Solver* from the *Data* ribbon. Click *Solve* from the Solver input window, and the results (flows) are put into the worksheet.

PROGRAM 9.6

Waukesha Maximal-Flow Solution in Excel 2013 Using Excel QM

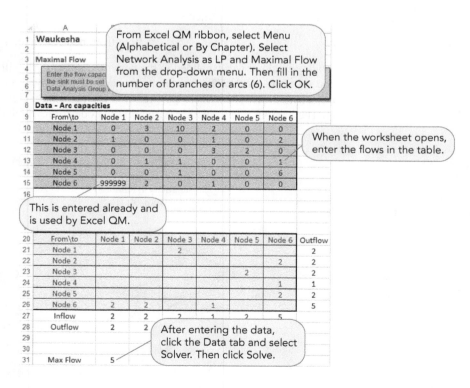

9.6 Shortest-Route Problem

The objective of the **shortest-route problem** is to find the shortest distance from one location to another. In a network, this often involves determining the shortest route from one node to each of the other nodes. This problem can be modeled as a linear program with 0–1 variables, or it could be modeled and solved using a specialized algorithm that is presented in Module 8. The following example is a typical shortest-route problem

Every day, Ray Design, Inc., must transport beds, chairs, and other furniture items from the factory to the warehouse. This involves going through several cities, and there are no direct interstate highways to make the delivery easier. Ray would like to find the route with the shortest distance. The road network is shown in Figure 9.5.

The shortest-route problem may be viewed as a special type of transshipment problem with one source having a supply of 1, one destination with a demand of 1, and a number of transshipment points. This type of problem can be modeled as a linear program with 0–1 variables. Ray is trying to decide which of the routes (arcs) to choose to be a part of the delivery system. Therefore, the decision variables will indicate whether a particular arc is chosen to be a part of the route taken. For the Ray Design, Inc., example, the objective is to minimize the total distance (cost) from the start to the finish. The constraints will specify that the number of units (either 0 or 1) going into a node must equal the number going out of that node. The variables are defined as

$$X_{ij} = 1 \text{ if arc from node } i \text{ to node } j \text{ is selected and } X_{ij} = 0 \text{ otherwise}$$

Since the starting point is node 1, we will not include variables going from node 2 or 3 back to node 1. Similarly, since node 6 is the final destination, we will not include any variable that starts at node 6. Viewing this as a transshipment problem, the origin node (node 1) must have one unit shipped out of it. This would be

$$X_{12} + X_{13} = 1$$

The final destination node (node 6) must have one unit shipped to it, and this is written as

$$X_{46} + X_{56} = 1$$

Each intermediate node will have a constraint requiring the amount coming into the node to equal the amount going out of that node (i.e., the flow into a node minus the flow out of a node must equal zero). For node 2 this would be

$$X_{12} + X_{32} = X_{23} + X_{24} + X_{25}$$

This simplifies to

$$X_{12} + X_{32} - X_{23} - X_{24} - X_{25} = 0$$

The other constraints would be constructed in a similar manner. The linear program is

Minimize distance $= 100X_{12} + 200X_{13} + 50X_{23} + 50X_{32} + 200X_{24} + 200X_{42} + 100X_{25}$
$+ 100X_{52} + 40X_{35} + 40X_{53} + 150X_{45} + 150X_{54} + 100X_{46} + 100X_{56}$

subject to

$$
\begin{array}{ll}
X_{12} + X_{13} = 1 & \text{Node 1} \\
X_{12} + X_{32} - X_{23} - X_{24} - X_{25} = 0 & \text{Node 2} \\
X_{13} + X_{23} - X_{32} - X_{35} = 0 & \text{Node 3} \\
X_{24} + X_{54} - X_{42} - X_{45} - X_{46} = 0 & \text{Node 4} \\
X_{25} + X_{35} + X_{45} - X_{52} - X_{53} - X_{54} - X_{56} = 0 & \text{Node 5} \\
X_{46} + X_{56} = 1 & \text{Node 6} \\
\text{All variables} = 0 \text{ or } 1
\end{array}
$$

FIGURE 9.5

Roads from Ray's Plant to Warehouse

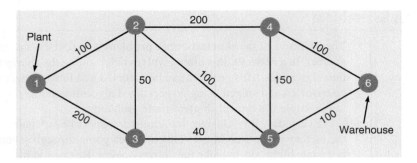

PROGRAM 9.7

Ray Designs, Inc. Solution in Excel 2013 Using Excel QM

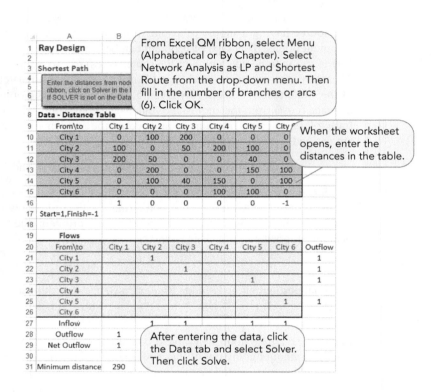

While this problem could be solved as a linear program, using Excel QM is the easiest to obtain the solutions. To solve a *shortest-route* problem, from the Excel QM ribbon select *Network Analysis as LP* and then choose *Shortest Path*. In the initialization window that opens, you enter the number of nodes (6) and click *OK*. A worksheet is developed as seen in Program 9.7. Enter the data for the distances, and then click *Solver* from the *Data* ribbon. Click *Solve* from the Solver input window, and the results (flows) are put into the worksheet. From Program 9.7 we see that

$$X_{12} = X_{23} = X_{35} = X_{56} = 1$$

So Ray will travel from city 1 to city 2, then to city 3, then to city 5, and from there to the final destination city 6. The total distance is 290 miles.

9.7 Minimal-Spanning Tree Problem

The **minimal-spanning tree problem** involves connecting all points of a network together while minimizing the total distance of these connections. Some common examples include telephone or cable companies trying to connect houses in a neighborhood, and network administrators trying to minimize the cable required to hard-wire computers in a network. While a linear programming model has been used for this, there are certain properties of this problem that make this quite complex. Fortunately, there is another method for finding the solution to such a problem that is very easy, and that will be presented here. The minimal-spanning tree technique problem will be presented using the following example.

Let us consider the Lauderdale Construction Company, which is currently developing a luxurious housing project in Panama City Beach, Florida. Melvin Lauderdale, owner and president of Lauderdale Construction, must determine the least expensive way to provide water and power to each house. The network of houses is shown in Figure 9.6.

As seen in Figure 9.6, there are eight houses on the gulf. The distance between each house in hundreds of feet is shown on the network. The distance between houses 1 and 2, for example, is 300 feet. (The number 3 is between nodes 1 and 2.) Now, the minimal-spanning tree technique is used to determine the minimal distance that can be used to connect all of the nodes. The approach is outlined as follows:

There are four steps for the minimal-spanning tree problem.

Steps for the Minimal-Spanning Tree Technique

1. Select any node in the network.
2. Connect this node to the nearest node that minimizes the total distance.
3. Considering all of the nodes that are now connected, find and connect the nearest node that is not connected. If there is a tie for the nearest node, select one arbitrarily. A tie suggests there may be more than one optimal solution.
4. Repeat the third step until all nodes are connected.

Step 1: We select node 1.
Step 2: We connect node 1 to node 3.

Now, we solve the network in Figure 9.6 for Melvin Lauderdale. We start by arbitrarily selecting node 1. Since the nearest node is the third node at a distance of 2 (200 feet), we connect node 1 to node 3. This is shown in Figure 9.7.

Considering nodes 1 and 3, we look for the next-nearest node. This is node 4, which is the closest to node 3. The distance is 2 (200 feet). Again, we connect these nodes (see Figure 9.8, part (a)).

We continue, looking for the nearest unconnected node to nodes 1, 3, and 4. This is node 2 or node 6, each at a distance of 3 from node 3. We will pick node 2 and connect it to node 3 (see Figure 9.8, part (b)).

FIGURE 9.6

Network for Lauderdale Construction

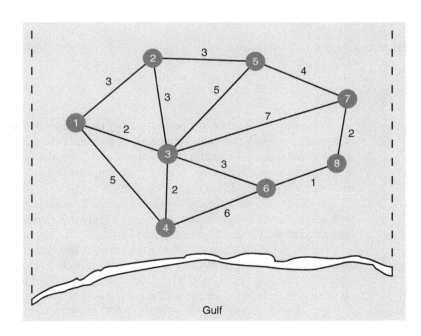

FIGURE 9.7
First Iteration for
Lauderdale Construction

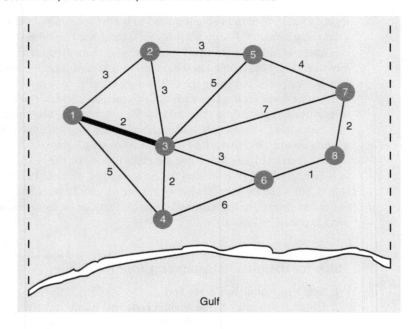

FIGURE 9.8   Second and Third Iterations

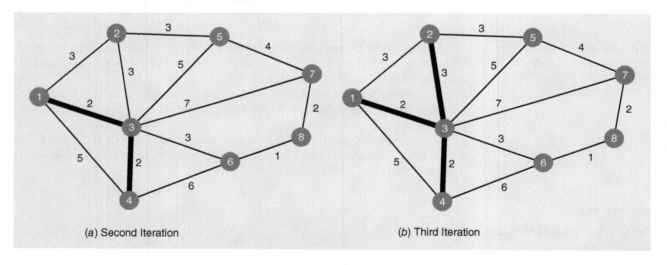

(a) Second Iteration   (b) Third Iteration

Step 3: We connect the next nearest node.

Step 4: We repeat the process.

We continue the process. There is another tie for the next iteration with a minimum distance of 3 (node 2–node 5 and node 3–node 6). You should note that we do not consider node 1–node 2 with a distance of 3 because both nodes 1 and 2 are already connected. We arbitrarily select node 5 and connect it to node 2 (see Figure 9.9, part (a)). The next nearest node is node 6, and we connect it to node 3 (see Figure 9.9, part (b)).

At this stage, we have only two unconnected nodes left. Node 8 is the nearest to node 6, with a distance of 1 and we connect it (see Figure 9.9, part (c)). Then the remaining node 7 is connected to node 8 (see Figure 9.9, part (d)).

The final solution can be seen in the seventh and final iteration. Nodes 1, 2, 4, and 6 are all connected to node 3. Node 2 is connected to node 5. Node 6 is connected to node 8, and node 8 is connected to node 7. All of the nodes are now connected. The total distance is found by adding the distances for the arcs used in the spanning tree. In this example, the distance is $2 + 2 + 3 + 3 + 3 + 1 + 2 = 16$ (or 1,600 feet). This is summarized in Table 9.4.

FIGURE 9.9 Last Four Iterations for Lauderdale Construction

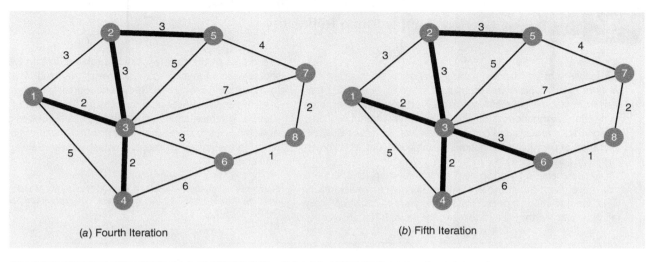

(a) Fourth Iteration   (b) Fifth Iteration

(c) Sixth Iteration   (d) Seventh Iteration

The minimal-spanning tree problem can be solved with Excel QM or QM for Windows. Using Excel QM in Excel 2013, select *Alphabetical* Menu from the ribbon, scroll down to *Network Analysis*, and select *Minimal Spanning Tree*. In the spreadsheet initialization window that opens, enter the number of branches or arcs (13 in this example). When the worksheet opens, for each

TABLE 9.4 Summary of Steps in Lauderdale Construction Minimal-Spanning Tree Problem

STEP	CONNECTED NODES	UNCONNECTED NODES	CLOSEST UNCONNECTED NODE	ARC SELECTED	ARC LENGTH	TOTAL DISTANCE
1	1	2, 3, 4, 5, 6, 7, 8	3	1–3	2	2
2	1, 3	2, 4, 5, 6, 7, 8	4	3–4	2	4
3	1, 3, 4	2, 5, 6, 7, 8	2 or 6	3–2	3	7
4	1, 2, 3, 4	5, 6, 7, 8	5 or 6	2–5	3	10
5	1, 2, 3, 4, 5	6, 7, 8	6	3–6	3	13
6	1, 2, 3, 4, 5, 6	7, 8	8	6–8	1	14
7	1, 2, 3, 4, 5, 6, 8	7	7	8–7	2	16

IN ACTION Facility Location Leads to Improved Supply-Chain Reliability

Supply chains are, at their physical level, an interconnected network of delivery routes (roads, bridges, shipping lanes, etc.) that lead from multiple sources (warehouse, factories, refineries, etc.) to multiple destinations (stores, outlets, other warehouses, etc.) along which products and commodities travel. In most cases, the allocation of particular destinations to particular sources is known and fairly constant.

Researchers, in trying to help companies plan for emergencies, have investigated the problem of supply-chain disruption. What would happen if one of the sources were to catastrophically fail due to an earthquake, a tornado, or worse? The answer lies

in the area of the facility location problem: Which warehouses should deliver to which stores addresses this issue. Analyzing the transportation problem with current sources eliminated one by one, the analysts were able to measure the impact of such disruption. The researchers concluded that "backup assignments" of warehouses to stores should be planned ahead of time to help mitigate the impact of possible catastrophes. It always pays to plan ahead!

Source: Based on L. Snyder and M. Daskin. "Reliability Models for Facility Location: The Expected Failure Cost Case," *Transportation Science* 39, 3 (2005): 400–416.

PROGRAM 9.8

Lauderdale Construction Minimal-Spanning Tree Example

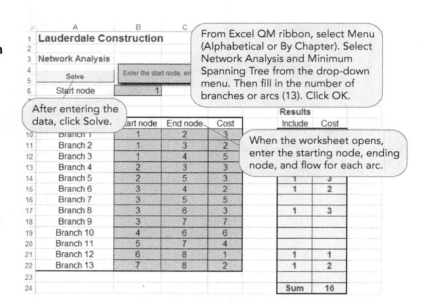

arc enter the beginning node, the ending node, and the distance between the two (i.e., the length of the arc) as shown in Program 9.8. Click the *Solve* button that appears in the spreadsheet, and the solution will be displayed as in Program 9.8. The problem could also be solved in QM for Windows by selecting the networks module and entering a new problem as a minimal-spanning tree. The input is very similar to the Excel QM input.

Summary

In this chapter we explored several problems that are commonly modeled as networks, with nodes and arcs representing a variety of situations. These problems were the transportation, assignment, transshipment, maximal-flow, shortest-route, and minimal-spanning tree problems. Linear programming models

were developed for all but the minimal-spanning tree, highlighting the fact that linear programming can be beneficial in many different areas. Computer software that takes advantage of the special structure of these problems can help solve large network problems very efficiently.

Glossary

Arc A line in a network that may represent a path or route. An arc or branch is used to connect the nodes in a network.

Assignment Problem A special type of network problem in which costs are minimized while assigning people to jobs (or other such assignments) on a one-to-one basis.

Destination A demand location in a transportation problem.

Facility Location Analysis An application of the transportation method to help a firm decide where to locate a new factory, warehouse, or other facility.

Maximal-Flow Problem A network problem with the objective of determining the maximum amount that may flow from the origin or source to the final destination or sink.

Minimal-Spanning Tree Problem A network problem with the objective of minimizing the total distance or cost required to connect all the nodes in the network.

Node A point in a network, often represented by a circle, that is at the beginning or end of an arc.

Shortest-Route Problem A network problem with the objective of finding the shortest distance from one location to another while passing through intermediate nodes.

Sink The final node or destination in a network.

Source An origin or supply location in a transportation problem. Also, the origin or beginning node in a maximal-flow network.

Transportation Problem A specific case of LP concerned with scheduling shipments from sources to destinations so that total transportation costs are minimized.

Solved Problems

Solved Problem 9-1

Don Yale, president of Hardrock Concrete Company, has plants in three locations and is currently working on three major construction projects, located at different sites. The shipping cost per truckload of concrete, plant capacities, and project requirements are provided in the accompanying table.

Formulate Hardrock's transportation problem as a linear program and solve using software.

FROM \ TO	PROJECT A	PROJECT B	PROJECT C	PLANT CAPACITIES
PLANT 1	$10	$4	$11	70
PLANT 2	$12	$5	$8	50
PLANT 3	$9	$7	$6	30
PROJECT REQUIREMENTS	40	50	60	150

Solution

Define the variables as

$$X_{ij} = \text{number of units shipped from Plant } i \text{ to Project } j$$

where

$i = 1, 2, 3$ with $1 = $ Plant 1, $2 = $ Plant 2, and $3 = $ Plant 3

$j = 1, 2, 3$ with $1 = $ Project A, $2 = $ Project B, and $3 = $ Project C

The linear program formulation is

Minimize total cost $= 10X_{11} + 4X_{12} + 11X_{13} + 12X_{21} + 5X_{22} + 8X_{23} + 9X_{31} + 7X_{32} + 6X_{33}$

subject to

$X_{11} + X_{21} + X_{31} = 40$ Project A requirements

$X_{12} + X_{22} + X_{32} = 50$ Project B requirements

$X_{13} + X_{23} + X_{33} = 60$ Project C requirements

$X_{11} + X_{12} + X_{13} \leq 70$ Plant 1 capacity

$X_{21} + X_{22} + X_{23} \leq 50$ Plant 2 capacity

$X_{31} + X_{32} + X_{33} \leq 30$ Plant 3 capacity

All variables ≥ 0

The computer output found using Excel QM gives the optimal solution. From Plant 1 Ship 20 units to Project A and 50 units to Project B. From Plant 2 Ship 50 units to Project C. From Plant 3 Ship 20 units to Project A and 10 units to Project B. The total cost of this solution is $1,040. While not shown in the computer output, there are alternate optimal solutions to this problem.

**Program for
Solved Problem 9-1**

	A	B	C	D	E	F	G	H
1	Solved Problem 9-1							
2								
3	Transportation							
4	Enter the transportation data in the shaded area. Then go to the DATA Tab on the ribbon, click on Solver							
5	in the Data Analysis Group and then click SOLVE.							
6	If SOLVER is not on the Data Tab then please see the Help file (Solver) for instructions.							
7								
8	Data							
9	COSTS	Project 1	Project 2	Project 3	Supply			
10	Plant 1	10	4	11	70			
11	Plant 2	12	5	8	50			
12	Plant 3	9	7	6	30			
13	Demand	40	50	60	150 \ 150			
14								
15	Shipments							
16	Shipments	Project 1	Project 2	Project 3	Row Total			
17	Plant 1	20	50		70			
18	Plant 2			50	50			
19	Plant 3	20		10	30			
20	Column Total	40	50	60	150 \ 150			
21								
22	Total Cost	1040						

Solved Problem 9-2

Prentice Hall, Inc., a publisher headquartered in New Jersey, wants to assign three recently hired college graduates, Jones, Smith, and Wilson to regional sales districts in Omaha, Dallas, and Miami. But the firm also has an opening in New York and would send one of the three there if it were more economical than a move to Omaha, Dallas, or Miami. It will cost $1,000 to relocate Jones to New York, $800 to relocate Smith there, and $1,500 to move Wilson. What is the optimal assignment of personnel to offices?

HIREE \ OFFICE	OMAHA	MIAMI	DALLAS
JONES	$800	$1,100	$1,200
SMITH	$500	$1,600	$1,300
WILSON	$500	$1,000	$2,300

Because there are three new hires and four offices when New York is included, the problem is not balanced. It is impossible for all four cities to have a person assigned (i.e., there is no feasible solution). Therefore, a dummy source (new hire) is added, and the costs are zero for this dummy. Thus, the variables could be omitted from the objective function, but they are included for the sake of completeness.

Define the variables as

X_{ij} = 1 if new hire i is assigned to office j

where

i = 1, 2, 3, 4 with 1 = Jones, 2 = Smith, 3 = Wilson, and 4 = Dummy hire

j = 1, 2, 3, 4 with 1 = Omaha, 2 = Miami, 3 = Dallas, and 4 = New York

The linear program formulation is

$$\text{Minimize total cost} = 800X_{11} + 1100X_{12} + 1200X_{13} + 1000X_{14} + 500X_{21} + 1600X_{22} + 1300X_{23} + 800X_{24} + 500X_{31} + 1000X_{32} + 2300X_{33} + 1500X_{34} + 0X_{41} + 0X_{42} + 0X_{43} + 0X_{44}$$

subject to

$$X_{11} + X_{21} + X_{31} + X_{41} \leq 1 \quad \text{Omaha Office}$$
$$X_{12} + X_{22} + X_{32} + X_{42} \leq 1 \quad \text{Miami Office}$$
$$X_{13} + X_{23} + X_{33} + X_{43} \leq 1 \quad \text{Dallas Office}$$
$$X_{14} + X_{24} + X_{34} + X_{44} \leq 1 \quad \text{New York Office}$$
$$X_{11} + X_{12} + X_{13} + X_{14} = 1 \quad \text{Jones}$$
$$X_{21} + X_{22} + X_{23} + X_{24} = 1 \quad \text{Smith}$$
$$X_{31} + X_{32} + X_{33} + X_{34} = 1 \quad \text{Wilson}$$
$$X_{41} + X_{42} + X_{43} + X_{44} = 1 \quad \text{Dummy hire}$$
$$\text{All variables} \geq 0$$

The solution found using Excel QM is shown below, and it provides the optimal solution: Jones is assigned to Miami ($X_{12} = 1$), Smith is assigned to New York ($X_{24} = 1$), Wilson is assigned to Omaha ($X_{31} = 1$), and no one (the dummy) is assigned to Dallas ($X_{43} = 1$). The total cost is $2,400.

Program for Solved Problem 9-2

	A	B	C	D	E	F	G
1	Solved Problem 9-2						
2							
3	Assignment						
4	Enter the assignment costs in the shaded area. Then go to the DATA Tab on the						
5	ribbon, click on Solver in the Data Analysis Group and then click SOLVE.						
6	If SOLVER is not on the Data Tab then please see the Help file (Solver) for						
7	instructions						
8	Data						
9	COSTS	Omaha	Miami	Dallas	NY		
10	Jones	800	1100	1200	1000		
11	Smith	500	1600	1300	800		
12	Wilson	500	1000	2300	1500		
13	Dummy	0	0	0	0		
14							
15	Assignments						
16	Shipments	Omaha	Miami	Dallas	NY	Row Total	
17	Jones		1			1	
18	Smith				1	1	
19	Wilson	1				1	
20	Dummy			1		1	
21	Column Total	1	1	1	1	4	
22							
23	Total Cost	2400					

Self-Test

- Before taking the self-test, refer to the learning objectives at the beginning of the chapter, the notes in the margins, and the glossary at the end of the chapter.
- Use the key at the back of the book to correct your answers.
- Restudy pages that correspond to any questions that you answered incorrectly or material you feel uncertain about.

1. If a transportation problem has 4 sources and 5 destinations, the linear program for this will have
   a. 4 variables and 5 constraints.
   b. 5 variable and 4 constraints.
   c. 9 variables and 20 constraints.
   d. 20 variables and 9 constraints.

2. An assignment problem may be viewed as a transportation problem with
   a. a cost of $1 for all shipping routes.
   b. all supplies and demands equal to 1.
   c. only demand constraints.
   d. only supply constraints.

3. A company is considering opening one new production facility, and three locations are being considered. For this facility location problem, how many transportation models must be developed and solved?
   a. 1
   b. 2
   c. 3
   d. 4

4. Four cranes are being assigned to five construction jobs. One of the jobs will be delayed until one of the cranes becomes available after finishing the first job. An assignment model will be used. To allow specialized software to find a solution to this problem,
   a. nothing special must be done to this problem.
   b. one dummy crane must be used in the model.
   c. one dummy job must be used in the model.
   d. both a dummy job and a dummy crane must be used in the model.

5. Which network model is used to determine how to connect all points of a network together while minimizing the total distance between them?
   a. The assignment model.
   b. The maximal-flow model.
   c. The shortest-route model.
   d. The minimal-spanning tree model.

6. In a typical shortest-route model, the objective is to
   a. minimize the number of nodes in the route.
   b. minimize the time or distance to get from one point to another.
   c. minimize the number of arcs in the route.
   d. travel through all nodes in the best way possible.

7. A large city is planning for the Olympic Games which will be coming in a few years. The transportation system is being evaluated to determine what expansion is needed to handle the large number of visitors to the games. Which of the following models would most likely help the city planners determine the capacity of the current system?
   a. The transportation model.
   b. The maximal-flow model.
   c. The shortest-route model.
   d. The minimal-spanning tree model.

8. The computing center of a large university is installing fiber-optic cables to fifteen building on campus. Which of the following models could be used to determine the least amount of cable required to connect all the buildings?
   a. The transportation model.
   b. The maximal-flow model.
   c. The shortest-route model.
   d. The minimal-spanning tree model.

Discussion Questions and Problems

Discussion Questions

9-1 Is the transportation model an example of decision making under certainty or decision making under uncertainty? Why?

9-2 Explain how to determine the number of variables and constraints that would be in a transportation problem simply by knowing the number of sources and the number of destinations.

9-3 Explain what it means for an assignment model to be balanced.

9-4 Explain the purpose of the transshipment constraints in the linear program for a transshipment model.

9-5 Describe a problem that can be solved by using the shortest-route model.

9-6 Explain how the maximal-flow model might be viewed as a transshipment model.

Problems*

9-7 The management of the Executive Furniture Corporation decided to expand the production capacity at its Des Moines factory and to cut back production at its other factories. It also recognizes a shifting market for its desks and revises the requirements at its three warehouses.

The table below provides the requirements at each of the warehouses, the capacities at each of the factories, and the shipping cost per unit to ship from each factory to each warehouse. Find the least cost way to meet the requirements given the capacity at each factory.

9-8 The Hardrock Concrete Company has plants in three locations and is currently working on three major construction projects, each located at a different site. The shipping cost per truckload of concrete, daily

FROM \ TO	ALBUQUERQUE	BOSTON	CLEVELAND	CAPACITY
DES MOINES	$5	$4	$3	300
EVANSVILLE	8	4	3	150
FORT LAUDERDALE	9	7	5	250
REQUIREMENTS	200	200	300	

plant capacities, and daily project requirements are provided in the table below.

Formulate this as a linear program to determine the least cost way to meet the requirements. Solve using any computer software.

9-9 Hardrock Concrete's owner has decided to increase the capacity at his smallest plant (see Problem 9-8). Instead of producing 30 loads of concrete per day at plant 3, that plant's capacity is doubled to 60 loads. Does this change the schedule developed previously?

9-10 The Saussy Lumber Company ships pine flooring to three building supply houses from its mills in Pineville, Oak Ridge, and Mapletown. Determine the best transportation schedule for the data given in the table below.

9-11 The Krampf Lines Railway Company specializes in coal handling. On Friday, April 13, Krampf had empty cars at the following towns in the quantities indicated:

TOWN	SUPPLY OF CARS
Morgantown	35
Youngstown	60
Pittsburgh	25

By Monday, April 16, the following towns will need coal cars as follows:

TOWN	DEMAND FOR CARS
Coal Valley	30
Coaltown	45
Coal Junction	25
Coalsburg	20

Using a railway city-to-city distance chart, the dispatcher constructs a mileage table for the preceding towns. The result is shown in the table below. Minimizing total miles over which cars are moved to new locations, compute the best shipment of coal cars.

9-12 An air conditioning manufacturer produces room air conditioners at plants in Houston, Phoenix, and Memphis. These are sent to regional distributors in Dallas, Atlanta, and Denver. The shipping costs vary, and the company would like to find the least-cost way to meet the demands at each of the distribution centers. Dallas needs to receive 800 air conditioners per month, Atlanta needs 600, and Denver needs 200. Houston has 850 air conditioners available each month, Phoenix has 650, and Memphis has 300. The

Table for Problem 9-8

FROM \ TO	PROJECT A	PROJECT B	PROJECT C	CAPACITY
PLANT 1	$10	$4	$11	70
PLANT 2	12	5	8	50
PLANT 3	9	7	6	30
REQUIREMENTS	40	50	60	

Table for Problem 9-10

FROM \ TO	SUPPLY HOUSE 1	SUPPLY HOUSE 2	SUPPLY HOUSE 3	MILL CAPACITY (TONS)
PINEVILLE	$3	$3	$2	25
OAK RIDGE	4	2	3	40
MAPLETOWN	3	2	3	30
SUPPLY HOUSE DEMAND	30	30	35	

Table for Problem 9-11

FROM \ TO	COAL VALLEY	COALTOWN	COAL JUNCTION	COALSBURG
MORGANTOWN	50	30	60	70
YOUNGSTOWN	20	80	10	90
PITTSBURGH	100	40	80	30

shipping cost per unit from Houston to Dallas is $8, to Atlanta is $12, and to Denver is $10. The cost per unit from Phoenix to Dallas is $10, to Atlanta is $14, and to Denver is $9. The cost per unit from Memphis to Dallas is $11, to Atlanta is $8, and to Denver is $12. How many units should be shipped from each plant to each regional distribution center? What is the total cost for this?

: 9-13 Finnish Furniture manufactures tables in facilities located in three cities—Reno, Denver, and Pittsburgh. The tables are then shipped to three retail stores located in Phoenix, Cleveland, and Chicago. Management wishes to develop a distribution schedule that will meet the demands at the lowest possible cost. The shipping cost per unit from each of the sources to each of the destinations is shown in the following table:

TO / FROM	PHOENIX	CLEVELAND	CHICAGO
RENO	10	16	19
DENVER	12	14	13
PITTSBURGH	18	12	12

The available supplies are 120 units from Reno, 200 from Denver, and 160 from Pittsburgh. Phoenix has a demand of 140 units, Cleveland has a demand of 160 units, and Chicago has a demand of 180 units. How many units should be shipped from each manufacturing facility to each of the retail stores if cost is to be minimized? What is the total cost?

: 9-14 The state of Missouri has three major power-generating companies (A, B, and C). During the months of peak demand, the Missouri Power Authority authorizes these companies to pool their excess supply and to distribute it to smaller independent power companies that do not have generators large enough to handle the demand. Excess supply is distributed on the basis of cost per kilowatt hour transmitted. The following table shows the demand and supply in millions of kilowatt hours and the cost per kilowatt hour of transmitting electric power to four small companies in cities W, X, Y, and Z:

TO / FROM	W	X	Y	Z	EXCESS SUPPLY
A	12¢	4¢	9¢	5¢	55
B	8¢	1¢	6¢	6¢	45
C	1¢	12¢	4¢	7¢	30
UNFILLED POWER DEMAND	40	20	50	20	

Find the least-cost distribution system.

: 9-15 The three blood banks in Franklin County are coordinated through a central office that facilitates blood delivery to four hospitals in the region. The cost to ship a standard container of blood from each bank to each hospital is shown in the table below. Also given are the biweekly number of containers available at each bank and the biweekly number of containers of blood needed at each hospital. How many shipments should be made biweekly from each blood bank to each hospital so that total shipment costs are minimized?

: 9-16 The B. Hall Real Estate Investment Corporation has identified four small apartment buildings in which it would like to invest. Mrs. Hall has approached three savings and loan companies regarding financing.

Table for Problem 9-15

TO / FROM	HOSPITAL 1	HOSPITAL 2	HOSPITAL 3	HOSPITAL 4	SUPPLY
BANK 1	$8	$9	$11	$16	50
BANK 2	12	7	5	8	80
BANK 3	14	10	6	7	120
DEMAND	90	70	40	50	

Table for Problem 9-16

SAVINGS AND LOAN COMPANY	PROPERTY (INTEREST RATES) (%)				MAXIMUM CREDIT LINE ($)
	HILL ST.	BANKS ST.	PARK AVE.	DRURY LANE	
FIRST HOMESTEAD	8	8	10	11	80,000
COMMONWEALTH	9	10	12	10	100,000
WASHINGTON FEDERAL	9	11	10	9	120,000
LOAN REQUIRED TO PURCHASE BUILDING	$60,000	$40,000	$130,000	$70,000	

Because Hall has been a good client in the past and has maintained a high credit rating in the community, each savings and loan company is willing to consider providing all or part of the mortgage loan needed on each property. Each loan officer has set differing interest rates on each property (rates are affected by the neighborhood of the apartment building, condition of the property, and desire by the individual savings and loan to finance various-size buildings), *and* each loan company has placed a maximum credit ceiling on how much it will lend Hall in total. This information is summarized in the table on the previous page.

Each apartment building is equally attractive as an investment to Hall, so she has decided to purchase all buildings possible at the lowest total payment of interest. From which savings and loan companies should she borrow to purchase which buildings? More than one savings and loan can finance the same property.

9-17 The J. Mehta Company's production manager is planning for a series of 1-month production periods for stainless steel sinks. The demand for the next 4 months is as follows:

MONTH	DEMAND FOR STAINLESS STEEL SINKS
1	120
2	160
3	240
4	100

The Mehta firm can normally produce 100 stainless steel sinks in a month. This is done during regular production hours at a cost of $100 per sink. If demand in any 1 month cannot be satisfied by regular production, the production manager has three other choices: (1) He can produce up to 50 more sinks per month in overtime but at a cost of $130 per sink; (2) he can purchase a limited number of sinks from a friendly competitor for resale (the maximum number of outside purchases over the 4-month period is 450 sinks, at a cost of $150 each); or (3) he can fill the demand from his on-hand inventory. The inventory carrying cost is $10 per sink per month. Back orders are not permitted. Inventory on hand at the beginning of month 1 is 40 sinks. Set up this "production smoothing" problem as a transportation problem to minimize cost.

9-18 Ashley's Auto Top Carriers currently maintains plants in Atlanta and Tulsa that supply major distribution centers in Los Angeles and New York. Because of an expanding demand, Ashley has decided to open a third plant and has narrowed the choice to one of two cities—New Orleans or Houston. The pertinent production and distribution costs, as well as the plant capacities and distribution demands, are shown in the table below.

Which of the new possible plants should be opened?

9-19 Marc Smith, vice president for operations of HHN, Inc., a manufacturer of cabinets for telephone switches, is constrained from meeting the 5-year forecast by limited capacity at the existing three plants. These three plants are Waterloo, Pusan, and Bogota. You, as his able assistant, have been told that because of existing capacity constraints and the expanding world market for HHN cabinets, a new plant is to be added to the existing three plants. The real estate department has advised Marc that two sites seem particularly good because of a stable political situation and tolerable exchange rate: Dublin, Ireland, and Fontainebleau, France. Marc suggests that you should be able to take the data on the next page and determine where the fourth plant should be

Data for Problem 9-18

FROM PLANTS \ TO DISTRIBUTION CENTERS	LOS ANGELES	NEW YORK	NORMAL PRODUCTION	UNIT PRODUCTION COST ($)
ATLANTA	$8	$5	600	6
TULSA	4	7	900	5
NEW ORLEANS	5	6	500	4 (anticipated)
HOUSTON	4	6	500	3 (anticipated)
FORECAST DEMAND	800	1,200	2,000	

Indicates distribution cost (shipping, handling, storage) will be $6 per carrier if sent from Houston to New York

Data for Problem 9-19

	PLANT LOCATION				
MARKET AREA	WATERLOO	PUSAN	BOGOTA	FONTAINEBLEAU	DUBLIN
Canada					
Demand 4,000					
Production cost	$50	$30	$40	$50	$45
Transportation cost	10	25	20	25	25
South America					
Demand 5,000					
Production cost	50	30	40	50	45
Transportation cost	20	25	10	30	30
Pacific Rim					
Demand 10,000					
Production cost	50	30	40	50	45
Transportation cost	25	10	25	40	40
Europe					
Demand 5,000					
Production cost	50	30	40	50	45
Transportation cost	25	40	30	10	20
Capacity	8,000	2,000	5,000	9,000	9,000

located on the basis of production costs and transportation costs. Which location is better?

9-20 Don Levine Corporation is considering adding an additional plant to its three existing facilities in Decatur, Minneapolis, and Carbondale. Both St. Louis and East St. Louis are being considered. Evaluating only the transportation costs per unit as shown in the tables below, which site is best?

	FROM EXISTING PLANTS			
TO	DECATUR	MINNEAPOLIS	CARBONDALE	DEMAND
Blue Earth	$20	$17	$21	250
Ciro	25	27	20	200
Des Moines	22	25	22	350
Capacity	300	200	150	

	FROM PROPOSED PLANTS	
TO	EAST ST. LOUIS	ST. LOUIS
Blue Earth	$29	$27
Ciro	30	28
Des Moines	30	31
Capacity	150	150

9-21 Using the data from Problem 9-20 plus the unit production costs shown in the following table, which locations yield the lowest cost?

LOCATION	PRODUCTION COSTS
Decatur	$50
Minneapolis	60
Carbondale	70
East St. Louis	40
St. Louis	50

9-22 In a job shop operation, four jobs may be performed on any of four machines. The hours required for each job on each machine are presented in the following table. The plant supervisor would like to assign jobs so that total time is minimized. Find the best solution. Which assignments should be made?

	MACHINE			
JOB	W	X	Y	Z
A12	10	14	16	13
A15	12	13	15	12
B2	9	12	12	11
B9	14	16	18	16

:9-23 Four automobiles have entered Bubba's Repair Shop for various types of work, ranging from a transmission overhaul to a brake job. The experience level of the mechanics is quite varied, and Bubba would like to minimize the time required to complete all of the jobs. He has estimated the time in minutes for each mechanic to complete each job. Billy can complete job 1 in 400 minutes, job 2 in 90 minutes, job 3 in 60 minutes, and job 4 in 120 minutes. Taylor will finish job 1 in 650 minutes, job 2 in 120 minutes, job 3 in 90 minutes, and job 4 in 180 minutes. Mark will finish job 1 in 480 minutes, job 2 in 120 minutes, job 3 in 80 minutes, and job 4 in 180 minutes. John will complete job 1 in 500 minutes, job 2 in 110 minutes, job 3 in 90 minutes, and job 4 in 150 minutes. Each mechanic should be assigned to just one of these jobs. What is the minimum total time required to finish the four jobs? Who should be assigned to each job?

:9-24 Baseball umpiring crews are currently in four cities where three-game series are beginning. When these are finished, the crews are needed to work games in four different cities. The distances (miles) from each of the cities where the crews are currently working to the cities where the new games will begin are shown in the following table:

	TO			
FROM	**KANSAS CITY**	**CHICAGO**	**DETROIT**	**TORONTO**
Seattle	1,500	1,730	1,940	2,070
Arlington	460	810	1,020	1,270
Oakland	1,500	1,850	2,080	X
Baltimore	960	610	400	330

The X indicates that the crew in Oakland cannot be sent to Toronto. Determine which crew should be sent to each city to minimize the total distance traveled. How many miles will be traveled if these assignments are made?

:9-25 In Problem 9-24, the minimum travel distance was found. To see how much better this solution is than the assignments that might have been made, find the assignments that would give the maximum distance traveled. Compare this total distance with the distance found in Problem 9-24.

:9-26 Roscoe Davis, chairman of a college's business department, has decided to apply a new method in assigning professors to courses next semester. As a criterion for judging who should teach each course, Professor Davis reviews the past two years' teaching evaluations (which were filled out by students). Since each of the four professors taught each of the four courses at one time or another during the two-year period, Davis is able to record a course rating for each instructor. These ratings are shown in the table at top of next column. Find the best assignment of professors to courses to maximize the overall teaching rating.

	COURSE			
PROFESSOR	**STATISTICS**	**MANAGEMENT**	**FINANCE**	**ECONOMICS**
Anderson	90	65	95	40
Sweeney	70	60	80	75
Williams	85	40	80	60
McKinney	55	80	65	55

:9-27 The hospital administrator at St. Charles General must appoint head nurses to four newly established departments: urology, cardiology, orthopedics, and obstetrics. In anticipation of this staffing problem, she had hired four nurses: Hawkins, Condriac, Bardot, and Hoolihan. Believing in the quantitative analysis approach to problem solving, the administrator has interviewed each nurse, considered his or her background, personality, and talents, and developed a cost scale ranging from 0 to 100 to be used in the assignment. A 0 for Nurse Bardot being assigned to the cardiology unit implies that she would be perfectly suited to that task. A value close to 100, on the other hand, would imply that she is not at all suited to head that unit. The accompanying table gives the complete set of cost figures that the hospital administrator felt represented all possible assignments. Which nurse should be assigned to which unit?

	DEPARTMENT			
NURSE	**UROLOGY**	**CARDIOLOGY**	**ORTHOPEDICS**	**OBSTETRICS**
Hawkins	28	18	15	75
Condriac	32	48	23	38
Bardot	51	36	24	36
Hoolihan	25	38	55	12

:9-28 The Gleaming Company has just developed a new dishwashing liquid and is preparing for a national television promotional campaign. The firm has decided to schedule a series of 1-minute commercials during the peak homemaker audience viewing hours of 1 P.M. to 5 P.M. To reach the widest possible audience, Gleaming wants to schedule one commercial on each of four networks and to have one commercial appear during each of the four 1-hour time blocks. The exposure ratings for each hour, which represent the number of viewers per $1,000 spent, are presented in the following table. Which network should be scheduled each hour to provide the maximum audience exposure?

	NETWORK			
VIEWING HOURS	**A**	**B**	**C**	**INDEPENDENT**
1–2 P.M.	27.1	18.1	11.3	9.5
2–3 P.M.	18.9	15.5	17.1	10.6
3–4 P.M.	19.2	18.5	9.9	7.7
4–5 P.M.	11.5	21.4	16.8	12.8

Data for Problem 9-29

MEDICAL DEVICES	PLANT							
	1	2	3	4	5	6	7	8
C53	$0.10	$0.12	$0.13	$0.11	$0.10	$0.06	$0.16	$0.12
C81	0.05	0.06	0.04	0.08	0.04	0.09	0.06	0.06
D5	0.32	0.40	0.31	0.30	0.42	0.35	0.36	0.49
D44	0.17	0.14	0.19	0.15	0.10	0.16	0.19	0.12
E2	0.06	0.07	0.10	0.05	0.08	0.10	0.11	0.05
E35	0.08	0.10	0.12	0.08	0.09	0.10	0.09	0.06
G99	0.55	0.62	0.61	0.70	0.62	0.63	0.65	0.59

9-29 The Patricia Garcia Company is producing seven new medical products. Each of Garcia's eight plants can add one more product to its current line of medical devices. The unit manufacturing costs for producing the different parts at the eight plants are shown in the table above. How should Garcia assign the new products to the plants to minimize manufacturing costs?

9-30 Haifa Instruments, an Israeli producer of portable kidney dialysis units and other medical products, develops an 8-month aggregate plan. Demand and capacity (in units) are forecast as shown in the table below.

The cost of producing each dialysis unit is $1,000 on regular time, $1,300 on overtime, and $1,500 on a subcontract. Inventory carrying cost is $100 per unit per month. There is no beginning or ending inventory in stock.

(a) Set up a production plan, using the transportation model, that minimizes cost. What is this plan's cost?

(b) Through better planning, regular time production can be set at exactly the same value, 275 per month. Does this alter the solution?

(c) If overtime costs rise from $1,300 to $1,400, does this change your answer to part (a)? What if they fall to $1,200?

9-31 NASA's astronaut crew currently includes 10 mission specialists who hold a doctoral degree in either astrophysics or astromedicine. One of these specialists will be assigned to each of the 10 flights scheduled for the upcoming nine months. Mission specialists are responsible for carrying out scientific and medical experiments in space or for launching, retrieving, or repairing satellites. The chief of astronaut personnel, himself a former crew member with three missions under his belt, must decide who should be assigned and trained for each of the very different missions. Clearly, astronauts with medical educations are more suited to missions involving biological or medical experiments, whereas those with engineering- or physics-oriented degrees are best suited to other types of missions. The chief assigns each astronaut a rating on a scale of 1 to 10 for each possible mission, with a 10 being a perfect match for the task at hand and a 1 being a mismatch. Only one specialist is assigned to each flight, and none is reassigned until all others have flown at least once.

(a) Who should be assigned to which flight?

(b) NASA has just been notified that Anderson is getting married in February and has been granted a highly sought publicity tour in Europe that month. (He intends to take his wife and let the trip double as a honeymoon.) How does this change the final schedule?

(c) Certo has complained that he was misrated on his January missions. Both ratings should be 10s, he claims to the chief, who agrees and

Data for Problem 9-30

CAPACITY SOURCE	JAN.	FEB.	MAR.	APR.	MAY	JUNE	JULY	AUG.
Labor								
Regular time	235	255	290	300	300	290	300	290
Overtime	20	24	26	24	30	28	30	30
Subcontract	12	15	15	17	17	19	19	20
Demand	255	294	321	301	330	320	345	340

Data for Problem 9-31

ASTRONAUT	MISSION									
	JAN. 12	JAN. 27	FEB. 5	FEB. 26	MAR. 26	APR. 12	MAY 1	JUN. 9	AUG. 20	SEP. 19
Vincze	9	7	2	1	10	9	8	9	2	6
Veit	8	8	3	4	7	9	7	7	4	4
Anderson	2	1	10	10	1	4	7	6	6	7
Herbert	4	4	10	9	9	9	1	2	3	4
Schatz	10	10	9	9	8	9	1	1	1	1
Plane	1	3	5	7	9	7	10	10	9	2
Certo	9	9	8	8	9	1	1	2	2	9
Moses	3	2	7	6	4	3	9	7	7	9
Brandon	5	4	5	9	10	10	5	4	9	8
Drtina	10	10	9	7	6	7	5	4	8	8

recomputes the schedule. Do any changes occur over the schedule set in part (b)?

(d) What are the strengths and weaknesses of this approach to scheduling?

9-32 The XYZ Corporation is expanding its market to include Texas. Each salesperson is assigned to potential distributors in one of five different areas. It is anticipated that the salesperson will spend about three to four weeks in their assigned area. A statewide marketing campaign will begin once the product has been delivered to the distributors. The five sales people who will be assigned to these areas (one

person for each area) have rated the areas on the desirability of the assignment as shown in the following table. The scale is 1 (least desirable) to 5 (most desirable). Which assignments should be made if the total of the ratings is to be maximized?

9-33 Bechtold Construction is in the process of installing power lines to a large housing development. Steve Bechtold wants to minimize the total length of wire used, which will minimize his costs. The housing development is shown as a network. Each house has been numbered, and the distances between houses are given in hundreds of feet. What do you recommend?

Table for Problem 9-32

	AUSTIN/SAN ANTONIO	DALLAS/FT. WORTH	EL PASO/WEST TEXAS	HOUSTON/ GALVESTON	CORPUS CHRISTI/RIO GRANDE VALLEY
Erica	5	3	2	3	4
Louis	3	4	4	2	2
Maria	4	5	4	3	3
Paul	2	4	3	4	3
Orlando	4	5	3	5	4

Network for Problem 9-33

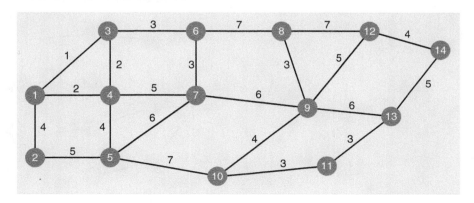

Network for Problem 9-34

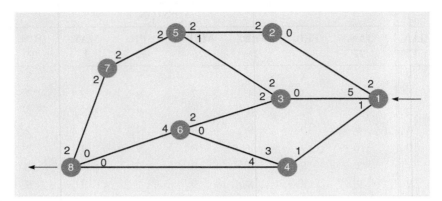

9-34   The city of New Berlin is considering making several of its streets one-way (see the network provided). Also, due to increased property taxes and an aggressive road development plan, the city of New Berlin has been considering increasing the road capacity of two of its roads. If this is done, traffic along road 1–2 (from node 1 to node 2) will be increased from 2 to 5, and traffic capacity along road 1–4 will increase from 1 to 3. What is the maximum number of cars per hour that can travel from east to west with the current road system? If the increases in capacity for road 1–2 and 2–5 were both made, how would that change the number of cars per hour that can travel from east to west?

9-35   The director of security wants to connect security video cameras to the main control site from five potential trouble locations. Ordinarily, cable would simply be run from each location to the main control site. However, because the environment is potentially explosive, the cable must be run in a special conduit that is continually air purged. This conduit is very expensive but large enough to handle five cables (the maximum that might be needed). Use the minimal-spanning tree technique to find a minimum distance route for the conduit between the locations noted in the figure. (Note that it makes no difference which one is the main control site.)

9-36   The road system around the hotel complex on International Drive (node 1) to Disney World (node 11) in Orlando, Florida, is shown in the network. The numbers by the nodes represent the traffic flow in hundreds of cars per hour. What is the maximum flow of cars from the hotel complex to Disney World?

Network for Problem 9-36

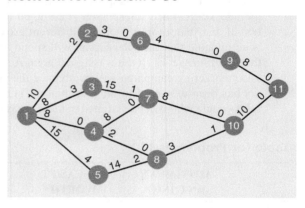

9-37   The numbers in the network below represent thousands of gallons per hour as they flow through a chemical processing plant. Two terminals in the chemical processing plant, represented by nodes 6

Network for Problem 9-35

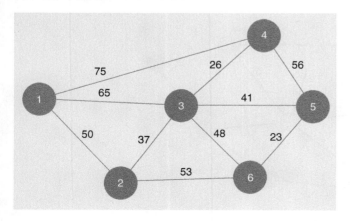

Network for Problem 9-37

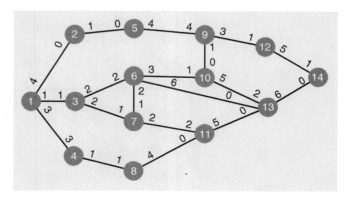

and 7, have had problems recently, and repairs on these are being considered. However, these repairs would require that these terminals (nodes) be shut down for a significant amount of time, and no material could flow into or out of these nodes until the repairs are finished. What impact would closing these nodes have on the capacity of the network?

9-38   The German towns around the Black Forest are represented by nodes in the network below. The distances between towns is shown in kilometers. Find the shortest route from city 1 to city 16. If flooding in cities 7 and 8 force closure of all roads leading into or coming out of those cities, how would that impact the shortest route?

Network for Problem 9-38

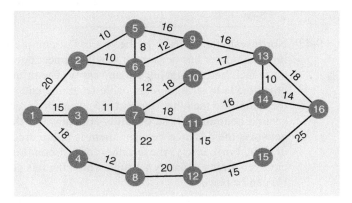

9-39   Grey Construction would like to determine the least expensive way of connecting houses it is building with cable TV. It has identified 11 possible branches or routes that could be used to connect the houses. The cost in hundreds of dollars and the branches are summarized in the following table.

(a) What is the least expensive way to run cable to the houses?

BRANCH	START NODE	END NODE	COST ($100s)
Branch 1	1	2	5
Branch 2	1	3	6
Branch 3	1	4	6
Branch 4	1	5	5
Branch 5	2	6	7
Branch 6	3	7	5
Branch 7	4	7	7
Branch 8	5	8	4
Branch 9	6	7	1
Branch 10	7	9	6
Branch 11	8	9	2

(b) After reviewing cable and installation costs, Grey Construction would like to alter the costs for installing cable TV between its houses. The first branches need to be changed. The changes are summarized in the following table. What is the impact on total costs?

BRANCH	START NODE	END NODE	COST ($100s)
Branch 1	1	2	5
Branch 2	1	3	1
Branch 3	1	4	1
Branch 4	1	5	1
Branch 5	2	6	7
Branch 6	3	7	5
Branch 7	4	7	7
Branch 8	5	8	4
Branch 9	6	7	1
Branch 10	7	9	6
Branch 11	8	9	2

9-40   In going from Quincy to Old Bainbridge, there are 10 possible roads that George Olin can take. Each road can be considered a branch in the shortest-route problem.

(a) Determine the best way to get from Quincy (node 1) to Old Bainbridge (node 8) that will minimize total distance traveled. All distances are in hundreds of miles.

BRANCH	START NODE	END NODE	DISTANCE (IN HUNDREDS OF MILES)
Branch 1	1	2	3
Branch 2	1	3	2
Branch 3	2	4	3
Branch 4	3	5	3
Branch 5	4	5	1
Branch 6	4	6	4
Branch 7	5	7	2
Branch 8	6	7	2
Branch 9	6	8	3
Branch 10	7	8	6

(b) George Olin made a mistake in estimating the distances from Quincy to Old Bainbridge. The new distances are in the following table. What impact does this have on the shortest route from Quincy to Old Bainbridge?

BRANCH	START NODE	END NODE	DISTANCE (IN HUNDREDS OF MILES)
Branch 1	1	2	3
Branch 2	1	3	2
Branch 3	2	4	3
Branch 4	3	5	1
Branch 5	4	5	1
Branch 6	4	6	4
Branch 7	5	7	2
Branch 8	6	7	2
Branch 9	6	8	3
Branch 10	7	8	6

9-41 South Side Oil and Gas, a new venture in Texas, has developed an oil pipeline network to transport oil from exploration fields to the refinery and other locations. There are 10 pipelines (branches) in the network. The oil flow in hundreds of gallons and the network of pipelines is given in the following table.

(a) What is the maximum that can flow through the network?

BRANCH	START NODE	END NODE	CAPACITY	REVERSE CAPACITY	FLOW
Branch 1	1	2	10	4	10
Branch 2	1	3	8	2	5
Branch 3	2	4	12	1	10
Branch 4	2	5	6	6	0
Branch 5	3	5	8	1	5
Branch 6	4	6	10	2	10
Branch 7	5	6	10	10	0
Branch 8	5	7	5	5	5
Branch 9	6	8	10	1	10
Branch 10	7	8	10	1	5

(b) South Side Oil and Gas needs to modify its pipeline network flow patterns. The new data is in the following table. What impact does this have on the maximum flow through the network?

BRANCH	START NODE	END NODE	CAPACITY	REVERSE CAPACITY	FLOW
Branch 1	1	2	10	4	10
Branch 2	1	3	8	2	5
Branch 3	2	4	12	1	10
Branch 4	2	5	0	0	0
Branch 5	3	5	8	1	5
Branch 6	4	6	10	2	10
Branch 7	5	6	10	10	0
Branch 8	5	7	5	5	5
Branch 9	6	8	10	1	10
Branch 10	7	8	10	1	5

9-42 The following table represents a network with the arcs identified by their starting and ending nodes. Draw the network and use the minimal-spanning tree to find the minimum distance required to connect these nodes.

ARC	DISTANCE
1–2	12
1–3	8
2–3	7
2–4	10
3–4	9
3–5	8
4–5	8
4–6	11
5–6	9

9-43 Northwest University is in the process of completing a computer bus network that will connect computer facilities throughout the university. The prime objective is to string a main cable from one end of the campus to the other (nodes 1–25) through underground conduits. These conduits are shown in the network; the distance between them is in hundreds of feet. Fortunately, these underground conduits have remaining capacity through which the bus cable can be placed.

(a) Given the network for this problem, how far (in hundreds of feet) is the shortest route from node 1 to node 25?

(b) In addition to the computer bus network, a new phone system is also being planned. The phone system would use the same underground conduits. If the phone system were installed, the following paths along the conduit would be at capacity and would not be available for the computer bus network: 6–11, 7–12, and 17–20. What changes (if any) would you have to make to the path used for the computer bus if the phone system were installed?

Network for Problem 9-43

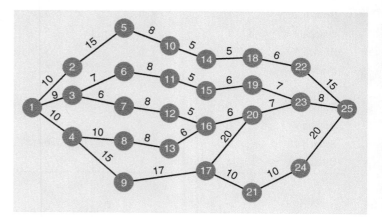

(c) The university *did* decide to install the new phone system before the cable for the computer network. Because of unexpected demand for computer networking facilities, an additional cable is needed for node 1 to node 25. Unfortunately, the cable for the first or original network has completely used up the capacity along its path. Given this situation, what is the best path for the second network cable?

Internet Homework Problems

See our Internet home page, at **www.pearsonhighered.com/render**, for additional problems, Problems 9-44 through 9-50.

Case Study

Andrew–Carter, Inc.

Andrew–Carter, Inc. (A–C), is a major Canadian producer and distributor of outdoor lighting fixtures. Its fixture is distributed throughout North America and has been in high demand for several years. The company operates three plants that manufacture the fixture and distribute it to five distribution centers (warehouses).

During the present recession, A–C has seen a major drop in demand for its fixture as the housing market has declined. Based on the forecast of interest rates, the head of operations feels that demand for housing and thus for its product will remain depressed for the foreseeable future. A–C is considering closing one of its plants, as it is now operating with a forecasted excess capacity of 34,000 units per week. The forecasted weekly demands for the coming year are

Warehouse 1	9,000 units
Warehouse 2	13,000 units
Warehouse 3	11,000 units
Warehouse 4	15,000 units
Warehouse 5	8,000 units

The plant capacities in units per week are

Plant 1, regular time	27,000 units
Plant 1, on overtime	7,000 units
Plant 2, regular time	20,000 units
Plant 2, on overtime	5,000 units
Plant 3, regular time	25,000 units
Plant 3, on overtime	6,000 units

If A–C shuts down any plants, its weekly costs will change, as fixed costs are lower for a nonoperating plant. Table 9.4 shows production costs at each plant, both variable at regular time and overtime, and fixed when operating and shut down. Table 9.5 shows distribution costs from each plant to each warehouse (distribution center).

Discussion Questions

1. Evaluate the various configurations of operating and closed plants that will meet weekly demand. Determine which configuration minimizes total costs.
2. Discuss the implications of closing a plant.

Source: Professor Michael Ballot, University of the Pacific.

TABLE 9.5
Andrew–Carter, Inc., Variable Costs and Fixed Production Costs per Week

PLANT	VARIABLE COST	FIXED COST PER WEEK	
		OPERATING	NOT OPERATING
No. 1, regular time	$2.80/unit	$14,000	$6,000
No. 1, overtime	3.52		
No. 2, regular time	2.78	12,000	5,000
No. 2, overtime	3.48		
No. 3, regular time	2.72	15,000	7,500
No. 3, overtime	3.42		

TABLE 9.6
Andrew–Carter, Inc., Distribution Costs per Unit

	TO DISTRIBUTION CENTER				
FROM PLANT	W1	W2	W3	W4	W5
No. 1	$0.50	$0.44	$0.49	$0.46	$0.56
No. 2	0.40	0.52	0.50	0.56	0.57
No. 3	0.56	0.53	0.51	0.54	0.35

Case Study

Northeastern Airlines

Northeastern Airlines is a regional airline serving nine cities in the New England states as well as cities in New York, New Jersey, and Pennsylvania. While nonstop flights are available for some of the routes, connecting flights are often necessary. The network shows the cities served and profit in U.S. dollars per passenger along each of these routes. The routes from Boston-to-Providence and from Providence-to-Boston make only $9 per passenger profit after all expenses. To service these cities, Northeastern operates a fleet of sixteen 122-passenger Embraer E-195 jets. These jets, which were first introduced by Embraer in late 2004, have helped Northeastern Airlines remain profitable for a number of years. However, in recent years, the profit margins have been falling, and Northeastern is facing the prospect of downsizing their operations.

Management at Northeastern Airlines has considered several options to reduce cost and increase profitability. Due to Federal Aviation Administration regulations, the company must continue to serve each of the nine cities. How they serve these cities, however, is up to the management at Northeastern. One

suggestion has been made to provide fewer direct flights, which would mean that a city served by Northeastern might only have direct flights to one other city. The company plans to hire a marketing analytics consultant to determine how demand would be impacted by longer flights with more connections, and to forecast the demand along each of the routes based on a modified flight operations map. Before hiring the consultant, the company would like to first determine the most profitable (on a profit per passenger basis) way to continue serving all of the cities.

Discussion Questions

1. Develop a flight operations map that still serves each of the nine cities, but maximizes the company's profit per passenger (*Hint:* Find the *maximal*-spanning tree)
2. Comment on how the 16 jets should be assigned.

Thanks to Professor Faizul Huq, College of Business, Ohio University, for providing this case.

**Northeastern Airlines
Service Area**

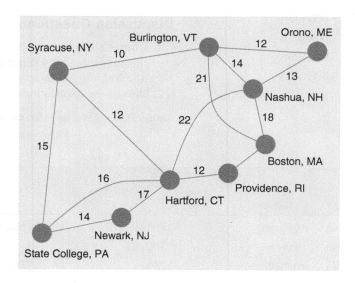

Case Study

Southwestern University Traffic Problems

Southwestern University (SWU), located in the small town of Stephenville, Texas, is experiencing increased interest in its football program now that a big-name coach has been hired. The increase in season ticket sales for the upcoming season means additional revenues, but it also means increased complaints due to the traffic problems associated with the football games. When a new stadium is built, this will only get worse. Marty Starr, SWU's president, has asked the University Planning Committee to look into this problem.

Based on traffic projections, Dr. Starr would like to have sufficient capacity so that 35,000 cars per hour could travel from the stadium to the interstate highway. To alleviate the anticipated traffic problems, some of the current streets leading from the university to the interstate highway are being considered for widening to increase the capacity. The current street capacities with the number of cars (in 1,000s) per hour are shown below. Since the major problem will be after the game, only the flows away from the stadium are indicated. These flows include some streets closest to the stadium being transformed into one-way streets for a short period after each game with police officers directing traffic.

Alexander Lee, a member of the University Planning Committee, has said that a quick check of the road capacities in the diagram indicates that the total number of cars per hour that may leave the stadium (node 1) is 33,000. The number of cars that may pass through nodes 2, 3, and 4 is 35,000 per hour, and the number of cars that may pass through nodes 5, 6, and 7 is even greater. Therefore, Dr. Lee has suggested that the current

capacity is 33,000 cars per hour. He has also suggested that a recommendation be made to the city manager for expansion of one of the routes from the stadium to the highway to permit an additional 2,000 cars per hour. He recommends expanding whichever route is cheapest. If the city chooses not to expand the roads, it is felt that the traffic problem would be a nuisance but would be manageable.

Based on past experience, it is believed that as long as the street capacity is within 2,500 cars per hour of the number that leave the stadium, the problem is not too severe. However, the severity of the problem grows dramatically for each additional 1,000 cars that are added to the streets.

Discussion Questions

1. If there is no expansion, what is the maximum number of cars that may actually travel from the stadium to the interstate per hour? Why is this number not equal to 33,000, as Dr. Lee suggested?
2. If the cost for expanding a street were the same for each street, which street(s) would you recommend expanding to increase the capacity to 33,000? Which streets would you recommend expanding to get the total capacity of the system to 35,000 per hour?

Roads from Stadium to Interstate

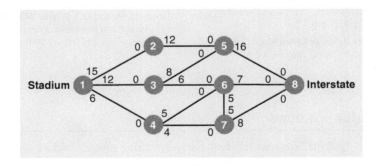

Internet Case Studies

See our Internet home page, at **www.pearsonhighered.com/render**, for these additional case studies:

(1) **Northwest General Hospital:** This case involves improving the food distribution system in a hospital to reduce the chances of food getting cold before it is delivered to the patients.

(2) **Custom Vans, Inc:** This case involves finding the best location for a plant that will manufacture showers used in customized vans.

(3) **Ranch Development Project:** This case involves finding the least-cost way to provide water and sewer services to homes in a new housing development.

(4) **Old Oregon Wood Store:** This case involves determining the best way to assign employees to jobs in a small manufacturing company.

(5) **Binder's Beverage:** This case is about finding the shortest route from a plant to a warehouse.

Bibliography

Adlakha, V., and K. Kowalski. "Simple Algorithm for the Source-Induced Fixed-Charge Transportation Problem," *Journal of the Operational Research Society* 55, 12 (2004): 1275–1280.

Bowman, E. "Production Scheduling by the Transportation Method of Linear Programming," *Operations Research* 4 (1956).

Dawid, Herbert, Johannes Konig, and Christine Strauss. "An Enhanced Rostering Model for Airline Crews," *Computers and Operations Research* 28, 7 (June 2001): 671–688.

Hezarkhani, Behzad, and Wieslaw Kubiak. "A Coordinating Contract for Transshipment In a Two-Company Supply Chain," *European Journal of Operational Research* 207, 1 (2010): 232–237.

Jacobs, T., B. Smith, and E. Johnson. "Incorporating Network Flow Effects into the Airline Fleet Assignment Process," *Transportation Science* 42, 4(2008): 514–529.

Johnsonbaugh, Richard. *Discrete Mathematics*, 5th ed. Upper Saddle River, NJ: Prentice Hall, 2001.

Kawatra, R., and D. Bricker. "A Multiperiod Planning Model for the Capacitated Minimal Spanning Tree Problem," *European Journal of Operational Research* 121, 2 (2000): 412–419.

Koksalan, Murat, and Haldun Sural. "Efes Beverage Group Makes Location and Distribution Decisions for Its Malt Plants," *Interfaces* 29, 2 (March–April, 1999): 89–103.

Liu, Jinming, and Fred Rahbar. "Project Time–Cost Trade-off Optimization by Maximal Flow Theory," *Journal of Construction Engineering & Management* 130, 4 (July/August 2004): 607–609.

Liu, Shiang-Tai. "The Total Cost Bounds of the Transportation Problem with Varying Demand and Supply," *Omega* 31, 4 (2003): 247–251.

Martello, Silvano. "Jeno Egervary: From the Origins of the Hungarian Algorithm to Satellite Communication," *Central European Journal of Operations Research* 18, 1 (2010): 47–58.

McKeown, P., and B. Workman. "A Study in Using Linear Programming to Assign Students to Schools," *Interfaces* 6, 4 (August 1976).

Render, B., and R. M. Stair. *Introduction to Management Science*. Boston: Allyn & Bacon, Inc., 1992.

Sancho, N. G. F. "On the Maximum Expected Flow in a Network," *Journal of Operational Research Society* 39 (May 1988): 481–485.

Sedeño-Noda, Antonio, Carlos González-Martín, and Sergio Alonso. "A Generalization of the Scaling Max-Flow Algorithm," *Computers & Operations Research* 31, 13 (November 2004): 2183–2198.

Troutt, M. D., and G. P White. "Maximal Flow Network Modeling of Production Bottleneck Problems," *Journal of the Operational Research Society* 52, 2 (February 2001): 182–187.

Appendix 9.1: Using QM for Windows

QM for Windows has both a transportation module and an assignment module in its menu. Both are easy to use in terms of data entry and easy to interpret in terms of output. Program 9.9A shows the input screen for the Executive Furniture transportation example. The starting solution technique may be specified. The results are shown in Program 9.9B. Program 9.10A provides the input screen for the Fix-It Shop assignment example. Simply enter the costs and then *click Solve*. Program 9.10B gives the solution to this.

PROGRAM 9.9A

QM for Windows Input for Executive Furniture Transportation Example

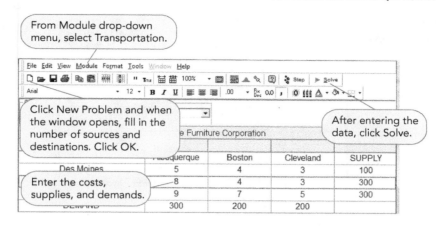

From Module drop-down menu, select Transportation.

Click New Problem and when the window opens, fill in the number of sources and destinations. Click OK.

After entering the data, click Solve.

Enter the costs, supplies, and demands.

	Albuquerque	Boston	Cleveland	SUPPLY
Des Moines	5	4	3	100
	8	4	3	300
	9	7	5	300
DEMAND	300	200	200	

PROGRAM 9.9B

QM for Windows Solution for Executive Furniture Transportation Example

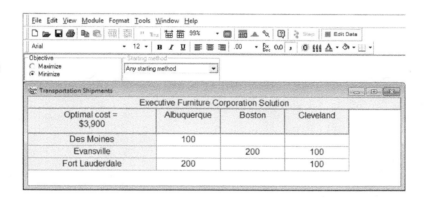

Objective
- Maximize
- Minimize

Starting method
Any starting method

Transportation Shipments

Optimal cost = $3,900	Albuquerque	Boston	Cleveland	
Des Moines	100			
Evansville		200	100	
Fort Lauderdale	200		100	

Executive Furniture Corporation Solution

PROGRAM 9.10A

QM for Windows Input for the Fix-It Shop Assignment Example

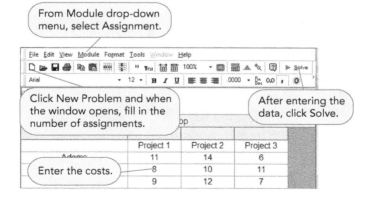

From Module drop-down menu, select Assignment.

Click New Problem and when the window opens, fill in the number of assignments.

After entering the data, click Solve.

Enter the costs.

	Project 1	Project 2	Project 3
Adams	11	14	6
	8	10	11
	9	12	7

PROGRAM 9.10B

QM for Windows Output for the Fix-It Shop Assignment Example

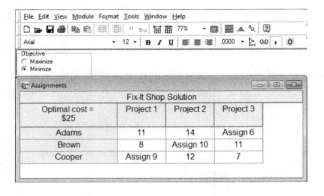

Fix-It Shop Solution			
Optimal cost = $25	Project 1	Project 2	Project 3
Adams	11	14	Assign 6
Brown	8	Assign 10	11
Cooper	Assign 9	12	7

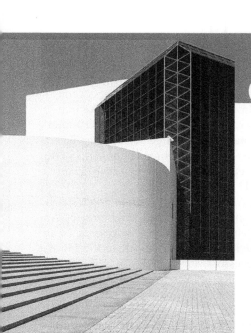

CHAPTER 11

Project Management

After completing this chapter, students will be able to:

1. Understand how to plan, monitor, and control projects with the use of PERT and CPM.

2. Determine earliest start, earliest finish, latest start, latest finish, and slack times for each activity, along with the total project completion time.

3. Reduce total project time at the least total cost by crashing the network using manual or linear programming techniques.

4. Understand the important role of software in project management.

CHAPTER OUTLINE

11.1 Introduction

11.2 PERT/CPM

11.3 PERT/Cost

11.4 Project Crashing

11.5 Other Topics in Project Management

Summary • Glossary • Key Equations • Solved Problems • Self-Test • Discussion Questions and Problems • Internet Homework Problems • Case Study: Southwestern University Stadium Construction ♦ Case Study: Family Planning Research Center of Nigeria • Internet Case Studies • Bibliography

Appendix 11.1: Project Management with QM for Windows

11.1 Introduction

Project management can be used to manage complex projects.

Most realistic projects that organizations like Microsoft, General Motors, or the U.S. Defense Department undertake are large and complex. A builder putting up an office building, for example, must complete thousands of activities costing millions of dollars. NASA must inspect countless components before it launches a rocket. The Bath Iron Works shipyard on the Kennebec River in Bath, Maine, must manage and coordinate thousands of complex activities simultaneously. Almost every industry worries about how to manage similar large-scale, complicated projects effectively. It is a difficult problem, and the stakes are high. Millions of dollars in cost overruns have been wasted due to poor planning of projects. Unnecessary delays have occurred due to poor scheduling. How can such problems be solved?

The first step in planning and scheduling a project is to develop the **work breakdown structure (WBS)**. This involves identifying the activities that must be performed in the project. An **activity** is a job or task that is a part of a project. The beginning or end of an activity is called an **event**. There may be varying levels of detail, and each activity may be broken into its most basic components. The time, cost, resource requirements, predecessors, and person(s) responsible are identified for each activity. When this has been done, a schedule for the project can be developed.

The **program evaluation and review technique (PERT)** and the **critical path method (CPM)** are two popular quantitative analysis techniques that help managers plan, schedule, monitor, and control large and complex projects. They were developed because there was a critical need for a better way to manage (see the History box).

PERT is probabilistic, whereas CPM is deterministic.

When they were first developed, PERT and CPM were similar in their basic approach, but they differed in the way activity times were estimated. For every PERT activity, three time estimates are combined to determine the expected activity completion time. Thus, PERT is a probabilistic technique. On the other hand, CPM is a deterministic method since it is assumed that the times are known with certainty. While these differences are still noted, the two techniques are so similar that the term PERT/CPM is often used to describe the overall approach. This reference is used in this chapter, and differences are noted where appropriate.

HISTORY   How PERT and CPM Started

Managers have been planning, scheduling, monitoring, and controlling large-scale projects for hundreds of years, but it has only been in the past 50 years that QA techniques have been applied to major projects. One of the earliest techniques was the *Gantt chart*. This type of chart shows the start and finish times of one or more activities, as shown in the accompanying chart.

In 1958, the Special Projects Office of the U.S. Navy developed the program evaluation and review technique (PERT) to plan and control the Polaris missile program. This project involved the coordination of thousands of contractors. Today PERT is still used to monitor countless government contract schedules. At about the same time (1957), the critical path method (CPM) was developed by J. E. Kelley, Jr. of Remington Rand and M. R. Walker of DuPont. Originally, CPM was used to assist in the building and maintenance of chemical plants at DuPont.

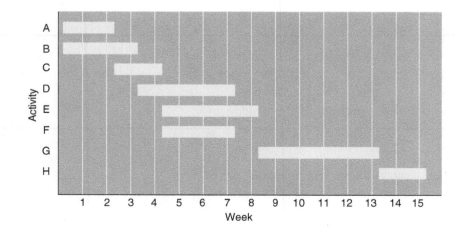

There are six steps common to both PERT and CPM. The procedure follows:

Six Steps of PERT/CPM

1. Define the project and all of its significant activities or tasks.
2. Develop the relationships among the activities. Decide which activities must precede others.
3. Draw the **network** connecting all of the activities.
4. Assign time and/or cost estimates to each activity.
5. Compute the longest time path through the network; this is called the **critical path**.
6. Use the network to help plan, schedule, monitor, and control the project.

The critical path is important because activities on the critical path can delay the entire project.

Finding the critical path is a major part of controlling a project. The activities on the critical path represent tasks that will delay the entire project if they are delayed. Managers derive flexibility by identifying noncritical activities and replanning, rescheduling, and reallocating resources such as personnel and finances.

11.2   PERT/CPM

Almost any large project can be subdivided into a series of smaller activities or tasks that can be analyzed with PERT/CPM. When you recognize that projects can have thousands of specific activities, you see why it is important to be able to answer questions such as the following:

Questions answered by PERT.

1. When will the entire project be completed?
2. What are the *critical* activities or tasks in the project, that is, the ones that will delay the entire project if they are late?
3. Which are the *noncritical* activities, that is, the ones that can run late without delaying the entire project's completion?
4. If there are three time estimates, what is the probability that the project will be completed by a specific date?
5. At any particular date, is the project on schedule, behind schedule, or ahead of schedule?
6. On any given date, is the money spent equal to, less than, or greater than the budgeted amount?
7. Are there enough resources available to finish the project on time?

General Foundry Example of PERT/CPM

General Foundry, Inc., a metalworks plant in Milwaukee, has long been trying to avoid the expense of installing air pollution control equipment. The local environmental protection group has recently given the foundry 16 weeks to install a complex air filter system on its main smokestack. General Foundry was warned that it will be forced to close unless the device is installed in the allotted period. Lester Harky, the managing partner, wants to make sure that installation of the filtering system progresses smoothly and on time.

The first step is to define the project and all project activities.

When the project begins, the building of the internal components for the device (activity *A*) and the modifications that are necessary for the floor and roof (activity *B*) can be started. The construction of the collection stack (activity *C*) can begin once the internal components are completed, and pouring of the new concrete floor and installation of the frame (activity *D*) can be completed as soon as the roof and floor have been modified. After the collection stack has been constructed, the high-temperature burner can be built (activity *E*), and the installation of the pollution control system (activity *F*) can begin. The air pollution device can be installed (activity *G*) after the high-temperature burner has been built, the concrete floor has been poured and the frame has been installed (activity *D*). Finally, after the control system and pollution device have been installed, the system can be inspected and tested (activity *H*).

All of these activities seem rather confusing and complex until they are placed in a network. First, all of the activities must be listed. This information is shown in Table 11.1. We see in the table that before the collection stack can be constructed (activity *C*), the internal components

TABLE 11.1

Activities and Immediate Predecessors for General Foundry, Inc.

ACTIVITY	DESCRIPTION	IMMEDIATE PREDECESSORS
A	Build internal components	—
B	Modify roof and floor	—
C	Construct collection stack	A
D	Pour concrete and install frame	B
E	Build high-temperature burner	C
F	Install control system	C
G	Install air pollution device	D, E
H	Inspect and test	F, G

MODELING IN THE REAL WORLD

PERT Helps Change the Face of British Airways

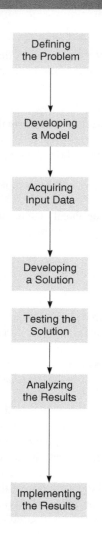

Defining the Problem

↓

Developing a Model

↓

Acquiring Input Data

↓

Developing a Solution

↓

Testing the Solution

↓

Analyzing the Results

↓

Implementing the Results

Defining the Problem

British Airways (BA) wanted to rejuvenate its image using international design consultants to help develop a new identity. The "makeover" was to be completed in all areas of BA's public image as quickly as possible.

Developing a Model

Using a computerized project management package—PERTMASTER from Abex Software—a BA team constructed a PERT model of all tasks involved.

Acquiring Input Data

Data were collected from each department involved. Printers were asked to develop time estimates for new company stationery, tickets, timetables, and baggage tags; clothing suppliers for uniforms; and Boeing Corp. for all the tasks involved in remaking the inside and outside of BA's jets.

Developing a Solution

All the data were entered into PERTMASTER for a schedule and critical path.

Testing the Solution

The resulting schedule did not please BA management. Boeing could not prepare a huge 747 in time for a December 4 gala launch date. Uniform designs were also going to delay the entire project.

Analyzing the Results

An analysis of the earliest possible date that all items for a refurbished airplane could be ready (new paint, upholstery, carpets, trim, and so on) revealed that there were just sufficient materials to totally convert a smaller Boeing 737 that was available in the Seattle plant. Critical path analysis also showed that uniforms—the work of British designer Roland Klein—would have to be launched six months later in a separate ceremony.

Implementing the Results

The smaller 737 was outfitted just in time for a brilliant light show in an auditorium specially built in a Heathrow Airport hangar. Ground vehicles were also prepared in time.

Source: Based on *Industrial Management and Data Systems* (March–April 1986): 6–7.

FIGURE 11.1

Network for General Foundry, Inc.

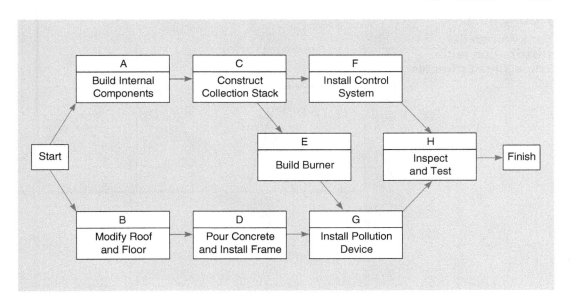

Immediate predecessors are determined in the second step.

must be built (activity *A*). Thus, activity *A* is the **immediate predecessor** of activity *C*. Similarly, both activities *D* and *E* must be performed just prior to installation of the air pollution device (activity *G*).

Drawing the PERT/CPM Network

Activities and events are drawn and connected in the third step.

Once the activities have all been specified (step 1 of the PERT procedure) and management has decided which activities must precede others (step 2), the network can be drawn (step 3).

There are two common techniques for drawing PERT networks. The first is called **activity-on-node (AON)** because the nodes represent the activities. The second is called **activity-on-arc (AOA)** because the arcs are used to represent the activities. In this book, we present the AON technique, as this is easier and is often used in commercial software.

In constructing an AON network, there should be one node representing the start of the project and one node representing the finish of the project. There will be one node (represented as a rectangle in this chapter) for each activity. Figure 11.1 gives the entire network for General Foundry. The arcs (arrows) are used to show the predecessors for the activities. For example, the arrows leading into activity *G* indicate that both *D* and *E* are immediate predecessors for *G*.

Activity Times

The next step in both CPM and PERT is to assign estimates of the time required to complete each activity. For some projects, such as construction projects, the time to complete each activity may be known with certainty. The developers of CPM assigned just one time estimate to each activity. These times are then used to find the critical path, as described in the sections that follow.

The fourth step is to assign activity times.

However, for one-of-a-kind projects or for new jobs, providing **activity time estimates** is not always an easy task. Without solid historical data, managers are often uncertain about the activity times. For this reason, the developers of PERT employed a probability distribution based on three time estimates for each activity. A weighted average of these times is used with PERT in place of the single time estimate used with CPM, and these averages are used to find the critical path. The time estimates in PERT are

Optimistic time (*a*) = time an activity will take if everything goes as well as possible. There should be only a small probability (say, $^1/_{100}$) of this occurring.

Pessimistic time (*b*) = time an activity would take assuming very unfavorable conditions. There should also be only a small probability that the activity will really take this long.

Most likely time (*m*) = most realistic time estimate to complete the activity.

The beta probability distribution is often used.

PERT often assumes that time estimates follow the **beta probability distribution** (see Figure 11.2). This continuous distribution has been found to be appropriate, in many cases, for determining an expected value and variance for activity completion times.

FIGURE 11.2
Beta Probability Distribution with Three Time Estimates

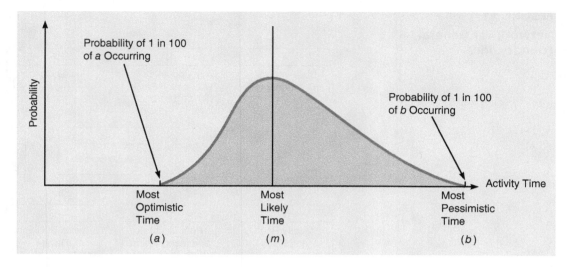

To find the **expected activity time** (*t*), the beta distribution weights the estimates as follows:

$$t = \frac{a + 4m + b}{6} \tag{11-1}$$

To compute the dispersion or **variance of activity completion time**, we use this formula:*

$$\text{Variance} = \left(\frac{b - a}{6}\right)^2 \tag{11-2}$$

Table 11.2 shows General Foundry's optimistic, most likely, and pessimistic time estimates for each activity. It also reveals the expected time (*t*) and variance for each of the activities, as computed with Equations 11-1 and 11-2.

How to Find the Critical Path

Once the expected completion time for each activity has been determined, we accept it as the actual time of that task. Variability in times will be considered later.

Although Table 11.2 indicates that the total expected time for all eight of General Foundry's activities is 25 weeks, it is obvious in Figure 11.3 that several of the tasks can be taking place simultaneously. To find out just how long the project will take, we perform the critical path analysis for the network.

The fifth step is to compute the longest path through the network—the critical path.

The *critical path* is the longest time path route through the network. If Lester Harky wants to reduce the total project time for General Foundry, he will have to reduce the length of some activity on the critical path. Conversely, any delay of an activity on the critical path will delay completion of the entire project.

To find the critical path, we need to determine the following quantities for each activity in the network:

1. **Earliest start (ES) time**: the earliest time an activity can begin without violation of immediate predecessor requirements
2. **Earliest finish (EF) time**: the earliest time at which an activity can end
3. **Latest start (LS) time**: the latest time an activity can begin without delaying the entire project
4. **Latest finish (LF) time**: the latest time an activity can end without delaying the entire project

---

*This formula is based on the statistical concept that from one end of the beta distribution to the other are 6 standard deviations (± 3 standard deviations from the mean). Because $b - a$ is 6 standard deviations, 1 standard deviation is $(b - a)/6$. Thus, the variance is $[(b - a)/6]^2$.

TABLE 11.2 Time Estimates (Weeks) for General Foundry, Inc.

ACTIVITY	OPTIMISTIC, a	MOST LIKELY, m	PESSIMISTIC, b	EXPECTED TIME, $t = [(a + 4m + b)/6]$	VARIANCE, $[(b - a)/6]^2$
A	1	2	3	2	$\left(\dfrac{3-1}{6}\right)^2 = \dfrac{4}{36}$
B	2	3	4	3	$\left(\dfrac{4-2}{6}\right)^2 = \dfrac{4}{36}$
C	1	2	3	2	$\left(\dfrac{3-1}{6}\right)^2 = \dfrac{4}{36}$
D	2	4	6	4	$\left(\dfrac{6-2}{6}\right)^2 = \dfrac{16}{36}$
E	1	4	7	4	$\left(\dfrac{7-1}{6}\right)^2 = \dfrac{36}{36}$
F	1	2	9	3	$\left(\dfrac{9-1}{6}\right)^2 = \dfrac{64}{36}$
G	3	4	11	5	$\left(\dfrac{11-3}{6}\right)^2 = \dfrac{64}{36}$
H	1	2	3	$\underline{2}$	$\left(\dfrac{3-1}{6}\right)^2 = \dfrac{4}{36}$
				25	

In the network, we represent these times as well as the activity times (t) in the nodes, as seen here:

ACTIVITY	t
ES	EF
LS	LF

We first show how to determine the earliest times. When we find these, the latest times can be computed.

FIGURE 11.3

General Foundry's Network with Expected Activity Times

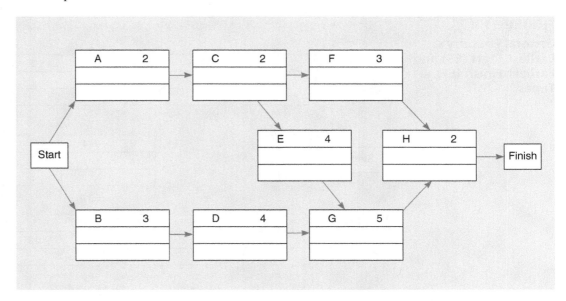

EARLIEST TIMES   There are two basic rules to follow when computing ES and EF times. The first rule is for the earliest finish time, which is computed as follows:

$$\text{Earliest finish time} = \text{Earliest start time} + \text{Expected activity time}$$
$$EF = ES + t \qquad\qquad (11\text{-}3)$$

Also, before any activity can be started, all of its predecessor activities must be completed. In other words, we search for the largest EF for all of the immediate predecessors in determining ES. The second rule is for the earliest start time, which is computed as follows:

The ES is the largest EF of the immediate predecessors.

$$\text{Earliest start} = \text{Largest of the earliest finish times of immediate predecessors}$$
$$ES = \text{Largest EF of immediate predecessors}$$

The start of the whole project will be set at time zero. Therefore, any activity that has no predecessors will have an earliest start time of zero. So ES = 0 for both A and B in the General Foundry problem, as seen here:

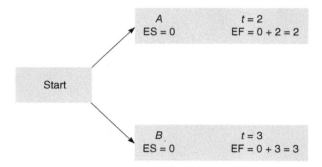

The earliest times are found by beginning at the start of the project and making a forward pass through the network.

The rest of the earliest times for General Foundry are shown in Figure 11.4. These are found using a **forward pass** through the network. At each step, EF = ES + t, and ES is the largest EF of the predecessors. Notice that activity G has an earliest start time of 8, since both D (with EF = 7) and E (with EF = 8) are immediate predecessors. Activity G cannot start until both predecessors are finished, and so we choose the larger of the earliest finish times for these. Thus, G has ES = 8. The finish time for the project will be 15 weeks, which is the EF for activity H.

LATEST TIMES   The next step in finding the critical path is to compute the latest start (LS) time and the latest finish (LF) time for each activity. We do this by making a **backward pass** through the network, that is, starting at the finish and working backward.

FIGURE 11.4

General Foundry's Earliest Start (ES) and Earliest Finish (EF) Times

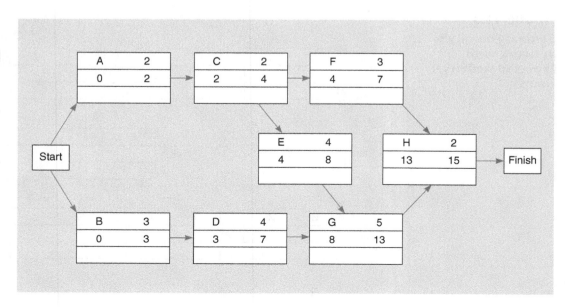

FIGURE 11.5

General Foundry's Latest Start (LS) and Latest Finish (LF) Times

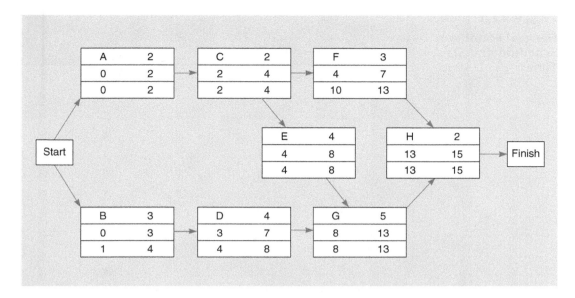

There are two basic rules to follow when computing the latest times. The first rule involves the latest start time, which is computed as

$$\text{Latest start time} = \text{Latest finish time} - \text{Activity time}$$
$$\text{LS} = \text{LF} - t \qquad (11\text{-}4)$$

The latest times are found by beginning at the finish of the project and making a backward pass through the network.

Also, since all immediate predecessors must be finished before an activity can begin, the latest start time for an activity determines the latest finish time for its immediate predecessors. If an activity is the immediate predecessor for two or more activities, it must be finished so that all following activities can begin by their latest start times. Thus, the second rule involves the latest finish time, which is computed as

The LF is the smallest LS of the activities that immediately follow.

$$\text{Latest finish time} = \text{Smallest of latest start times for following activities, or}$$
$$\text{LF} = \text{Smallest LS of following activities}$$

To compute the latest times, we start at the finish and work backwards. Since the finish time for the General Foundry project is 15, activity H has LF = 15. The latest start for activity H is

$$\text{LS} = \text{LF} - t = 15 - 2 = 13 \text{ weeks}$$

Continuing to work backward, this latest start time of 13 becomes the latest finish time for immediate predecessors F and G. All of the latest times are shown in Figure 11.5. Notice that for activity C, which is the immediate predecessor for two activities (E and F), the latest finish time is the smaller of the latest start times (4 and 10) for activities E and F.

 IN ACTION   **Project Management in an Office-Less, Cloud-Based Work Environment**

Stillwater Associates is an energy supply chain consulting company with a unique characteristic: They are an *office-less* company. They do not have a building, per se. All of their associates are scattered across the country. Needless to say, in some ways, not having a "brick and mortar" office helped Stillwater. For example, Stillwater's overhead costs are extremely low when compared to their competition. In other ways, however, not having an office hindered the company . . . especially in the area of project management. Employees were duplicating effort and experienced trouble communicating. As a result, schedules slipped, budgets busted, and clients became irritated.

Stillwater turned to Project Insight, a software tool by Metafuse, Inc. Project Insight allowed Stillwater employees to "log-in" to particular projects from any work site and from any platform. As soon as Stillwater Associates' employees logged in, the software kept track of their hours on any task, on any project, from anywhere.

As a result, Stillwater Associates budget overruns became a thing of the past, allowing their employees to more effectively respond to their client's needs.

Source: Project Insight Drives Budget Management Success at Stillwater Associates, *Wall Street Journal*, May 21, 2013, <online.wsj.com>

TABLE 11.3

General Foundry's Schedule and Slack Times

ACTIVITY	EARLIEST START, ES	EARLIEST FINISH, EF	LATEST START, LS	LATEST FINISH, LF	SLACK, LS − ES	ON CRITICAL PATH?
A	0	2	0	2	0	Yes
B	0	3	1	4	1	No
C	2	4	2	4	0	Yes
D	3	7	4	8	1	No
E	4	8	4	8	0	Yes
F	4	7	10	13	6	No
G	8	13	8	13	0	Yes
H	13	15	13	15	0	Yes

Slack time is free time for an activity.

CONCEPT OF SLACK IN CRITICAL PATH COMPUTATIONS When ES, LS, EF, and LF have been determined, it is a simple matter to find the amount of **slack time**, or free time, that each activity has. Slack is the length of time an activity can be delayed without delaying the whole project. Mathematically,

$$\text{Slack} = \text{LS} - \text{ES}, \quad \text{or} \quad \text{Slack} = \text{LF} - \text{EF} \qquad (11\text{-}5)$$

Table 11.3 summarizes the ES, EF, LS, LF, and slack times for all of General Foundry's activities. Activity *B*, for example, has 1 week of slack time since LS − ES = 1 − 0 = 1 (or, similarly, LF − EF = 4 − 3 = 1). This means that it can be delayed up to 1 week without causing the project to run any longer than expected.

Critical activities have no slack time.

On the other hand, activities *A, C, E, G,* and *H* have *no* slack time; this means that none of them can be delayed without delaying the entire project. Because of this, they are called *critical activities* and are said to be on the *critical path*. Lester Harky's critical path is shown in network form in Figure 11.6. The total project completion time (*T*), 15 weeks, is seen as the largest number in the EF or LF columns of Table 11.3. Industrial managers call this a boundary timetable.

FIGURE 11.6

General Foundry's Critical Path (A–C–E–G–H)

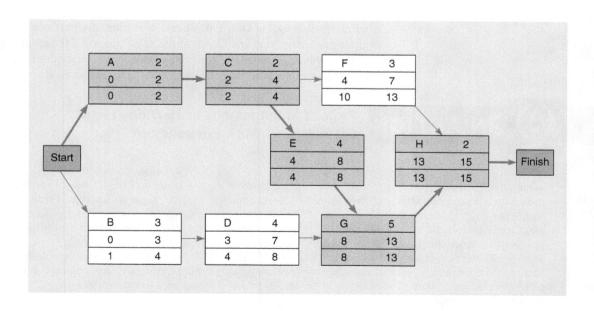

Probability of Project Completion

The **critical path analysis** helped us determine that the foundry's expected project completion time is 15 weeks. Harky knows, however, that if the project is not completed in 16 weeks, General Foundry will be forced to close by environmental controllers. He is also aware that there is significant variation in the time estimates for several activities. Variation in activities that are on the critical path can affect overall project completion—possibly delaying it. This is one occurrence that worries Harky considerably.

Computing project variance is done by summing activity variances along the critical path.

PERT uses the variance of critical path activities to help determine the variance of the overall project. If the activity times are statistically independent, the project variance is computed by summing the variances of the critical activities:

$$\text{Project variance} = \sum \text{variances of activities on the critical path} \qquad (11\text{-}6)$$

From Table 11.2 we know that

CRITICAL ACTIVITY	VARIANCE
A	$^4/_{36}$
C	$^4/_{36}$
E	$^{36}/_{36}$
G	$^{64}/_{36}$
H	$^4/_{36}$

Hence, the project variance is

$$\text{Project variance} = {}^4/_{36} + {}^4/_{36} + {}^{36}/_{36} + {}^{64}/_{36} + {}^4/_{36} = {}^{112}/_{36} = 3.111$$

We know that the standard deviation is just the square root of the variance, so

Computing the standard deviation.

$$\text{Project standard deviation} = \sigma_T = \sqrt{\text{Project variance}}$$
$$= \sqrt{3.111} = 1.76 \text{ weeks}$$

How can this information be used to help answer questions regarding the probability of finishing the project on time? In addition to assuming that the activity times are independent, we also assume that total project completion time follows a normal probability distribution. With these assumptions, the bell-shaped curve shown in Figure 11.7 can be used to represent project

PERT has two assumptions.

FIGURE 11.7

Probability Distribution for Project Completion Times

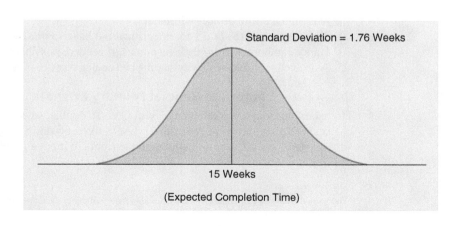

Standard Deviation = 1.76 Weeks

15 Weeks

(Expected Completion Time)

FIGURE 11.8

Probability of General Foundry's Meeting the 16-Week Deadline

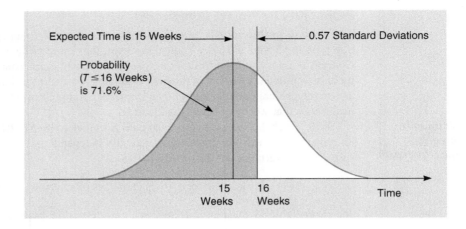

completion dates. It also means that there is a 50% chance that the entire project will be completed in less than the expected 15 weeks and a 50% chance that it will exceed 15 weeks.*

For Harky to find the probability that his project will be finished on or before the 16-week deadline, he needs to determine the appropriate area under the normal curve. The standard normal equation can be applied as follows:

Computing the probability of project completion.

$$Z = \frac{\text{Due date} - \text{Expected date of completion}}{\sigma_T} \qquad (11\text{-}7)$$

$$= \frac{16 \text{ weeks} - 15 \text{ weeks}}{1.76 \text{ weeks}} = 0.57$$

where

Z is the number of standard deviations the due date or target date lies from the mean or expected completion date.

Referring to the normal table in Appendix *A*, we find a probability of 0.71566. Thus, there is a 71.6% chance that the pollution control equipment can be put in place in 16 weeks or less. This is shown in Figure 11.8.

What PERT Was Able to Provide

PERT has thus far been able to provide Lester Harky with several valuable pieces of management information:

The sixth and final step is to monitor and control the project using the information provided by PERT.

1. The project's expected completion date is 15 weeks.
2. There is a 71.6% chance that the equipment will be in place within the 16-week deadline. PERT can easily find the probability of finishing by any date Harky is interested in.
3. Five activities (*A, C, E, G, H*) are on the critical path. If any one of them is delayed for any reason, the entire project will be delayed.
4. Three activities (*B, D, F*) are not critical but have some slack time built in. This means that Harky can borrow from their resources, if needed, possibly to speed up the entire project.
5. A detailed schedule of activity starting and ending dates has been made available (see Table 11.3).

Using Excel QM for the General Foundry Example

This example can be worked using Excel QM. To do this, select *Excel QM* from the *Add-Ins* tab in Excel 2013, as shown in Program 11.1A. In the drop-down menu, put the cursor over *Project Management*, and choices will appear to the right. To input a problem that is presented in a table

---

*You should be aware that noncritical activities also have variability (as shown in Table 11.2). In fact, a different critical path can evolve because of the probabilistic situation. This may also cause the probability estimates to be unreliable. In such instances, it is better to use simulation to determine the probabilities.

PROGRAM 11.1A

Excel QM Initialization Screen for General Foundry Example with 3 Time Estimate

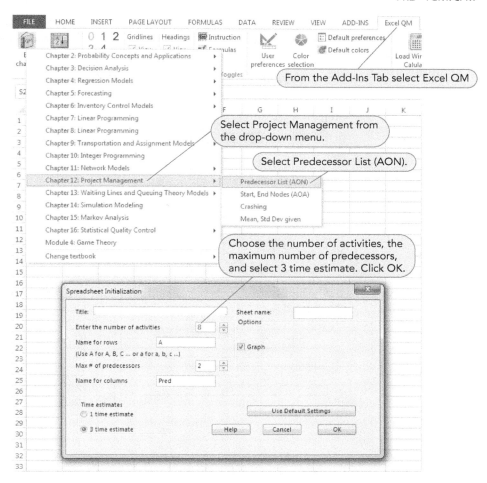

with the immediate predecessors and three time estimates, select *Predecessor List (AON)*, and the initialization window will appear. Specify the number of activities, the maximum number of immediate predecessors for the activities, and select the *3 Time Estimate* option. If you wish to see a Gantt chart, check *Graph*. Click *OK* when finished, and a spreadsheet will appear, with all the necessary rows and columns labeled. For this example, enter the three time estimates in cells B8:D15 and then enter the immediate predecessors in cells C18:D25, as shown in Program 11.1B. No other inputs or steps are required.

As these data are being entered, Excel QM calculates the expected times and variances for all activities, and a table will automatically display the earliest, latest, and slack times for all the activities. A **Gantt chart** is displayed, and this chart shows the critical path and slack time for the activities.

Sensitivity Analysis and Project Management

During any project, the time required to complete an activity can vary from the projected or expected time. If the activity is on the critical path, the total project completion time will change, as discussed previously. In addition to having an impact on the total project completion time, there is also an impact on the earliest start, earliest finish, latest start, latest finish, and slack times for other activities. The exact impact depends on the relationship between the various activities.

In previous sections we define an *immediate predecessor* activity as an activity that comes immediately before a given activity. In general, a *predecessor activity* is one that must be completed before the given activity can be started. Consider activity G (install pollution device) for

PROGRAM 11.1B

Excel QM Input Screen and Solution for General Foundry Example with 3 Time Estimates

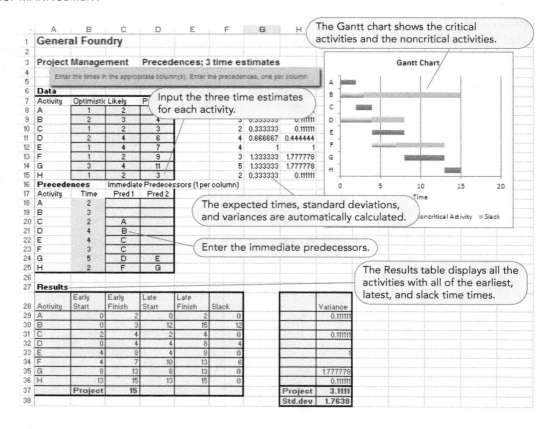

the General Foundry example. As seen previously, this activity is on the critical path. Predecessor activities are *A, B, C, D,* and *E.* All of these activities must be completed before activity *G* can be started. A *successor activity* is an activity that can be started only after the given activity is finished. Activity *H* is the only successor activity for activity *G.* A *parallel activity* is an activity that does not directly depend on the given activity. Again consider activity *G.* Are there any parallel activities for this activity? Looking at the network for General Foundry, it can be seen that activity *F* is a parallel activity of activity *G.*

After predecessor, successor, and parallel activities have been defined, we can explore the impact that an increase (decrease) in an activity time for a critical path activity would have on other activities in the network. The results are summarized in Table 11.4. If the time it takes to complete activity *G* increases, there will be an increase in the earliest start, earliest finish, latest start, and latest finish times for all successor activities. Because these activities follow activity *G,* these times will also increase. Because slack time is equal to latest finish time minus the earliest finish time (or the latest start time minus earliest start time; LF − EF or LS − ES), there will be no change in the slack for successor activities. Because activity *G*

TABLE 11.4

Impact of an Increase (Decrease) in an Activity Time for a Critical Path Activity

ACTIVITY TIME	SUCCESSOR ACTIVITY	PARALLEL ACTIVITY	PREDECESSOR ACTIVITY
Earliest start	Increase (decrease)	No change	No change
Earliest finish	Increase (decrease)	No change	No change
Latest start	Increase (decrease)	Increase (decrease)	No change
Latest finish	Increase (decrease)	Increase (decrease)	No change
Slack	No change	Increase (decrease)	No change

is on the critical path, an increase in activity time will increase the total project competition time. This would mean that the latest finish, latest start, and slack time will also increase for all parallel activities. You can prove this to yourself by completing a backward pass through the network using a higher total project competition time. There are no changes for predecessor activities.

11.3 PERT/Cost

Using PERT/Cost to plan, schedule, monitor, and control project cost helps accomplish the sixth and final step of PERT.

Although PERT is an excellent method of monitoring and controlling project length, it does not consider another very important factor, project *cost*. **PERT/Cost** is a modification of PERT that allows a manager to plan, schedule, monitor, and control cost as well as time.

We begin this section by investigating how costs can be planned and scheduled. Then we see how costs can be monitored and controlled.

Planning and Scheduling Project Costs: Budgeting Process

The overall approach in the budgeting process of a project is to determine how much is to be spent every week or month. This is accomplished as follows:

Four Steps of the Budgeting Process

1. Identify all costs associated with each of the activities. Then add these costs together to get one estimated cost or budget for each activity.
2. If you are dealing with a large project, several activities can be combined into larger work packages. A work *package* is simply a logical collection of activities. Since the General Foundry project we have been discussing is small, each activity will be a work package.
3. Convert the budgeted cost per activity into a cost per time period. To do this, we assume that the cost of completing any activity is spent at a uniform rate over time. Thus, if the budgeted cost for a given activity is $48,000 and the activity's expected time is four weeks, the budgeted cost per week is $12,000 (=$48,000/4weeks).
4. Using the earliest and latest start times, find out how much money should be spent during each week or month to finish the project by the date desired.

BUDGETING FOR GENERAL FOUNDRY   Let us apply this budgeting process to the General Foundry problem. The Gantt chart for this problem, shown in Figure 11.9, illustrates this process. In this chart, a horizontal bar shows when each activity will be performed based on the earliest times. To develop a budget schedule, we will determine how much will be spent on each activity during each week and fill these amounts into the chart in place of the bars. Lester Harky has carefully computed the costs associated with each of his eight activities. He has also divided the total budget for each activity by the activity's expected completion time to determine the weekly

FIGURE 11.9
Gantt Chart for General Foundry Example

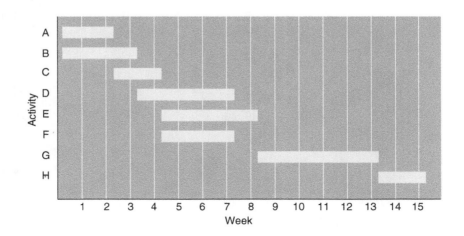

IN ACTION

California Needs Project Management for $25 Billion Water Project

The budget crunch in California has affected many lives. Amidst the turmoil, a new project to divert water from the Sacramento River via two enormous tunnels routed to the southern part of the state. The project would take 10 years to finish and is expected to have 50 years of useful life.

Advocates say the water project would improve the water quality, improve sustainability, increase earthquake robustness, minimize overall exports, and decrease demand from existing fish-killing water facilities in the southern part of California. The biggest challenge for the proposed massive double-tunnel, water diversion project will be the coordination of state and federal agencies, administration of the construction and excavation contractors, and the supervision of the overall expenses . . . in other words, the management of the project.

The state of California has estimated that building the two tunnels will cost $14.5 billion, the net present value of the operation and maintenance of the two tunnels over their 50 year useful life equivocates to $4.8 billion, and the ensuing habit restoration would require another $4.1 billion. In this case, sound project management is not just a nicety . . . it is a necessity.

Source: California plan to overhaul water system hub to cost $25 billion, *Los Angeles Times*, May 29, 2013, <articles.latimes.com>

---

budget for the activity. The budget for activity A, for example, is $22,000 (see Table 11.5). Since its expected time (t) is 2 weeks, $11,000 is spent each week to complete the activity. Table 11.5 also provides two pieces of data we found earlier using PERT: the earliest start time (ES) and latest start time (LS) for each activity.

Looking at the total of the budgeted activity costs, we see that the entire project will cost $308,000. Finding the weekly budget will help Harky determine how the project is progressing on a week-to-week basis.

A budget is computed using ES.

The weekly budget for the project is developed from the data in Table 11.5. The earliest start time for activity A, for example, is 0. Because A takes 2 weeks to complete, its weekly budget of $11,000 should be spent in weeks 1 and 2. For activity B, the earliest start time is 0, the expected completion time is 3 weeks, and the budgeted cost per week is $10,000. Thus, $10,000 should be spent for activity B in each of weeks 1, 2, and 3. Using the earliest start time, we can find the exact weeks during which the budget for each activity should be spent. These weekly amounts can be summed for all activities to arrive at the weekly budget for the entire project. This is shown in Table 11.6. Notice the similarities between this chart and the Gantt chart shown in Figure 11.9.

Do you see how the weekly budget for the project (total per week) is determined in Table 11.6? The only two activities that can be performed during the first week are activities A and B because their earliest start times are 0. Thus, during the first week, a total of $21,000

TABLE 11.5 Activity Cost for General Foundry, Inc.

ACTIVITY	EARLIEST START TIME, ES	LATEST START TIME, LS	EXPECTED TIME, t	TOTAL BUDGETED COST ($)	BUDGETED COST PER WEEK ($)
A	0	0	2	22,000	11,000
B	0	1	3	30,000	10,000
C	2	2	2	26,000	13,000
D	3	4	4	48,000	12,000
E	4	4	4	56,000	14,000
F	4	10	3	30,000	10,000
G	8	8	5	80,000	16,000
H	13	13	2	16,000	8,000
				Total 308,000	

TABLE 11.6   Budgeted Cost (Thousands of Dollars) for General Foundry, Inc., Using Earliest Start Times

ACTIVITY	1	2	3	4	5	6	7	8	9	10	11	12	13	14	15	TOTAL
A	11	11														22
B	10	10	10													30
C			13	13												26
D				12	12	12	12									48
E					14	14	14	14								56
F					10	10	10									30
G									16	16	16	16	16			80
H														8	8	16
																308
Total per week	21	21	23	25	36	36	36	14	16	16	16	16	16	8	8	
Total to date	21	42	65	90	126	162	198	212	228	244	260	276	292	300	308	

should be spent. Because activities A and B are still being performed in the second week, a total of $21,000 should also be spent during that period. The earliest start time for activity C is at the end of week 2 (ES = 2 for activity C). Thus, $13,000 is spent on activity C in both weeks 3 and 4. Because activity B is also being performed during week 3, the total budget in week 3 is $23,000. Similar computations are done for all activities to determine the total budget for the entire project for each week. Then these weekly totals can be added to determine the total amount that should be spent to date (total to date). This information is displayed in the bottom row of the table.

Another budget is computed using LS.

Those activities along the critical path must spend their budgets at the times shown in Table 11.6. The activities that are *not* on the critical path, however, can be started at a later date. This concept is embodied in the latest starting time, LS, for each activity. Thus, if *latest starting times* are used, another budget can be obtained. This budget will delay the expenditure of funds until the last possible moment. The procedures for computing the budget when LS is used are the same as when ES is used. The results of the new computations are shown in Table 11.7.

TABLE 11.7   Budgeted Cost (Thousands of Dollars) for General Foundry, Inc., Using Latest Start Times

ACTIVITY	1	2	3	4	5	6	7	8	9	10	11	12	13	14	15	TOTAL
A	11	11														22
B		10	10	10												30
C			13	13												26
D					12	12	12	12								48
E					14	14	14	14								56
F											10	10	10			30
G									16	16	16	16	16			80
H														8	8	16
																308
Total per week	11	21	23	23	26	26	26	26	16	16	26	26	26	8	8	
Total to date	11	32	55	78	104	130	156	182	198	214	240	266	292	300	308	

FIGURE 11.10
Budget Ranges for General Foundry

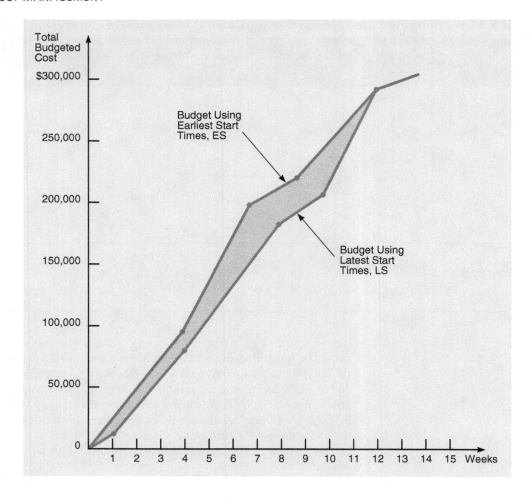

Compare the budgets given in Tables 11.6 and 11.7. The amount that should be spent to date (total to date) for the budget in Table 11.7 uses fewer financial resources in the first few weeks. This is because this budget is prepared using the latest start times. Thus, the budget in Table 11.7 shows the *latest* possible time that funds can be expended and still finish the project on time. The budget in Table 11.6 reveals the *earliest* possible time that funds can be expended. Therefore, a manager can choose any budget that falls between the budgets presented in these two tables. These two tables form feasible budget ranges. This concept is illustrated in Figure 11.10.

The budget ranges for General Foundry were established by plotting the total-to-date budgets for ES and LS. Lester Harky can use any budget between these feasible ranges and still complete the air pollution project on time. Budgets like the ones shown in Figure 11.10 are normally developed before the project is started. Then, as the project is being completed, funds expended should be monitored and controlled.

Although there are cash flow and money management advantages to delaying activities until their latest start times, such delays can create problems with finishing the project on schedule. If an activity is not started until its latest start time, there is no slack remaining. Any subsequent delays in this activity will delay the project. For this reason, it may not be desirable to schedule all activities to start at the latest start time.

Is the project on schedule and within its budget?

Monitoring and Controlling Project Costs

The purpose of monitoring and controlling project costs is to ensure that the project is progressing on schedule and that cost overruns are kept to a minimum. The status of the entire project should be checked periodically.

Lester Harky wants to know how his air pollution project is going. It is now the sixth week of the 15-week project. Activities A, B, and C have been finished. These activities incurred costs of $20,000, $36,000, and $26,000, respectively. Activity D is only 10% completed and so far the cost expended has been $6,000. Activity E is 20% completed with an incurred cost of $20,000,

TABLE 11.8 Monitoring and Controlling Budgeted Cost

ACTIVITY	TOTAL BUDGETED COST ($)	PERCENT OF COMPLETION	VALUE OF WORK COMPLETED ($)	ACTUAL COST ($)	ACTIVITY DIFFERENCE ($)
A	22,000	100	22,000	20,000	−2,000
B	30,000	100	30,000	36,000	6,000
C	26,000	100	26,000	26,000	0
D	48,000	10	4,800	6,000	1,200
E	56,000	20	11,200	20,000	8,800
F	30,000	20	6,000	4,000	−2,000
G	80,000	0	0	0	0
H	16,000	0	0	0	0
			Total 100,000	112,000	12,000
				Overrun	

and activity *F* is 20% completed with an incurred cost of $4,000. Activities *G* and *H* have not been started. Is the air pollution project on schedule? What is the value of work completed? Are there any cost overruns?

The value of work completed, or the budgeted cost to date for any activity, can be computed as follows:

$$\text{Value of work completed} = (\text{Percentage of work completed})$$
$$\times (\text{Total activity budget}) \qquad (11\text{-}8)$$

The activity difference is also of interest:

$$\text{Activity difference} = \text{Actual cost} - \text{Value of work completed} \qquad (11\text{-}9)$$

If an activity difference is negative, there is a cost underrun, but if the number is positive, there has been a cost overrun.

Compute the value of work completed by multiplying budgeted cost times percent of completion.

Table 11.8 provides this information for General Foundry. The second column contains the total budgeted cost (from Table 11.6), and the third column contains the percent of completion. With these data and the actual cost expended for each activity, we can compute the value of work completed and the overruns or underruns for every activity.

One way to measure the value of the work completed is to multiply the total budgeted cost times the percent of completion for every activity.* Activity *D*, for example, has a value of work completed of $4,800 (=$48,000 times 10%). To determine the amount of overrun or underrun for any activity, the value of work completed is subtracted from the actual cost. These differences can be added to determine the overrun or underrun for the project. As you see, at week 6 there is a $12,000 cost overrun. Furthermore, the value of work completed is only $100,000, and the actual cost of the project to date is $112,000. How do these costs compare with the budgeted costs for week 6? If Harky had decided to use the budget for earliest start times (see Table 11.6) we can see that $162,000 should have been spent. Thus, the project is behind schedule and there are cost overruns. Harky needs to move faster on this project to finish on time, and he must control future costs carefully to try to eliminate the current cost overrun of $12,000. To monitor and control costs, the budgeted amount, the value of work completed, and the actual costs should be computed periodically.

In the next section we see how a project can be shortened by spending additional money. The technique is called crashing and is part of the critical path method (CPM).

*The percentage of completion for each activity can be measured in other ways as well. For example, one might examine the ratio of labor hours expended to total labor hours estimated.

IN ACTION   Small Companies Utilize Project Management in Five Phases

Recently, small companies have incorporated project management tools into their workplaces. For small companies, proprietors and managers assign activities in the project to employees, including themselves. Researchers have identified five basic phases of a project to help small businesses. These five are conception, planning and design, execution, control, and closing.

Conception
During conception, small business decision makers integrate their ideas and align them with the company's goals. The decision to go forward with the project is made during this phase.

Planning and Design
The second phase involves determining the tasks and milestones that need to happen for the project to be successful. It also involves the assignment of activities to departments and preparing the PERT network.

Execution
Beginning at the project's start is the execution phase. Managers direct employees to perform tasks and make note of their completion times.

Control
The control phase can overlap the execution phase above and involves ensuring deadlines and milestones are met on time and on budget. Resources may need to be re-allocated during this phase.

Closing
This phase is aptly named as presentations are performed, analyses are finished, and reports are filed.

Source: Major Activities in Project Management Phases, *Houston Chronicle*, May 21, 2013, <smallbusiness.chron.com>

11.4   Project Crashing

Shortening a project is called crashing.

At times, projects have deadlines that may be impossible to meet using the normal procedures for completion of the project. However, by using overtime, working weekends, hiring extra workers, or using extra equipment, it may be possible to finish a project in less time than is normally required. However, the cost of the project will usually increase as a result. When CPM was developed, the possibility of reducing the project completion time was recognized; this process is called **crashing**.

When crashing a project, the *normal time* for each activity is used to find the critical path. The *normal cost* is the cost for completing the activity using normal procedures. If the project completion time using normal procedures meets the deadline that has been imposed, there is no problem. However, if the deadline is before the normal project completion time, some extraordinary measures must be taken. Another set of times and costs is then developed for each activity. The *crash time* is the shortest possible activity time, and this requires the use of additional resources. The *crash cost* is the price of completing the activity in an earlier-than-normal time. If a project must be crashed, it is desirable to do this at the least additional cost.

Project crashing with CPM involves four steps:

Four Steps of Project Crashing

1. Find the normal critical path and identify the critical activities.
2. Compute the crash cost per week (or other time period) for all activities in the network. This process uses the following formula:*

$$\text{Crash cost/Time period} = \frac{\text{Crash cost} - \text{Normal cost}}{\text{Normal time} - \text{Crash time}} \qquad (11\text{-}10)$$

3. Select the activity on the critical path with the smallest crash cost per week. Crash this activity to the maximum extent possible or to the point at which your desired deadline has been reached.
4. Check to be sure that the critical path you were crashing is still critical. Often, a reduction in activity time along the critical path causes a noncritical path or paths to become critical. If the critical path is still the longest path through the network, return to step 3. If not, find the new critical path and return to step 3.

---

*This formula assumes that crash costs are linear. If they are not, adjustments must be made.

TABLE 11.9   Normal and Crash Data for General Foundry, Inc.

ACTIVITY	TIME (WEEKS)		COST ($)		CRASH COST PER WEEK ($)	CRITICAL PATH?
	NORMAL	CRASH	NORMAL	CRASH		
A	2	1	22,000	23,000	1,000	Yes
B	3	1	30,000	34,000	2,000	No
C	2	1	26,000	27,000	1,000	Yes
D	4	3	48,000	49,000	1,000	No
E	4	2	56,000	58,000	1,000	Yes
F	3	2	30,000	30,500	500	No
G	5	2	80,000	86,000	2,000	Yes
H	2	1	16,000	19,000	3,000	Yes

General Foundry Example

Suppose that General Foundry had been given 14 weeks instead of 16 weeks to install the new pollution control equipment or face a court-ordered shutdown. Or suppose that there was a bonus on the line for Lester if the equipment is installed in 12 weeks or less. As you recall, the length of Lester Harky's critical path was 15 weeks. What can he do? We see that Harky cannot possibly meet the deadline unless he is able to shorten some of the activity times.

General Foundry's normal and crash times and normal and crash costs are shown in Table 11.9. Note, for example, that activity B's normal time is 3 weeks (this estimate was also used for PERT) and its crash time is 1 week. This means that the activity can be shortened by 2 weeks if extra resources are provided. The normal cost is $30,000, and the crash cost is $34,000. This implies that crashing activity B will cost General Foundry an additional $4,000. Crash costs are assumed to be linear. As shown in Figure 11.11, activity B's crash cost per week is $2,000. Crash costs for all other activities can be computed in a similar fashion. Then steps 3 and 4 can be applied to reduce the project's completion time.

FIGURE 11.11

Crash and Normal Times and Costs for Activity B

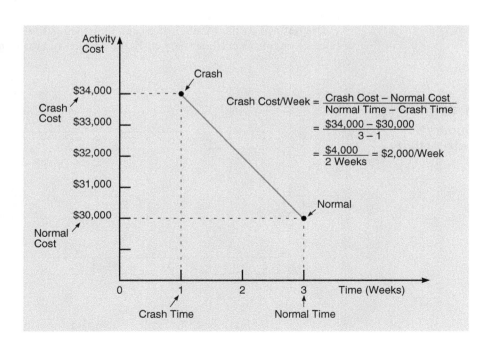

Activities *A, C,* and *E* are on the critical path, and each have a minimum crash cost per week of $1,000. Harky can crash activity *A* by 1 week to reduce the project completion time to 14 weeks. The cost is an additional $1,000.

There are now two critical paths.

At this stage, there are two critical paths. The original critical path consists of activities *A, C, E, G,* and *H,* with a total completion time of 14 weeks. The new critical path consists of activities *B, D, G,* and *H,* also with a total completion time of 14 weeks. Any further crashing must be done to both critical paths. For example, if Harky wants to reduce the project completion time by an additional 2 weeks, both paths must be reduced. This can be done by reducing activity *G,* which is on both critical paths, by two weeks for an additional cost of $2,000 per week. The total completion time would be 12 weeks, and total crashing cost would be $5,000 ($1,000 to reduce activity *A* by one week and $4,000 to reduce activity *G* by two weeks).

For small networks, such as General Foundry's, it is possible to use the four-step procedure to find the least cost of reducing the project completion dates. For larger networks, however, this approach is difficult and impractical, and more sophisticated techniques, such as linear programming, must be employed.

Project Crashing with Linear Programming

Linear programming (see Chapters 7 and 8) is another approach to finding the best project crashing schedule. We illustrate its use on General Foundry's network. The data needed are derived from Table 11.9 and Figure 11.12.

The first step is to define decision variables for the linear program.

We begin by defining the decision variables. If *X* is the earliest finish time for an activity, then

$$X_A = \text{EF for activity } A$$
$$X_B = \text{EF for activity } B$$
$$X_C = \text{EF for activity } C$$
$$X_D = \text{EF for activity } D$$
$$X_E = \text{EF for activity } E$$
$$X_F = \text{EF for activity } F$$
$$X_G = \text{EF for activity } G$$
$$X_H = \text{EF for activity } H$$
$$X_{\text{start}} = \text{start time for project (usually 0)}$$
$$X_{\text{finish}} = \text{earliest finish time for the project}$$

Although the starting node has a variable (X_{start}) associated with it, this is not necessary since it will be given a value of 0, and this could be used instead of the variable.

Y is defined as the number of weeks that each activity is crashed. Y_A is the number of weeks we decide to crash activity *A,* Y_B the amount of crash time used for activity *B,* and so on, up to Y_H.

FIGURE 11.12

General Foundry's Network with Activity Times

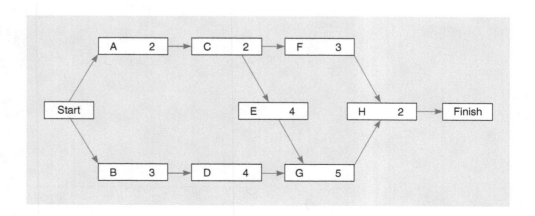

The next step is to determine the objective function.

OBJECTIVE FUNCTION   Since the objective is to minimize the cost of crashing the total project, our LP objective function is

$$\text{Minimize crash cost} = 1{,}000Y_A + 2{,}000Y_B + 1{,}000Y_C + 1{,}000Y_D + 1{,}000Y_E$$
$$+ 500Y_F + 2{,}000Y_G + 3{,}000Y_H$$

(These cost coefficients were drawn from the sixth column of Table 11.9.)

Crash constraints are determined next.

CRASH TIME CONSTRAINTS   Constraints are required to ensure that each activity is not crashed more than its maximum allowable crash time. The maximum for each Y variable is the difference between the normal time and the crash time (from Table 11.9):

$$Y_A \le 1$$
$$Y_B \le 2$$
$$Y_C \le 1$$
$$Y_D \le 1$$
$$Y_E \le 2$$
$$Y_F \le 1$$
$$Y_G \le 3$$
$$Y_H \le 1$$

The final step is to determine event constraints.

PROJECT COMPLETION CONSTRAINT   This constraint specifies that the last event must take place before the project deadline date. If Harky's project must be crashed down to 12 weeks, then

$$X_{\text{finish}} \le 12$$

CONSTRAINTS DESCRIBING THE NETWORK   The final set of constraints describes the structure of the network. Every activity will have one constraint for each of its predecessors. The form of these constraints is

$$\text{Earliest finish time} \ge \text{Earliest finish time for predecessor} + \text{Activity time}$$
$$EF \ge EF_{\text{predecessor}} + (t - Y)$$
or
$$X \ge X_{\text{predecessor}} + (t - Y)$$

The activity time is given as $t - Y$, or the normal activity time minus the time saved by crashing. We know $EF = ES + \text{Activity time}$, and $ES = \text{Largest EF of predecessors}$.

   We begin by setting the start of the project to time zero: $X_{\text{start}} = 0$.

For activity A,

$$X_A \ge X_{\text{start}} + (2 - Y_A)$$
or
$$X_A - X_{\text{start}} + Y_A \ge 2$$

For activity B,

$$X_B \ge X_{\text{start}} + (3 - Y_B)$$
or
$$X_B - X_{\text{start}} + Y_B \ge 3$$

For activity C,

$$X_C \ge X_A + (2 - Y_C)$$
or
$$X_C - X_A + Y_C \ge 2$$

For activity D,

$$X_D \ge X_B + (4 - Y_D)$$
or
$$X_D - X_B + Y_D \ge 4$$

For activity E,

$$X_E \geq X_C + (4 - Y_E)$$

or

$$X_E - X_C + Y_E \geq 4$$

For activity F,

$$X_F \geq X_C + (3 - Y_F)$$

or

$$X_F - X_C + Y_F \geq 3$$

For activity G, we need two constraints since there are two predecessors. The first constraint for activity G is

$$X_G \geq X_D + (5 - Y_G)$$

or

$$X_G - X_D + Y_G \geq 5$$

The second constraint for activity G is

$$X_G \geq X_E + (5 - Y_G)$$

or

$$X_G - X_E + Y_G \geq 5$$

For activity H we need two constraints since there are two predecessors. The first constraint for activity H is

$$X_H \geq X_F + (2 - Y_H)$$

or

$$X_H - X_F + Y_H \geq 2$$

The second constraint for activity H is

$$X_H \geq X_G + (2 - Y_H)$$

or

$$X_H - X_G + Y_H \geq 2$$

To indicate the project is finished when activity H is finished, we have

$$X_{\text{finish}} \geq X_H$$

After adding nonnegativity constraints, this LP problem can be solved for the optimal Y values. This can be done with QM for Windows or Excel QM. Program 11.2 provides the Excel QM solution to this problem.

PROGRAM 11.2

Solution to Crashing Problem via Solver in Excel

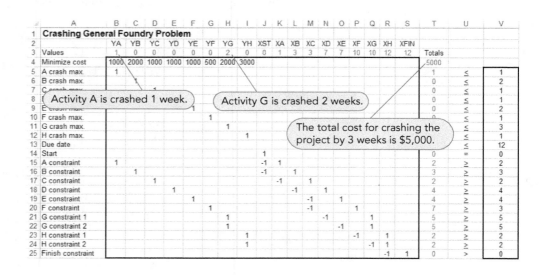

11.5 Other Topics in Project Management

We have seen how to schedule a project and develop budget schedules. However, there are other things that are important and helpful to a project manager. We now briefly introduce these.

Subprojects

For extremely large projects, an activity may be made of several smaller subactivities. Each activity might be viewed as a smaller project or a subproject of the original project. The person in charge of the activity might wish to create a PERT/CPM chart for managing this subproject. Many software packages have the ability to include several levels of subprojects.

Milestones

Major events in a project are often referred to as **milestones**. These are often reflected in Gantt charts and PERT charts to highlight the importance of reaching these events.

Resource Leveling

In addition to managing the time and costs involved in a project, a manager must also be concerned with the resources used in a project. These resources might be equipment or people. In planning a project (and often as part of the work breakdown structure), a manager must identify which resources are needed with each activity. For example, in a construction project there may be several activities requiring the use of heavy equipment such as a crane. If the construction company has only one such crane, then conflicts will occur if two activities requiring the use of this crane are scheduled for the same day. To alleviate problems such as this, **resource leveling** is employed. This means that one or more activities are moved from the earliest start time to another time (no later than the latest start time) so that the resource utilization is more evenly distributed over time. If the resources are construction crews, this is very beneficial in that the crews are kept busy and overtime is minimized.

Software

There are numerous project management software packages on the market for both mainframe computers and personal computers. There are numerous project management software packages on the market. Some are hosted locally while others are cloud-based. Some of them include Microsoft Project, Clarizen (cloud-based), OmniPlan, and OpenProj. They can be used to develop budget schedules, automatically adjust future start times based on the actual start times for prior activities, and level the resource utilization.

Good software for personal computers ranges in price from a few hundred dollars to several thousand dollars. For mainframe computers, software may cost considerably more. Companies have paid several hundred thousand dollars for project management software and support because it helps management make better decisions and keep track of things that would otherwise be unmanageable.

Summary

The fundamentals of PERT and CPM are presented in this chapter. Both of these techniques are excellent for controlling large and complex projects.

PERT is probabilistic and allows three time estimates for each activity. These estimates are used to compute the project's expected completion time, variance, and the probability that the project will be completed by a given date. PERT/Cost, an extension of standard PERT, can be used to plan, schedule, monitor, and control project costs. Using PERT/Cost, it is possible to determine if there are cost overruns or underruns at any point in time. It is also possible to determine whether the project is on schedule.

CPM, although similar to PERT, has the ability to crash projects by reducing their completion time through additional resource expenditures. Finally, we see that linear programming can also be used to crash a network by a desired amount at a minimum cost.

Glossary

Activity A time-consuming job or task that is a key subpart of the total project.

Activity-on-Arc (AOA) A network in which the activities are represented by arcs.

Activity-on-Node (AON) A network in which the activities are represented by nodes. This is the model illustrated in our book.

Activity Time Estimates Three time estimates that are used in determining the expected completion time and variance for an activity in a PERT network.

Backward Pass A procedure that moves from the end of the network to the beginning of the network. It is used in determining the latest finish and latest start times.

Beta Probability Distribution A probability distribution that is often used in computing the expected activity completion times and variances in networks.

CPM Critical path method. A deterministic network technique that is similar to PERT but allows for project crashing.

Crashing The process of reducing the total time that it takes to complete a project by expending additional funds.

Critical Path The series of activities that have zero slack. It is the longest time path through the network. A delay for any activity that is on the critical path will delay the completion of the entire project.

Critical Path Analysis An analysis that determines the total project completion time, the critical path for the project, slack, ES, EF, LS, and LF for every activity.

Earliest Finish Time (EF) The earliest time that an activity can be finished without violation of precedence requirements.

Earliest Start Time (ES) The earliest time that an activity can start without violation of precedence requirements.

Event A point in time that marks the beginning or ending of an activity.

Expected Activity Time The average time that it should take to complete an activity. $t = (a + 4m + b)/6$.

Forward Pass A procedure that moves from the beginning of a network to the end of the network. It is used in determining earliest activity start times and earliest finish times.

Gantt Chart A bar chart indicating when the activities (represented by bars) in a project will be performed.

Immediate Predecessor An activity that must be completed before another activity can be started.

Latest Finish Time (LF) The latest time that an activity can be finished without delaying the entire project.

Latest Start Time (LS) The latest time that an activity can be started without delaying the entire project.

Milestone A major event in a project.

Most Likely Time (m) The amount of time that you would expect it would take to complete the activity.

Network A graphical display of a project that contains both activities and events.

Optimistic Time (a) The shortest amount of time that could be required to complete the activity.

PERT Program evaluation and review technique. A network technique that allows three time estimates for each activity in a project.

PERT/Cost A technique that allows a decision maker to plan, schedule, monitor, and control project *cost* as well as project time.

Pessimistic Time (b) The greatest amount of time that could be required to complete the activity.

Resource Leveling The process of smoothing out the utilization of resources in a project.

Slack Time The amount of time that an activity can be delayed without delaying the entire project. Slack is equal to the latest start time minus the earliest start time, or the latest finish time minus the earliest finish time.

Variance of Activity Completion Time A measure of dispersion of the activity completion time. Variance $= [(b - a)/6]^2$.

Work Breakdown Structure (WBS) A list of the activities that must be performed in a project.

Key Equations

(11-1) $t = \dfrac{a + 4m + b}{6}$

Expected activity completion time for activity.

(11-2) Variance $= \left(\dfrac{b - a}{6}\right)^2$

Activity variance.

(11-3) $EF = ES + t$

Earliest finish time.

(11-4) $LS = LF - t$

Latest start time.

(11-5) Slack $= LS - ES$ *or*   Slack $= LF - EF$

Slack time in an activity.

(11-6) Project variance $= \Sigma$ variances of activities on critical path

(11-7) $Z = \dfrac{\text{Due date} - \text{Expected date of completion}}{\sigma_T}$

Number of standard deviations the target date lies from the expected date, using the normal distribution.

(11-8) Value of work completed $=$ (Percentage of work completed) $\times$ (Total activity budget)

(11-9) Activity difference $=$ Actual cost $-$ Value of work completed

(11-10) Crash cost/Time period $= \dfrac{\text{Crash cost} - \text{Normal cost}}{\text{Normal time} - \text{Crash time}}$

The cost in CPM of reducing an activity's length per time period.

Solved Problems

Solved Problem 11-1

To complete the wing assembly for an experimental aircraft, Scott DeWitte has laid out the major steps and seven activities involved. These activities have been labeled A through G in the following table, which also shows their estimated completion times (in weeks) and immediate predecessors. Determine the expected time and variance for each activity.

ACTIVITY	a	m	b	IMMEDIATE PREDECESSORS
A	1	2	3	—
B	2	3	4	—
C	4	5	6	A
D	8	9	10	B
E	2	5	8	C, D
F	4	5	6	B
G	1	2	3	E

Solution

Although not required for this problem, a diagram of all the activities can be useful. A PERT diagram for the wing assembly is shown in Figure 11.13.

FIGURE 11.13

PERT Diagram for Scott DeWitte (Solved Problem 11-1)

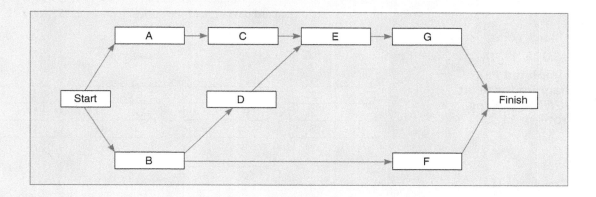

Expected times and variances can be computed using the formulas presented in the chapter. The results are summarized in the following table:

ACTIVITY	EXPECTED TIME (IN WEEKS)	VARIANCE
A	2	$1/9$
B	3	$1/9$
C	5	$1/9$
D	9	$1/9$
E	5	1
F	5	$1/9$
G	2	$1/9$

Solved Problem 11-2

Referring to Solved Problem 11-1, now Scott would like to determine the critical path for the entire wing assembly project as well as the expected completion time for the total project. In addition, he would like to determine the earliest and latest start and finish times for all activities.

Solution

The critical path, earliest start times, earliest finish times, latest start times, and latest finish times can be determined using the procedures outlined in the chapter. The results are shown in Figure 11.14 and are summarized in the following table:

ACTIVITY	ACTIVITY TIME				SLACK
	ES	EF	LS	LF	
A	0	2	5	7	5
B	0	3	0	3	0
C	2	7	7	12	5
D	3	12	3	12	0
E	12	17	12	17	0
F	3	8	14	19	11
G	17	19	17	19	0

Expected project length = 19 weeks
Variance of the critical path = 1.333
Standard deviation of the critical path = 1.155 weeks

FIGURE 11.14
Completed PERT Diagram for Scott DeWitte (Solved Problem 11-2)

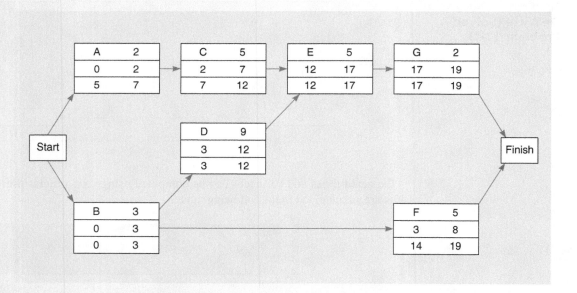

The activities along the critical path are *B, D, E,* and *G*. These activities have zero slack, as shown in the table. The expected project completion time is 19 weeks. The earliest and latest start and finish times are shown in the table.

Self-Test

- Before taking the self-test, refer to the learning objectives at the beginning of the chapter, the notes in the margins, and the glossary at the end of the chapter.
- Use the key at the back of the book to correct your answers.
- Restudy pages that correspond to any questions that you answered incorrectly or material you feel uncertain about.

1. Network models such as PERT and CPM are used
   a. to plan large and complex projects.
   b. to schedule large and complex projects.
   c. to monitor large and complex projects.
   d. to control large and complex projects.
   e. for all of the above.

2. The primary difference between PERT and CPM is that
   a. PERT uses one time estimate.
   b. CPM has three time estimates.
   c. PERT has three time estimates.
   d. with CPM, it is assumed that all activities can be performed at the same time.

3. The earliest start time for an activity is equal to
   a. the largest EF of the immediate predecessors.
   b. the smallest EF of the immediate predecessors.
   c. the largest ES of the immediate predecessors.
   d. the smallest ES of the immediate predecessors.

4. The latest finish time for an activity is found during the backward pass through the network. The latest finish time is equal to
   a. the largest LF of the activities for which it is an immediate predecessor.
   b. the smallest LF of the activities for which it is an immediate predecessor.
   c. the largest LS of the activities for which it is an immediate predecessor.
   d. the smallest LS of the activities for which it is an immediate predecessor.

5. When PERT is used and probabilities are found, one of the assumptions that is made is that
   a. all activities are on the critical path.
   b. activity times are independent.
   c. all activities have the same variance.
   d. the project variance is equal to the sum of the variances of all activities in the project.
   e. all of the above.

6. In PERT, the time estimate b represents
   a. the most optimistic time.
   b. the most likely time.
   c. the most pessimistic time.
   d. the expected time.
   e. none of the above.

7. In PERT, slack time equals
   a. ES $+ t$.
   b. LS $-$ ES.
   c. 0.
   d. EF $-$ ES.
   e. none of the above.

8. The standard deviation for the PERT project is approximately
   a. the square root of the sum of the variances along the critical path.
   b. the sum of the critical path activity standard deviations.
   c. the square root of the sum of the variances of the project activities.
   d. all of the above.
   e. none of the above.

9. The critical path is the
   a. shortest path in a network.
   b. longest path in a network.
   c. path with the smallest variance.
   d. path with the largest variance.
   e. none of the above.

10. If the project completion time is normally distributed and the due date for the project is greater than the expected completion time, then the probability that the project will be finished by the due date is
    a. less than 0.50.
    b. greater than 0.50.
    c. equal to 0.50.
    d. undeterminable without more information.

11. If activity A is not on the critical path, then the slack for A will equal
    a. LF $-$ EF.
    b. EF $-$ ES.
    c. 0.
    d. all of the above.

12. If a project is to be crashed at the minimum possible additional cost, then the first activity to be crashed must be
    a. on the critical path.
    b. the one with the shortest activity time.
    c. the one with the longest activity time.
    d. the one with the lowest cost.

13. _____ activities are ones that will delay the entire project if they are late or delayed.

14. PERT stands for _____.

15. Project crashing can be performed using a

    _____.

16. PERT can use three estimates for activity time. These three estimates are _____, _____, and _____.

17. The latest start time minus the earliest start time is called the _____ time for any activity.

18. The percent of project completion, value of work completed, and actual activity costs are used to _____ projects.

Discussion Questions and Problems

Discussion Questions

11-1 What are some of the questions that can be answered with PERT and CPM?

11-2 What are the major differences between PERT and CPM?

11-3 What is an activity? What is an event? What is an immediate predecessor?

11-4 Describe how expected activity times and variances can be computed in a PERT network.

11-5 Briefly discuss what is meant by critical path analysis. What are critical path activities, and why are they important?

11-6 What are the earliest activity start time and latest activity start time? How are they computed?

11-7 Describe the meaning of slack and discuss how it can be determined.

11-8 How can we determine the probability that a project will be completed by a certain date? What assumptions are made in this computation?

11-9 Briefly describe PERT/Cost and how it is used.

11-10 What is crashing, and how is it done by hand?

11-11 Why is linear programming useful in CPM crashing?

Problems*

: 11-12 Sid Davidson is the personnel director of Babson and Willcount, a company that specializes in consulting and research. One of the training programs that Sid is considering for the middle-level managers of Babson and Willcount is leadership training. Sid has listed a number of activities that must be completed before a training program of this nature could be conducted. The activities and immediate predecessors appear in the following table:

ACTIVITY	IMMEDIATE PREDECESSORS
A	—
B	—
C	—
D	B
E	A, D
F	C
G	E, F

Develop a network for this problem.

11-13 Sid Davidson was able to determine the activity times for the leadership training program. He would like to determine the total project completion time and the critical path. The activity times appear in the following table (see Problem 11-12):

ACTIVITY	TIME (DAYS)
A	2
B	5
C	1
D	10
E	3
F	6
G	8
	35

•11-14 Jean Walker is making plans for spring break at the beaches in Florida. In applying techniques she learned in her quantitative methods class, she has identified the activities that are necessary to prepare for her trip. The following table lists the activities and the immediate predecessors. Draw the network for this project.

ACTIVITY	IMMEDIATE PREDECESSORS
A	—
B	—
C	A
D	B
E	C, D
F	A
G	E, F

11-15 The following are the activity times for the project in Problem 11-14. Find the earliest, latest, and slack times for each activity. Then find the critical path.

ACTIVITY	TIME (DAYS)
A	3
B	7
C	4
D	2
E	5
F	6
G	3

---

*Note: means the problem may be solved with QM for Windows; means the problem may be solved with Excel QM; and means the problem may be solved with QM for Windows and/or Excel.

•11-16 Monohan Machinery specializes in developing weed-harvesting equipment that is used to clear small lakes of weeds. George Monohan, president of Monohan Machinery, is convinced that harvesting weeds is far better than using chemicals to kill weeds. Chemicals cause pollution, and the weeds seem to grow faster after chemicals have been used. George is contemplating the construction of a machine that would harvest weeds on narrow rivers and waterways. The activities that are necessary to build one of these experimental weed-harvesting machines are listed in the following table. Construct a network for these activities.

ACTIVITY	IMMEDIATE PREDECESSORS
A	—
B	—
C	A
D	A
E	B
F	B
G	C, E
H	D, F

Q:11-17 After consulting with Butch Radner, George Monohan was able to determine the activity times for constructing the weed-harvesting machine to be used on narrow rivers. George would like to determine ES, EF, LS, LF, and slack for each activity. The total project completion time and the critical path should also be determined. (See Problem 11-16 for details.) The activity times are shown in the following table:

ACTIVITY	TIME (WEEKS)
A	6
B	5
C	3
D	2
E	4
F	6
G	10
H	7

Q:11-18 A project was planned using PERT with three time estimates. The expected completion time of the project was determined to be 40 weeks. The variance of the critical path is 9.

(a) What is the probability that the project will be finished in 40 weeks or less?
(b) What is the probability that the project takes longer than 40 weeks?
(c) What is the probability that the project will be finished in 46 weeks or less?

(d) What is the probability that the project will take longer than 46 weeks?
(e) The project manager wishes to set the due date for the completion of the project so that there is a 90% chance of finishing on schedule. Thus, there would only be a 10% chance the project would take longer than this due date. What should this due date be?

Q:11-19 Tom Schriber, a director of personnel of Management Resources, Inc., is in the process of designing a program that its customers can use in the job-finding process. Some of the activities include preparing resumés, writing letters, making appointments to see prospective employers, researching companies and industries, and so on. Some of the information on the activities is shown in the following table:

ACTIVITY	DAYS a	DAYS m	DAYS b	IMMEDIATE PREDECESSORS
A	8	10	12	—
B	6	7	9	—
C	3	3	4	—
D	10	20	30	A
E	6	7	8	C
F	9	10	11	B, D, E
G	6	7	10	B, D, E
H	14	15	16	F
I	10	11	13	F
J	6	7	8	G, H
K	4	7	8	I, J
L	1	2	4	G, H

(a) Construct a network for this problem.
(b) Determine the expected time and variance for each activity.
(c) Determine ES, EF, LS, LF, and slack for each activity.
(d) Determine the critical path and project completion time.
(e) Determine the probability that the project will be finished in 70 days or less.
(f) Determine the probability that the project will be finished in 80 days or less.
(g) Determine the probability that the project will be finished in 90 days or less.

Q:11-20 Using PERT, Ed Rose was able to determine that the expected project completion time for the construction of a pleasure yacht is 21 months and the project variance is 4.

(a) What is the probability that the project will be completed in 17 months or less?
(b) What is the probability that the project will be completed in 20 months or less?

(c) What is the probability that the project will be completed in 23 months or less?

(d) What is the probability that the project will be completed in 25 months or less?

:11-21 The air pollution project discussed in the chapter has progressed over the past several weeks, and it is now the end of week 8. Lester Harky would like to know the value of the work completed, the amount of any cost overruns or underruns for the project, and the extent to which the project is ahead of or behind schedule by developing a table like Table 11.8. The revised cost figures are shown in the following table:

ACTIVITY	PERCENT OF COMPLETION	ACTUAL COST ($)
A	100	20,000
B	100	36,000
C	100	26,000
D	100	44,000
E	50	25,000
F	60	15,000
G	10	5,000
H	10	1,000

:11-22 Fred Ridgeway has been given the responsibility of managing a training and development program. He knows the earliest start time, the latest start time, and the total costs for each activity. This information is given in the following table.

(a) Using earliest start times, determine Fred's total monthly budget.

(b) Using latest start times, determine Fred's total monthly budget.

ACTIVITY	ES	LS	t	TOTAL COST ($1,000s)
A	0	0	6	10
B	1	4	2	14
C	3	3	7	5
D	4	9	3	6
E	6	6	10	14
F	14	15	11	13
G	12	18	2	4
H	14	14	11	6
I	18	21	6	18
J	18	19	4	12
K	22	22	14	10
L	22	23	8	16
M	18	24	6	18

:11-23 General Foundry's project crashing data are shown in Table 11.9. Crash this project to 13 weeks using CPM. What are the final times for each activity after crashing?

:11-24 Bowman Builders manufactures steel storage sheds for commercial use. Joe Bowman, president of Bowman Builders, is contemplating producing sheds for home use. The activities necessary to build an experimental model and related data are given in the accompanying table.

(a) What is the project completion date?

(b) Formulate an LP problem to crash this project to 10 weeks.

ACTIVITY	NORMAL TIME	CRASH TIME	NORMAL COST ($)	CRASH COST ($)	IMMEDIATE PREDECESSORS
A	3	2	1,000	1,600	—
B	2	1	2,000	2,700	—
C	1	1	300	300	—
D	7	3	1,300	1,600	A
E	6	3	850	1,000	B
F	2	1	4,000	5,000	C
G	4	2	1,500	2,000	D, E

:11-25 The Bender Construction Co. is involved in constructing municipal buildings and other structures that are used primarily by city and state municipalities. This requires developing legal documents, drafting feasibility studies, obtaining bond ratings, and so forth. Recently, Bender was given a request to submit a proposal for the construction of a municipal building. The first step is to develop legal documents and to perform all steps necessary before the construction contract is signed. This requires more than 20 separate activities that must be completed. These activities, their immediate predecessors, and time requirements are given in Table 11.10 on the next page.

As you can see, optimistic (a), most likely (m), and pessimistic (b) time estimates have been given for all of the activities described in the table. Using the data, determine the total project completion time for this preliminary step, the critical path, and slack time for all activities involved.

:11-26 Getting a degree from a college or university can be a long and difficult task. Certain courses must be completed before other courses may be taken. Develop a network diagram, in which every activity is a particular course that must be taken for a given degree program. The immediate predecessors will

TABLE 11.10   Data for Problem 11-25, Bender Construction Company

| ACTIVITY | TIME REQUIRED (WEEKS) | | | DESCRIPTION OF ACTIVITY | IMMEDIATE PREDECESSORS |
	a	m	b		
1	1	4	5	Draft of legal documents	—
2	2	3	4	Preparation of financial statements	—
3	3	4	5	Draft of history	—
4	7	8	9	Draft demand portion of feasibility study	—
5	4	4	5	Review and approval of legal documents	1
6	1	2	4	Review and approval of history	3
7	4	5	6	Review of feasibility study	4
8	1	2	4	Draft final financial portion of feasibility study	7
9	3	4	4	Draft facts relevant to the bond transaction	5
10	1	1	2	Review and approval of financial statements	2
11	18	20	26	Receive firm price of project	—
12	1	2	3	Review and completion of financial portion of feasibility study	8
13	1	1	2	Completion of draft statement	6, 9, 10, 11, 12
14	.10	.14	.16	All material sent to bond rating services	13
15	.2	.3	.4	Statement printed and distributed to all interested parties	14
16	1	1	2	Presentation to bond rating services	14
17	1	2	3	Bond rating received	16
18	3	5	7	Marketing of bonds	15, 17
19	.1	.1	.2	Purchase contract executed	18
20	.1	.14	.16	Final statement authorized and completed	19
21	2	3	6	Purchase contract	19
22	.1	.1	.2	Bond proceeds available	20
23	0	.2	.2	Sign construction contract	21, 22

be course prerequisites. Don't forget to include all university, college, and departmental course requirements. Then try to group these courses into semesters or quarters for your particular school. How long do you think it will take you to graduate? Which courses, if not taken in the proper sequence, could delay your graduation?

Q:11-27 Dream Team Productions was in the final design phases of its new film, *Killer Worms*, to be released next summer. Market Wise, the firm hired to coordinate the release of *Killer Worms* toys, identified 16 critical tasks to be completed before the release of the film.

(a) How many weeks in advance of the film release should Market Wise start its marketing campaign? What are the critical path activities? The tasks are as follows:

Table for Problem 11-27

ACTIVITY	IMMEDIATE PREDECESSORS	MOST OPTIMISTIC TIME	LIKELY TIME	PESSIMISTIC TIME
Task 1	—	1	2	4
Task 2	—	3	3.5	4
Task 3	—	10	12	13
Task 4	—	4	5	7
Task 5	—	2	4	5
Task 6	Task 1	6	7	8
Task 7	Task 2	2	4	5.5
Task 8	Task 3	5	7.7	9
Task 9	Task 3	9.9	10	12
Task 10	Task 3	2	4	5
Task 11	Task 4	2	4	6
Task 12	Task 5	2	4	6
Task 13	Tasks 6, 7, 8	5	6	6.5
Task 14	Tasks 10, 11, 12	1	1.1	2
Task 15	Tasks 9, 13	5	7	8
Task 16	Task 14	5	7	9

(b) If Tasks 9 and 10 were not necessary, what impact would this have on the critical path and the number of weeks needed to complete the marketing campaign?

⚙:11-28 The estimated times (in weeks) and immediate predecessors for the activities in a project are given in the following table. Assume that the activity times are independent.

ACTIVITY	IMMEDIATE PREDECESSORS	a	m	b
A	—	9	10	11
B	—	4	10	16
C	A	9	10	11
D	B	5	8	11

(a) Calculate the expected time and variance for each activity.
(b) What is the expected completion time of the critical path? What is the expected completion time of the other path in the network?
(c) What is the variance of the critical path? What is the variance of the other path in the network?
(d) If the time to complete path A–C is normally distributed, what is the probability that this path will be finished in 22 weeks or less?
(e) If the time to complete path B–D is normally distributed, what is the probability that this path will be finished in 22 weeks or less?
(f) Explain why the probability that the critical path will be finished in 22 weeks or less is not necessarily the probability that the project will be finished in 22 weeks or less.

⚙:11-29 The following costs have been estimated for the activities in a project:

ACTIVITY	IMMEDIATE PREDECESSORS	TIME	COST ($)
A	—	8	8,000
B	—	4	12,000
C	A	3	6,000
D	B	5	15,000
E	C, D	6	9,000
F	C, D	5	10,000
G	F	3	6,000

(a) Develop a cost schedule based on earliest start times.
(b) Develop a cost schedule based on latest start times.
(c) Suppose that it has been determined that the $6,000 for activity G is not evenly spread over the three weeks. Instead, the cost for the first week is $4,000, and the cost is $1,000 per week for each of the last two weeks. Modify the cost schedule based on earliest start times to reflect this situation.

⚙:11-30 The Scott Corey accounting firm is installing a new computer system. Several things must be done to make sure the system works properly before all the accounts are put into the new system. The following table provides information about this project. How long will it take to install the system? What is the critical path?

ACTIVITY	IMMEDIATE PREDECESSORS	TIME (WEEKS)
A	—	3
B	—	4
C	A	6
D	B	2
E	A	5
F	C	2
G	D, E	4
H	F, G	5

⚙:11-31 The managing partner of the Scott Corey accounting firm (see Problem 11-30) has decided that the system must be up and running in 16 weeks. Consequently, information about crashing the project was put together and is shown in the following table:

ACTIVITY	IMMEDIATE PREDECESSORS	NORMAL TIME (WEEKS)	CRASH TIME (WEEKS)	NORMAL COST ($)	CRASH COST ($)
A	—	3	2	8,000	9,800
B	—	4	3	9,000	10,000
C	A	6	4	12,000	15,000
D	B	2	1	15,000	15,500
E	A	5	3	5,000	8,700
F	C	2	1	7,500	9,000
G	D, E	4	2	8,000	9,400
H	F, G	5	3	5,000	6,600

(a) If the project is to be finished in 16 weeks, which activity or activities should be crashed to do this at the least additional cost? What is the total cost of this?
(b) List all the paths in this network. After the crashing in part (a) has been done, what is the time required for each path? If the project completion time must be reduced another week so that the total time is 15 weeks, which activity or activities should be crashed? Solve this by inspection. Note that it is sometimes better to crash an activity that is not the least cost for crashing if it is on several paths rather than to crash several activities on separate paths when there is more than one critical path.

✖:11-32 The L. O. Gystics Corporation is in need of a new regional distribution center. The planning is in the early stages of this project, but the activities have been identified along with their predecessors and their activity times in weeks. The table below provides this information. Develop a linear program that could be used to determine the length of the critical path (i.e., the minimum time required to complete the project). Solve this linear program to find the critical path and the time required to complete the project.

ACTIVITY	IMMEDIATE PREDECESSORS	TIME (WEEKS)
A	—	4
B	—	8
C	A	5
D	B	11
E	A, B	7
F	C, E	10
G	D	16
H	F	6

11-33 The Laurenster Corporation needs to perform the following tasks in weeks.

ACTIVITY	IMMEDIATE PREDECESSORS	OPTIMISTIC TIME	MOST LIKELY TIME	PESSIMISTIC TIME
A		2	3	4
B		4	6	8
C		2	5	8
D	A	3	4	5
E	B	6	7	8
F	C	4	7	10
G	A	1	5	9
H	B	2	5	8
I	C	3	5	7
J	D, G	2	2	2
K	E, H	4	4	4
L	F, I	3	3	3

Determine the associated PERT network diagram and determine the probability that the project will be complete in 16 weeks or less.

11-34 The Laurenster Corporation has determined the client will pay them a $10,000 bonus if they complete the project in Problem 11-33 in 14 weeks or less. The associated normal times and costs as well as the crash times and costs are shown below.

ACTIVITY	NORMAL TIME	CRASH TIME	NORMAL COST ($)	CRASH COST ($)
A	3	2	600	1,200
B	6	4	1,200	2,400
C	5	2	1,200	2,400
D	4	3	1,200	1,800
E	7	6	1,200	1,800
F	7	4	1,200	3,000
G	5	1	2,400	4,800
H	5	2	1,200	3,000
I	5	3	1,800	2,400
J	2	2	300	300
K	4	4	300	300
L	3	3	300	300

Considering the costs involved to crash the project, determine if the Laurenster Corporation should crash the project to 14 weeks to receive the bonus.

Internet Homework Problems

See our Internet home page, at **www.pearsonhighered.com/render**, for additional homework problems, Problems 11–35 to 11–42.

Case Study

Southwestern University Stadium Construction

After six months of study, much political arm wrestling, and some serious financial analysis, Dr. Martin Starr, president of Southwestern University, had reached a decision. To the delight of its students, and to the disappointment of its athletic boosters, SWU would not be relocating to a new football site but would expand the capacity at its on-campus stadium.

Adding 21,000 seats, including dozens of luxury skyboxes, would not please everyone. The influential football coach, Billy Bob Taylor, had long argued the need for a first-class stadium, one with built-in dormitory rooms for his players and a palatial office appropriate for the coach of a future NCAA champion

TABLE 11.11   Southwestern University Stadium Project

ACTIVITY	DESCRIPTION	PREDECESSORS	OPTIMISTIC	MOST LIKELY	PESSIMISTIC	CRASH COST/DAY($)
			TIME ESTIMATES (DAYS)			
A	Bonding, insurance, tax structuring	—	20	30	40	1,500
B	Foundation, concrete footings for boxes	A	20	65	80	3,500
C	Upgrading skyboxes, stadium seating	A	50	60	100	4,000
D	Upgrading walkways, stairwells, elevators	C	30	50	100	1,900
E	Interior wiring, lathes	B	25	30	35	9,500
F	Inspection approvals	E	1	1	1	0
G	Plumbing	D, E	25	30	35	2,500
H	Painting	G	10	20	30	2,000
I	Hardware/air conditioning/metal workings	H	20	25	60	2,000
J	Tile/carpeting/windows	H	8	10	12	6,000
K	Inspection	J	1	1	1	0
L	Final detail work/cleanup	I, K	20	25	60	4,500

Source: Adapted from J. Heizer and B. Render. *Operations Management*, 6th ed. Upper Saddle River, NJ: Prentice Hall, 2000: 693–694.

team. But the decision was made, and *everyone*, including the coach, would learn to live with it.

The job now was to get construction going immediately after the current season ended. This would allow exactly 270 days until the upcoming season opening game. The contractor, Hill Construction (Bob Hill being an alumnus, of course), signed the contract. Bob Hill looked at the tasks his engineers had outlined and looked President Starr in the eye. "I guarantee the team will be able to take the field on schedule next year," he said with a sense of confidence. "I sure hope so," replied Starr. "The contract penalty of $10,000 per day for running late is nothing compared to what Coach Bill Bob Taylor will do to you if our opening game with Penn State is delayed or cancelled." Hill, sweating slightly, did not respond. In football-crazy Texas, Hill Construction would be *mud* if the 270-day target were missed.

Back in his office, Hill again reviewed the data. (See Table 11.11 and note that optimistic time estimates can be used as crash times.) He then gathered his foremen. "People, if we're not 75% sure we'll finish this stadium in less than 270 days, I want this project crashed! Give me the cost figures for a target date of 250 days—also for 240 days. I want to be *early*, not just on time!"

Discussion Questions

1. Develop a network drawing for Hill Construction and determine the critical path. How long is the project expected to take?
2. What is the probability of finishing in 270 days?
3. If it were necessary to crash to 250 or 240 days, how would Hill do so, and at what costs? As noted in the case, assume that optimistic time estimates can be used as crash times.

Case Study

Family Planning Research Center of Nigeria

Dr. Adinombe Watage, deputy director of the Family Planning Research Center in Nigeria's Over-the-River Province, was assigned the task of organizing and training five teams of field workers to perform educational and outreach activities as part of a large project to demonstrate acceptance of a new method of birth control. These workers already had training in family planning education but must receive specific training regarding

the new method of contraception. Two types of materials must also be prepared: (1) those for use in training the workers, and (2) those for distribution in the field. Training faculty must be brought in and arrangements made for transportation and accommodations for the participants.

Dr. Watage first called a meeting of his office staff. Together they identified the activities that must be carried out,

TABLE 11.12   Family Planning Research Center Activities

ACTIVITY	MUST FOLLOW	TIME (DAYS)	STAFFING NEEDED
A. Identify faculty and their schedules	—	5	2
B. Arrange transport to base	—	7	3
C. Identify and collect training materials	—	5	2
D. Arrange accommodations	A	3	1
E. Identify team	A	7	4
F. Bring in team	B, E	2	1
G. Transport faculty to base	A, B	3	2
H. Print program material	C	10	6
I. Have program materials delivered	H	7	3
J. Conduct training program	D, F, G, I	15	0
K. Perform fieldwork training	J	30	0

TABLE 11.13   Family Planning Research Center Costs

ACTIVITY	NORMAL		MINIMUM		AVERAGE COST PER DAY SAVED ($)
	TIME	COST ($)	TIME	COST ($)	
A. Identify faculty	5	400	2	700	100
B. Arrange transport	7	1,000	4	1,450	150
C. Identify materials	5	400	3	500	50
D. Make accommodations	3	2,500	1	3,000	250
E. Identify team	7	400	4	850	150
F. Bring team in	2	1,000	1	2,000	1,000
G. Transport faculty	3	1,500	2	2,000	500
H. Print materials	10	3,000	5	4,000	200
I Deliver materials	7	200	2	600	80
J. Train team	15	5,000	10	7,000	400
K. Do fieldwork	30	10,000	20	14,000	400

their necessary sequences, and the time that they would require. Their results are displayed in Table 11.12.

Louis Odaga, the chief clerk, noted that the project had to be completed in 60 days. Whipping out his solar-powered calculator, he added up the time needed. It came to 94 days. "An impossible task, then," he noted. "No," Dr. Watage replied, "some of these tasks can go forward in parallel." "Be careful, though," warned Mr. Oglagadu, the chief nurse, "there aren't that many of us to go around. There are only 10 of us in this office."

"I can check whether we have enough heads and hands once I have tentatively scheduled the activities," Dr. Watage responded. "If the schedule is too tight, I have permission from the Pathminder Fund to spend some funds to speed it up, just so long as I can prove that it can be done at the least cost necessary. Can you help me prove that? Here are the costs for the activities with the elapsed time that we planned and the costs and times if we shorten them to an absolute minimum." Those data are given in Table 11.13.

Discussion Questions

1. Some of the tasks in this project can be done in parallel. Prepare a diagram showing the required network of tasks and define the critical path. What is the length of the project without crashing?
2. At this point, can the project be done given the personnel constraint of 10 persons?
3. If the critical path is longer than 60 days, what is the least amount that Dr. Watage can spend and still achieve this schedule objective? How can he prove to Pathminder Foundation that this is the minimum-cost alternative?

Source: Professor Curtis P. McLaughlin, Kenan-Flagler Business School, University of North Carolina at Chapel Hill.

Internet Case Studies

See our Internet home page, at **www.pearsonhighered.com/render**, for these additional case studies:

(1) **Alpha Beta Gamma Record:** This case involves publishing a monthly magazine for a fraternity.

(2) **Bay Community Hospital:** This case involves the acquisition and installation of equipment to be used in a new medical procedure.

(3) **Cranston Construction Company:** This case involves the construction of a new building at a university.

(4) **Haygood Brothers Construction Company:** This case involves planning the construction of a house.

(5) **Shale Oil Company:** This case involves planning the shutdown of a petrochemical plant for routine maintenance.

Bibliography

Ahuja, V., and V. Thiruvengadam. "Project Scheduling and Monitoring: Current Research Status," *Construction Innovation* 4, 1 (2004): 19–31.

Griffith, Andrew F. "Scheduling Practices and Project Success," *Cost Engineering* 48, 9 (2006): 24–30.

Herroelen, Willy, and Roel Leus. "Project Scheduling Under Uncertainty: Survey and Research Potentials," *European Journal of Operational Research* 165, 2 (2005): 289–306.

Jorgensen, Trond, and Stein W. Wallace. "Improving Project Cost Estimation by Taking into Account Managerial Flexibility," *European Journal of Operational Research* 127, 2 (2000): 239–251.

Lancaster, John, and Mustafa Ozbayrak. "Evolutionary Algorithms Applied to Project Scheduling Problems—A Survey of the State-of-the-art," *International Journal of Production Research* 45, 2 (2007): 425–450.

Lu, Ming, and Heng Li. "Resource-Activity Critical-Path Method for Construction Planning," *Journal of Construction Engineering & Management* 129, 4 (2003): 412–420.

Mantel, Samuel J., Jack R. Meredith, Scott M. Shafer, and Margaret M. Sutton. *Project Management in Practice.* New York: John Wiley & Sons, Inc., 2001.

Premachandra, I. M. "An Approximation of the Activity Duration Distribution in PERT," *Computers and Operations Research* 28, 5 (April 2001): 443–452.

Roe, Justin. "Bringing Discipline to Project Management," *Harvard Business Review* (April 1998): 153–160.

Sander, Wayne. "The Project Manager's Guide," *Quality Progress* (January 1998): 109.

Vaziri, Kabeh, Paul G. Carr, and Linda K. Nozick. "Project Planning for Construction under Uncertainty with Limited Resources," *Journal of Construction Engineering & Management* 133, 4 (2007): 268–276.

Walker II, Edward D. "Introducing Project Management Concepts Using a Jewelry Store Robbery," *Decision Sciences Journal of Innovative Education* 2, 1 (2004): 65–69.

Appendix 11.1: Project Management with QM for Windows

PERT is one of the most popular project management techniques. In this chapter, we explore the General Foundry, Inc., example. When expected times and variances have been computed for each activity, we can use the data to determine slack, the critical path, and the total project completion time. Program 11.3A shows the QM for Windows input screen for the General Foundry problem. By selecting the precedence list as the type of network, the data can be input without even constructing the network. The method indicated is for three time estimates, although this can be changed to a single time estimate, crashing, or cost budgeting. Program 11.3B provides the output for the General Foundry problem. The critical path consists of the activities with zero slack.

In addition to basic project management, QM for Windows also allows for project crashing, in which additional resources are used to reduce project completion time. Program 11.4A shows the input screen for the General Foundry data from Table 11.9. The output is shown in Program 11.4B. This indicates that the normal time is 15 weeks, but the project may be finished in 7 weeks if necessary; it may be finished in any number of weeks between 7 and 15. Selecting *Windows—Crash Schedule* provides additional information regarding these other times.

Monitoring and controlling projects is always an important aspect of project management. In this chapter we demonstrate how to construct budgets using the earliest and latest start times. Programs 11.5 and 11.6 show how QM for Windows can be used to develop budgets using earliest and latest starting times for a project. The data come from the General Foundry example in Tables 11.6 and Table 11.7.

PROGRAM 11.3A

QM for Windows Input Screen for General Foundry, Inc.

File Edit View Module Format Tools Window Help

Network type
◉ Immediate predecessor list
○ Start/end node numbers

Method
Triple time estimate

PERT Example

Activity	Optimistic time	Most Likely time	Pessimistic time	Predecessor 1	Predecessor 2
A	1	2	3		
B	2	3	4		
C	1	2	3	A	
D	2	4	6	B	
E	1	4	7	C	
F	1	2	9	C	
G	3	4	11	D	E
H	1	2	3	F	G

PROGRAM 11.3B

QM for Windows Solution Screen for General Foundry, Inc.

File Edit View Module Format Tools Window Help

Network type
◉ Immediate predecessor list
○ Start/end node numbers

Method
Triple time estimate

Project Management (PERT/CPM) Results

PERT Example Solution

Activity	Activity time	Early Start	Early Finish	Late Start	Late Finish	Slack	Standard Deviation
Project	15						1.76
A	2	0	2	0	2	0	0.33
B	3	0	3	1	4	1	0.33
C	2	2	4	2	4	0	0.33
D	4	3	7	4	8	1	0.67
E	4	4	8	4	8	0	1
F	3	4	7	10	13	6	1.33
G	5	8	13	8	13	0	1.33
H	2	13	15	13	15	0	0.33

PROGRAM 11.4A

QM for Windows Input Screen for Crashing General Foundry Example

Network type
◉ Immediate predecessor list
○ Start/end node numbers

Method
Crashing

General Foundry

Activity	Normal time	Crash time	Normal Cost	Crash Cost	Predecessor 1	Predecessor 2
A	2	1	22,000	23,000		
B	3	1	30,000	34,000		
C	2	1	26,000	27,000	A	
D	4	3	48,000	49,000	B	
E	4	2	56,000	58,000	C	
F	3	2	30,000	30,500	C	
G	5	2	80,000	86,000	D	E
H	2	1	16,000	19,000	F	G

PROGRAM 11.4B

QM for Windows Output Screen for Crashing General Foundry Example

Network type
- Immediate predecessor list
- Start/end node numbers

Method: Crashing

Project Management (PERT/CPM) Results

General Foundry Solution

Activity	Normal time	Crash time	Normal Cost	Crash Cost	Crash cost/pd	Crash by	Crashing cost
Project	15	7					
A	2	1	22,000	23,000	1,000	1	1,000
B	3	1	30,000	34,000	2,000	2	4,000
C	2	1	26,000	27,000	1,000	1	1,000
D	4	3	48,000	49,000	1,000	1	1,000
E	4	2	56,000	58,000	1,000	2	2,000
F	3	2	30,000	30,500	500	0	0
G	5	2	80,000	86,000	2,000	3	6,000
H	2	1	16,000	19,000	3,000	1	3,000
TOTALS			308,000				18,000

PROGRAM 11.5

QM for Windows for Budgeting with Earliest Start Times for General Foundry

Early Start Budget

General Foundry Solution

	Period 1	Period 2	Period 3	Period 4	Period 5	Period 6	Period 7	Period 8	Period 9	Period 10	Period 11	Period 12	Period 13	Period 14	Period 15
A	11	11													
B	10	10	10												
C			13	13											
D				12	12	12	12								
E					14	14	14	14							
F					10	10	10								
G									16	16	16	16	16		
H														8	8
Total in Period	21	21	23	25	36	36	36	14	16	16	16	16	16	8	8
Cumulative from	21	42	65	90	126	162	198	212	228	244	260	276	292	300	308

PROGRAM 11.6

QM for Windows for Budgeting with Latest Start Times for General Foundry

Late Start Budget

General Foundry Solution

	Period 1	Period 2	Period 3	Period 4	Period 5	Period 6	Period 7	Period 8	Period 9	Period 10	Period 11	Period 12	Period 13	Period 14	Period 15
A	11	11													
B		10	10	10											
C			13	13											
D					12	12	12	12							
E					14	14	14	14							
F											10	10	10		
G									16	16	16	16	16		
H														8	8
Total in Period	11	21	23	23	26	26	26	26	16	16	26	26	26	8	8
Cumulative from	11	32	55	78	104	130	156	182	198	214	240	266	292	300	308

Index

A

ABC analysis, 216
Abex Software, 398
Absorbing states, 518–522
Acceptance sampling tables, 539
Accounting data, 15
Accounts receivable application, 518–522
Activities
    cost to date for, 413
    defining, 396, 397–399
Activity difference, 413
Activity-on-arc (AOA), 399
Activity-on-node (AON), 399
Activity times estimates, 399–400
Adaptive smoothing, 177
Additive time-series models, 153
Additivity, 240
Airbus Industries simulation, 470
Airlines schedules maximizing profit, 375
Alabama Airlines, 504–505
Algorithms, 6
Alternate optimal solutions, 265–266
Alternatives, 66
Ambulances in Chile evaluate and improve
    performance metrics, 447
American Express financial advisors, 479
American Food, 513–514
American Meteorological Society (AMS), 63
AMS. See American Meteorological Society
    (AMS)
Analysis of variance (ANOVA) table, 123–124
Andrew-Carter, Inc., 357–358
Annual carrying costs and production run
    model, 199
Annual holding costs, calculating with safety
    stock, 209–211
Annual ordering costs, 199
Annual setup costs, 199. See also Annual
    ordering costs
ARCO p-charts, 546–547
Arcs, 324
Area of feasible solutions, 246
Arena, 494
Arnold's Muffler Shop
    exponential distribution, 49–50
    multichannel queuing model, 448–450
    single-channel queuing model, 443–447

Arrivals, 438
Aspen Technology, 271
Assignable variations, 541
Assignment problems, 312, 330–332
Assumptions, simplifying, 15
Athens Olympic Games Organizing
    Committee (ATHOC), 16
ATHOC. See Athens Olympic Games
    Organizing Committee (ATHOC)
Atlas Foods, 513–514
@Risk, 494
Attributes, 546–549
Average queue length, 450
Average waiting time, 450
Averaging techniques
    exponential smoothing, 158–163
    moving averages, 156
AVX-Kyocera statistical process control,
    607

B

Backward pass, 402
Backwards stepwise procedure, 133
Bad decisions, 66
Bagwell Chemical Company, 368
Balking, 438
Bank of America pecuniary corruption
    statistics, 540
Bath Iron Works, 396
Bayes, Thomas, 31
Bayes' theorem
    calculating revised probabilities, 85–87
    estimating probability values, 85–88
    general form of, 31
    probabilities and, 29–31
Bell Laboratories, 539
BEP. See Break-even point (BEP)
Bernoulli process, 37
Best level of service, 436
Beta probability distribution, 399–400
Bias, 156
Bill of materials (BOM), 217
Binary variables
    modeling, 370–375
    regression models, 131–132
Binding constraint, 253
Binomial distribution, 37–40

Binomial formula and problem solving, 38
Binomial probabilities, 560–564
Binomial tables and problem solving, 39–40
Blake Electronics, 110–111
Boeing Corporation simulation, 470
BOM. See Bill of materials (BOM)
Box filling example, 542–543
    Excel QM for, 543
Brass Department Store quantity discount
    model, 204–205
Break-even point (BEP), 9
Brier, 41
British Airways (BA) program evaluation and
    review technique/critical path method
    (PERT/CPM), 398
Brownian motion, 510
Brown Manufacturing production run model,
    200–202
Budgeting process, 409–412
Business analytics, 3
Business games, 492–493
Business system simulation, 470

C

Cable & Moore, 321–322
Café du Donut marginal analysis, 213–214
CALEB Technologies, 375
Calling population, 438
Canadian Men's Curling Championships, 41
Capital budgeting 0-1 (binary) variables,
    370–372
Carnegie-Mellon University, 376
Carrying costs, 199, 207, 210
Causal models, 151
Causation, 136–137
c-charts, 548–549
    and Excel QM, 549
    and Red Top Cab Company, 549
CELM. See Customer Equity Loyalty
    Management (CELM)
Centered moving averages (CMA), 169, 396
Centers for Disease Control and Prevention,
    441
Central limit theorem, 541
Central planning engine (CPE), 369
Chase Manhattan Bank, 322

Chicago Tribune newspaper marginal analysis with normal distribution, 214–215
Classical method, of objective probability, 25
Cloud-based work environment, 403
CMA. *See* Centered moving averages (CMA)
Coefficient of correlation, 118–119
Coefficient of determination, 118
Coefficient of realism, 69, 76
Collectively exhaustive events, 26–27, 34, 514
Collectively exhaustive states, 510
Collinear, 133
Complete enumeration, 6
Complex queuing models, 454–455
Components and material structure tree, 217–218
Computer languages and simulation, 471
Computers
    quantitative analysis role, 10–13
    simulation, 454–455
    simulation role, 494
Computer software and regression, 124–128
Conditional probabilities and decision trees, 82, 83
Conditional probability, 28–29
Conditional values, 67, 69
Conflicting viewpoints in defining problems, 14
Constant service time model, 450–452
Constraints
    binding and nonbinding, 253
    dual price, 272
    graphical representation, 243–247
    inequality, 244
    nonbinding, 253
    redundant, 264–265
    right-hand-side values, 271–273
    solution points that satisfy, 244
Consumer market survey, 151
Continental Airlines CrewSolver system, 375
Continuous distribution and exponential distribution, 48–49
Continuous random variables, 33–34, 36–37
Control charts
    attributes, 546–549
    building, 539
    c-charts, 548–549
    defects, 548–549
    QM for Windows, 555–556
    R-chart, 541, 546, 550
    variables, 541–546
    $\bar{x}$-chart (x-bar chart), 541–545
Controllable inputs, 480
Controllable variables, 5
Corner point method, 250–252, 260–261
Corporate operating system simulation, 493
Correlation, 136
Cost analysis simulation, 489–491
Cost data, 410
Costs
    fixed, 8, 11, 18
    project, 409–412
    single-channel queuing model, 442–447
    variable, 8
    waiting lines, 436
CPM. *See* Critical path method (CPM)
Crashing, 414–418
Crash time, 414
    constraints, 417

CrewSolver system, 375
Criterion of realism, 69–70
Critical path, 400–405
Critical path method (CPM), 396, 413–418
    crashing, 414–418
    start of, 397
Crystal Ball, 494
CSX Transportation, Inc. optimization models, 7
Cumulative probability and relation between intervals, 474
Cumulative probability distribution, 473, 480
Curling champions, probability assessments of, 39
Current state to future state, 512
Customer Equity Loyalty Management (CELM), 518
Cyclical (C) component of time-series, 152

D

Daily unloading rate variable, 484
Dantzig, George D., 242
Data Analysis add-in, 124
Data envelopment analysis (DEA), 312
DEA. *See* Data envelopment analysis (DEA)
Decision analysis utility theory, 88–93
Decision making, 87–88, 150
    automating process, 2
    under certainty, 67
    decision trees, 79
    group, 150
    and minimization, 75–77
    model, 150
    under risk, 68, 71–79
    six steps in, 66–67
    types of, 67–68
    under uncertainty, 65, 67, 68–71
Decision-making environments, 67–68
Decision nodes, 79
Decision points, 79
Decisions, good and bad, 66
Decision table, 67
Decision theory, 66
    and Ford Motor Company, 71
Decision trees, 79–85
    alternatives, 81
    analyzing problems, 80
    conditional probabilities, 82
    decision making, 80
    expected monetary value (EMV), 83–84
    expected value of sample information (EVSI), 84–85
    lottery ticket, 88–89
    possible outcomes and alternatives, 81–84
    posterior probabilities, 82
    sample information efficiency, 84
    sensitivity analysis, 84–85
    sequential decisions, 81–84
    state-of-nature nodes, 79, 81
Decision variables, 5, 242, 364. *See also* Controllable variables
Decomposition method, 170–173
    software for, 173
Decoupling function, 189
Defects and control charts, 548–549
Delphi method, 25, 150–151

Demand
    fluctuating, 208
    inventory, 191
    irregular, 189
    single time period, 211–216
Department of Agriculture, operations research, 13
Department of Commerce finite population model, 453–454
Department of Health and Rehabilitative Services (HRS), 479
Dependent demand, 216–221
Dependent events, 28
Dependent selections and 0-1 (binary) variables, 372
Dependent variables, 114, 129
Descriptive analytics, 3
Deseasonalized data, 168
Destinations, 325
Deterministic assumptions, 266
Deterministic inventory models, 480
Deterministic models, 9
Deviation. *See* Errors, forecast
Deviational variables, 376
Diet problems, 308–309
Disaster response research, 5
Discrete probability distribution, 36–37. *See also* Poisson distribution
Discrete random variables, 33, 34
Disney World forecasting, 175
DMEP. *See* Dual Mode Equipment Procedure (DMEP)
Drawing cards, 28
Drexel Corp., 297
Dual Mode Equipment Procedure (DMEP), 478
Dual price, 272
Dummy variables. *See* Binary variables
DuPont, 396
Dynamic Car-Planning (DCP) system, 7

E

Earliest finish time, 400, 402
Earliest possible time, 412
Earliest start time, 400, 402, 410
Econometric models, 493
Economic order quantity (EOQ), 192–195
    formula, 196–197
    without instantaneous receipt assumption, 198–202
Economic systems and simulation, 493
Empirical rule and normal distribution, 46
Employee scheduling applications, 301–303
EMV. *See* Expected monetary value (EMV)
Enumeration and integer programming problems, 365
EOL. *See* Expected opportunity loss (EOL)
Equally likely, 70
Equilibrium conditions, 515–518, 520
Equilibrium probabilities, 515
Equilibrium share, 515
Equilibrium states, 517
Errors, forecast, 153
Events, 28–29
    collectively exhaustive, 26–27, 34, 514
    dependent and independent, 28–29
    mutually exclusive, 26–27, 34, 514
    statistically independent, 29, 30
    union of, 27

Every day, 337
Excel
  activating add-ins, 571
  add-ins, 11, 494
  Data Analysis add-in, 124
  developing regression model, 124–125
  F distribution, 48
  forecasting, 160–163
  Goal Seek, 11, 13
  integer programming model, 369
  linear programming (LP) problems, 254–259
  linear regression equation, 133–136
  Markov analysis with, 535–536
  mean, variance, and standard deviation, 36
  nonlinear relationship, 134
  for Port of New Orleans simulation, 486
  regression calculations, 124
  Solver, 11
  Solver and changes right-hand-side values, 272–273
  Solver and objective function coefficients changes, 269–270
  sum of squares error, 124
  SUMPRODUCT function, 255
Excel 2010
  Solver add-in, 571
Excel 2013, 10–11
  activating add-ins, 571
  to develop regression model, 174
  and Poisson distribution, 52
  and regression, 124–125
  regression line, 166
  Solver add-in, 254–257
  and transportation problems, 325–326
Excel QM, 11, 571
  for analysis of Arnold's multichannel queuing model, 450
  on Arnold's Muffler shop queue, 444
  box filling example, 543–544
  c-chart, 549
  decision theory problems, 77–78
  decomposition method, 173
  to develop regression model, 174
  economic order quantity (EOQ), 195
  forecasting, 160–163
  installing, 571
  linear programming (LP) problems, 257–259
  minimal spanning tree problem, 341
  and payoff table problems, 78–79
  p-chart, 548
  production run models, 201, 209
  program crashing, 418
  program evaluation and review technique/critical path method (PERT/CPM), 406–407
  quantity discount problems, 205
  regression calculations, 125–126
  safety stock and reorder point, 210–211
  simulation module, 479
  for Super Cola example, 545
  technical support, 571
  and transportation problems, 325–326
  trend-adjusted exponential smoothing, 165
  trend analysis, 166
Excel spreadsheets, 10–11
  integer programming problems, 366
  simulation, 478–479

Executive Furniture Corporation, 325
Expected activity time, 400
Expected demand, 476
Expected monetary value (EMV), 71–72, 74, 83
Expected opportunity loss (EOL), 74
Expected value of perfect information (EVPI), 72–74
Expected value of probability distribution, 34–35
Expected value of sample information (EVSI), 84
Expected value with perfect information (EV wPI), 72–74
Expenses, 8, 9
Explanatory variable, 114
Exponential distribution, 48–50
Exponential smoothing, 158–160
  and Midwestern Manufacturing, 165
  with trend model, 163–165
ExtendSim, 494
Extreme point, 250. *See also* Corner point

F

Facility location
  analysis, 327–329
  supply-chain reliability, 342
Family Planning Research Center (Nigeria), 430–431
Favorable market (FM), 85
FB Badpoore Aerospace, 506–507
F distribution, 46–48, 121–124, 566–567
Feasible region, 246
Feasible region corner points, 250
Feasible solution, 246
Federal Aviation Administration (FAA) simulation, 484
Fifth Avenue Industries, 296–298
Financial applications, 303–308
Financial investment 0-1 (binary) variables, 374–375
Finite population model, 452–454
Finnair, 518
First-in, first-out (FIFO) rule, 438
First in, first served (FIFS), 439
Fixed-charge problem example, 372–374
Fixed costs, 8, 11, 18
Flair Furniture Company
  entering problem data, 255
  feasible corner points and profits for, 252
  graphical solution approach, 243
  linear programming (LP) problems, 241–243
  LP problem solving using Excel QM, 257–259
  LP problem solving using Excel's Solver Command, 254–257
  LP problem solving using QM for Windows, 253–254
Flight safety and probability analysis, 32
Flowchart, 480
Flow diagram, 480
Food and Beverages, 21
Food Mart, 513–514
Ford and decision theory, 71
Forecasting
  decomposition method, 170–173
  Disney World, 175

Excel and Excel QM, 160–163
  exponential smoothing, 168–163
  inventory, 188
  models, 163–177
  monthly sales, 185–186
  moving averages, 156
  time series, 151, 165–168
  with trend, seasonal, and random variations, 170–175
Forecasts
  bias, 156
  causal models, 151
  combinations of weights, 157
  errors, 153
  mean absolute deviation (MAD), 153–154
  mean absolute percent error (MAPE), 156
  mean squared error (MSE), 155
  measures of accuracy, 153–156
  monitoring and controlling, 175–177
  naïve model, 154
  qualitative models, 150–151
  scatter diagrams, 151
  time-series models, 151
  tracking signals, 175–177
  types of, 150–151
Formulas and regression calculations, 147–148
Fortune 100 firm inventory policy for service vehicles, 200, 210
Forward pass, 402
Forward stepwise procedure, 133
4-month moving average, 156
FREQUENCY function, 479
Frosty machine transshipment data, 333
F test, 137
Fundamental matrix, 518–522
Future state from current state, 512

G

Gantt charts, 396, 407
Garbage in, garbage out, 5
Garcia-Golding Recycling, Inc., constant service time model, 451–452
General Electric, 539
General Foundry, 415–416
  budgeting for, 409–412
  and Excel QM, 406–407
General Motors, 396, 476
Geographic information system (GIS), 368
The Glass Slipper, 186
Global Optimization (GO) Academy, 324
Global optimum, 379
Goal programming, 364, 375–379
  and continental airlines, 375
  and Harrison Electric Company, 376–377
  for tuberculosis drug allocation, 378
  with weighted goals, 378–379
Goals
  hierarchy of importance, 376
  multiple, 375–379
  ranking with priority levels, 377–378
  satisfices, 376
  weighted, 378–379
Goal Seek, 11
Goodman Shipping, 306–308
Greater-than-or-equal-to constraint, 252–253
Greenberg Motors, Inc., 297
Gross material requirements, 218–219

H

Harky, Lester, 405–406, 409, 412
Harrah's Cherokee Casino, 313
Harrison Electric Company
    and goal programming, 376–377
    integer programming, 364–366
    and QM for Windows, 379
Harry's Auto Tire, Monte Carlo simulation, 472–477
Haynes Construction Company, 43–46
Hewlett Packard sales increment, 248
High Note Sound Company, 267, 269–270
    and objective function coefficient change, 268
    and QM for Windows and objective function coefficient change, 268
Highway Corridor Analytical Program (HCAP), 368
Hill Construction, 430
Hinsdale Company safety stock, 208–209
Holding costs, 191–193, 199
Holiday Meal Turkey Ranch minimization problems, 260–263
Hong Kong Bank of Commerce and Industry, 302–303
Hurricane landfall location forecasts mean absolute deviation (MAD), 154
Hurwicz criterion, 69, 76

I

IBM Systems and Technology Group, 369
ICT. *See* International City Trust (ICT)
Immediate predecessors, 399, 407, 408
Independent events, 28–29
Independent variables, 114, 129–130, 133
Indicator variables, 131
Industrial dynamics, 493
Inequality constraints, 244
Infeasible solution, 246
Ingersoll Rand, 119
Ingredient blending applications, 309–311
Input data, 5, 15
Instantaneous inventory receipt assumption, 198–202
Integer programming, 364–370
    and enumeration method, 365
    and Excel spreadsheets, 366–367
    and Harrison Electric Company, 364–366
    limiting number of alternatives, 372
    mixed-integer programming problems, 368–370
    objective function measured in one dimension, 375
    and QM for Windows, 366–367
    and U.S. Postal Service (USPS), 368
    variables required integer values, 364
    zero-one integer programming problems, 364
Integer programming problems, 308
    enumeration, 365
    mathematical statement, 371
    rounding off, 365
Integer values, 364
Intel, improving inventory operations, 204
International City Trust (ICT), 303–306
International Organization for Standardization (ISO), 539

Intersection, 28–29
Intervals and cumulative probability, 474
Inventory, 188
    ABC analysis, 216
    annual ordering cost, 199
    annual setup cost, 199
    average dollar value, 196
    controlling levels, 188
    cost analysis, 483–484
    cost factors, 191
    decisions, 190–191
    demand, 191
    dependent demand, 216–221
    economic order quantity (EOQ), 191–197
    forecasting, 188
    how much to order, 191–197
    just-in-time inventory (JIT), 221–222
    lead time, 197
    optimal production quantity, 200
    purchase cost, 195–196
    quantity discount models, 202–205, 210–213
    reorder point (ROP), 197
    safety stock, 206–211
    single-period inventory models, 211–216
    stockouts, 188
    usage curve, 191
Inventory analysis and simulation, 480–484
Inventory control, 189
Inventory costs, 190–191
    economic order quantity (EOQ), 192–194
Inventory models
    deterministic, 480
    single-period, 211–216
Inventory planning and control system, 188
Inventory problem, 480
Irregular supply and demand, 189
ISO 9000 certified, 539
Isocost line approach minimization problems, 262–263
Isoprofit line method, 247–250

J

Jackson Memorial Hospital's operating rooms simulation, 491
Jenny Wilson Realty model, 130–131
Joint probability, 27
Jury of executive opinion, 151
Just-in-time inventory (JIT), 221–222

K

Kanban, 221–222
Kantorovich, Leonid, 242
Karmarkar, Narendra, 242
Kelley, J. E., 396
Kendall, D. G., 439
Kendall notation, 439–442
Koopmans, Tjalling, 242

L

Labor
    planning, 302–303
    stored in inventory, 189
Laplace, 70
Last in, first served (LIFS), 439

Latest finish time, 400, 402, 403
Latest start time, 400, 402, 403, 411
Lauderdale Construction, 339–342
Law of addition for events not mutually exclusive, 29–30
Lead time, 197, 208
Lead time variable, 480
Least-squares regression, 116, 166
Less-than-or-equal to constraint, 252–253
Limited queue length, 438
Linear constraints, 380
Linear objective function, 382
Linear programming (LP), 240–241
    alternative courses of action, 240
    applications, 311–312
    assignment problem, 330–332
    beginning of, 242
    conditions of certainty, 240
    constraints describing network, 482
    crash time constraints, 482
    defining decision variables, 416–418
    goal programming, 364
    integer programming, 364–370
    and linear equations, 240
    maximal-flow problem, 335–336
    non-linear programming, 364
    objective function, 375, 417
    project completion constraint, 482
    project crashing, 416–418
    properties of, 241
    shortest-route problem, 337–338
    and Swift & Company, 271
    transportation problem, 325
    transshipment problem, 332–334
Linear programming (LP) models
    employee scheduling applications, 302–303
    financial applications, 303–308
    ingredient blending applications, 308–311
    manufacturing applications, 296–301
    marketing applications, 292–296
Linear programming (LP) problems
    alternate optimal solutions, 265–266
    corner point method, 250–252
    deterministic assumptions, 266
    divisibility assumption, 240
    Excel, 254–259
    feasible region, 246
    formulating, 241–243
    graphical solution, 243–253
    isoprofit line method, 247–250
    no feasible solution, 263
    objective function, 240
    optimal solution, 247–250
    product mix problem, 241
    redundancy, 264–265
    requirements, 240–241
    sensitivity analysis, 266–274
    slack, 252–253
    solution points satisfying constraints simultaneously, 246
    solving minimization problems, 260–263
    special cases, 263–266
    surplus, 252–253
    unboundedness, 264
Linear trends, 170
Little's Flow Equations, 454
Liver transplants in United States, 26

Local optimum, 379
Logical method, of objective probability, 25
Los Alamos Scientific Laboratory, 471
Low Knock Oil Company, 310–311, 312

M

Machine operations, and Markov analysis, 514–515
MAD. *See* Mean absolute deviation (MAD)
Maintenance policy simulation model, 487–492
Management science, 2
Management Sciences Associates (MSA), 293–295
Management system simulation, 470
Managing Today's energy supply chain, 190
Manufacturing applications
    production mix, 296–297
    production scheduling, 297–301
MAPE. *See* Mean absolute percent error (MAPE)
Mapka Institute of Technology, 378
Marginal analysis, 211–216
Marginal loss (ML), 212
Marginal probability, 30, 32
Marginal profit (MP), 212
Marketing applications, 293–295
Marketing research, 293–295
Market shares, 511–512
Market values equilibrium share, 515
Markov analysis, 510
    absorbing states, 518–522
    accounts receivable application, 518–522
    airline uses, 518
    assumptions of, 510
    equilibrium conditions, 515–518
    with Excel, 535–536
    fundamental matrix, 518–522
    machine operations, 514–515
    matrix of transition probabilities, 510, 512–513
    predicting future market shares, 513–514
    with QM for Windows, 534–535
    reducing market costs, 518
    states, 510–512
    system starting in initial state or condition, 510
    vector of state probabilities, 511–512
    and volleyball skills, 522
Markovian volleyball, 522
Material cost quantity discounts, 202
Material requirements planning (MRP), 216–221, 222
Material structure tree, 217–218
Mathematical models, 5, 8–10, 14–15, 470
    advantages of, 9
    categorized by risk, 9–10
Mathematical programming, 240
Mathematics of probability, 24
Matrix of transition probabilities, 510, 512–513, 519–520
MAU. *See* Multiattribute utility model (MAU)
Maximal-flow problem, 335–336
Maximal-flow technique, 335–336
Maximax criterion, 68
Maximin criterion, 69, 74

Mean, 34–35, 71
    Poisson distribution, 51
    standard normal distribution, 42–43
Mean absolute deviation (MAD), 153–154
Mean absolute percent error (MAPE), 156
Mean squared error (MSE), 121, 155, 166
Media selection, 292–293
MEIO. *See* Multi-echelon inventory optimization (MEIO) system
Melvin Lauderdale, 339
Mexicana Wire Winding, Inc., 288–289
Meyers Marketing Research, Inc., 532
Microsoft Corporation, 151, 396
Midwestern Manufacturing Company, 164
    and exponential smoothing with trend forecasts, 164
    and time observations, 168
Milestones, 419
Military games, 492
Minimal-spanning tree problem, 338–342
Minimal-spanning tree technique, 339
Minimax regret, 70–71
Minimization problems, 260–261
Mitigation, 5
Mixed-integer programming problems, 368–370
    and IBM supply chain, 369
Modeling
    real world, 8
    0-1 (binary) variables, 370–375
Models, 4–5, 8–13. *See also* specific model
    building, 132–133
    developing, 14–15
    testing, 121–122
Modified-distribution (MODI) method, 330
Monitoring solutions, 6
Monte Carlo simulation, 472–479, 480
    QM for Windows for, 477–478
    random numbers, 492–493
Montgomery County (Maryland) Public Health Service, 441
Monthly sales, forecasting, 185–186
Most likely time, 399
Moving averages, 156
MSA. *See* Management Sciences Associates (MSA)
MSE. *See* Mean squared error (MSE)
Multiattribute utility model (MAU), 93
Multichannel queuing model, 447–450
Multichannel system, 439
Multicollinearity, 133, 136
Multi-echelon inventory optimization (MEIO) system, 204
Multiphase system, 439
Multiple goals, 377
Multiple regression model, 128–131
    equations for, 448
    evaluation, 129–130
    multicollinearity, 136
    with trend and seasonal components, 174–175
Multiplicative time-series models, 153
Multiplicative-time-series seasonal index, 168
Mutually exclusive events, 26–27, 34, 514
Mutually exclusive states, 510

N

Naïve model, 154
NASA, 66, 392, 396

National Academy of Sciences, 93
National Broadcasting Company (NBC)
    linear, integer, and goal programming selling advertising slots, 261
National Hurricane Center (NHC), 154
National Weather Service, 154
Natural variations, 540–541
Negative exponential distribution, 48–49
Negative exponential probability distribution, 439
Net material requirements plan, 218–219
Network problems
    maximal-flow problem, 335–336
    minimal-spanning tree problem, 338–342
    shortest-route problem, 337–338
Networks
    backward pass, 402
    forward pass, 402
    program evaluation and review technique/ critical path method (PERT/CPM), 396, 399
New England Foundry, Inc., 465–466
NHC. *See* National Hurricane Center (NHC)
Nodes, 324
Nonbinding constraints, 253
Nonlinear constraints, 380–381
    linear objective function with, 382
Nonlinear objective function, 380
Nonlinear programming (NLP), 364, 379–383
Nonlinear regression, 133–136
Nonnegative variables, 241
Nonnegativity constraints, 243
Normal cost, 414
Normal curve, 558–559
    area under, 42
Normal distribution, 40–46
    marginal analysis, 214–216
    safety stock, 207
Normal time, 414
NORMINV function, 479
Northeastern Airlines, 358
North-South Airline, 146
n-period moving average, 156
Nuclear weapons, multiattribute utility model in disposal of, 93
Numerical formatting, 569

O

Oakton River bridge, 393
Objective approach of probability, 25
Objective function, 240, 376
    coefficient changes, 268
    linear programming (LP), 417
Objective probability, 25, 32
Oil spills and operations research, 5
Olympic Games, 16
OnStar, strategic alternatives evaluation, 476
Operating characteristics, 442, 454
Operational gaming, 492–493
Operations research, 2, 4, 17
Opinion polls, 25
Opportunity loss, 71, 74
Opportunity loss table, 68, 70, 71, 74
Optimality analysis, 266. *See also* Sensitivity analysis
Optimal production quantity, 200
Optimistic criterion, 68

Optimistic time, 399
OptSolver system, 375
Oracle, 222
Ordering costs, 191, 192–193, 199
Organizations, best level of service, 436
Origins, 325
Outlier analysis, 540

P

Package delivery, 324
Parallel activity, 408
Parameters, 5, 8
Parametric programming, 266. *See also*
     Sensitivity analysis
Parents and material structure tree, 217
Partitioning matrix of transition probabilities,
     520
Payoff/cost table, 207
Payoff table, 67, 77–79
P-chart, 546–548
     and Excel QM, 548
People, assigning projects to, 330–332
Perfect information, 72
PERT/Cost, 409–412
PERTMASTER, 398
PERT networks, 399
Pessimistic criterion, 69, 76
Pessimistic time, 399
Physical models, 4, 470
Pilot plants, 4
Pittsburgh Pirates, 13
Plutonium, 93
Poisson arrivals, 447–450
Poisson distribution, 50–52, 438
     c-charts, 549
     and Excel 2013, 52
     values for use in, 565–567
Polls, queuing, 451
POM-QM for Windows, 10, 568–570
Portfolio selection, 303–306
Port of Baltimore exponential smoothing,
     159–160
Port of New Orleans simulation, 484–486
     Excel for, 486
Posterior probabilities, 29–30, 82, 85–87.
     See also Conditional probabilities
Postoptimality analysis, 6, 266. *See also*
     Sensitivity analysis
Predecessor activity, 408
Predicting future market shares, 513–514
Predictive analytics, 3
Predictor variable, 114
Preparedness, 5
Prescriptive analytics, 3
Presently known probabilities, 510
Present value, 370
Preventive maintenance simulation, 492
Prior probabilities, 29, 30, 86
Pritsker Corp., 26
Probabilistic models, 10
Probabilities, 24
     assessments of curling champions, 41
     Bayes' theorem and, 29–31, 85–88
     binomial distribution, 37–40
     classical or logical method, 25
     collectively exhaustive events and, 26–27
     conditional, 28–29, 81
     decision trees, 79–85

equilibrium share, 515
exponential distribution, 48–50
F distribution, 46–48
flight safety and, 32
independent events, 28–29
joint, 30
marginal, 30
mathematics of, 24
mutually exclusive events and,
     26–27
normal distribution, 40–46
objective, 25
Poisson distribution, 50–52
posterior, 29–30, 81, 82, 87
presently known, 510
prior, 29, 30, 85–87
random variables, 32–33
relative frequency of demand, 25, 27
revision, 29, 31–32, 85–87
rules of, 24–25
simple, 24
sports and, 41
statistically dependent events, 30
statistically independent events, 29
subjective, 25
table of normal curve areas, 43, 44
types of, 25
Probability analysis and flight safety, 32
Probability density function, 37
Probability distributions, 15, 24, 34–37, 479,
     480
     central tendency, 34
     continuous random variables, 36–37
     discrete random variable, 33–34
     expected value, 34–35
     Kendall notation, 439
     mean, 34–35
     Monte Carlo simulation, 472–473
     variables, 472–473
     variance, 35–36
Probability function, 37
Problems, 13–16
     quantitative analysis, 4
     solutions to, 572–575
Problem solving, 38–40
Process control system, 541
Processes
     assignable variations, 541
     average, 545
     dispersion, 545
     natural variations, 540–541
     states, 510
     variability, 539–541, 545
Process Logistics Advanced Technical
     Optimization (PLATO) project, 16
Procomp reorder point for chips, 198
Production mix, 296–297
Production/operations management (POM),
     2–3, 10, 568
Production process setup cost, 199
Production run model, 198–202
Production scheduling, 297–301
Product mix problem, 241
Product quality, 538
Profit contribution, 241
Profit models, 8, 9
Program crashing, 418
Program evaluation and review technique
     (PERT), 396, 397–399, 406

Program evaluation and review technique/
     critical path method (PERT/CPM)
     activity time estimates, 399–400
     beta probability distribution, 399
     critical path, 400–404
     defining project and activities, 397–399
     drawing network, 399
     expected activity time, 400
     general foundry example, 397–398
     history of, 396
     immediate predecessors, 399
     information provided by, 406
     most likely time, 399
     networks, 396
     optimistic time, 399
     pessimistic time, 399
     probability of project completion,
         405–406
     project management, 407–409
     projects in smaller activities or tasks, 397
     questions answered by, 397
     sensitivity analysis, 407–409
     variance of activity completion time, 400
Programming, 240
Project costs, 409–412
     monitoring and controlling, 412–413
Project crashing, 414–418
     with linear programming, 416–418
Project management, 419
     in office-less, cloud-based work
         environment, 403
     QM for Windows, 432
     sensitivity analysis, 407–409
     and small companies, 414
     and water project in California, 410
Projects
     assigning people, 330–332
     defining, 397–398
     identifying activities, 397
     probability of completion, 405–406
     standard deviation, 405
     weekly budget, 411
Project variance, computing, 405
ProModel, 494
Proof 5, 494
Proportionality, 240
Purchase cost, 195–196, 202

Q

QM for Windows
     and changes in right-hand-side values, 272
     control charts, 555–556
     decomposition method, 173
     file extension, 569
     to forecast, 160
     goal programming module, 379
     integer programming model, 369
     integer programming problems, 366–367
     linear programming (LP) problems,
         253–254
     with Markov analysis, 533–534
     maximal-flow problem, 336
     minimal spanning tree problem, 341
     minimization problems, 260–261
     Monte Carlo simulation, 477–478
     and objective function coefficients
         changes, 268–269
     and payoff table problems, 77–78

program crashing, 418
project management, 432
queuing problems, 468
regression calculations, 127–128
right-hand-side values changes, 272
and transportation module, 360–362
Quadratic programming problem, 380
Qualitative factors, 2
Qualitative models, 150–151
Quality, 538
Quality control (QC), 538
history of, 539
hospital uses, 543
Quantitative analysis, 2–3
approach, 4–8
computers and spreadsheet models role, 10–13
developing model, 4–5
implementing results, 6
lack of commitment, 17
origin of, 4
possible problems in, 13–16
real-world, 8
resistance to change, 17
Quantitative analysis/quantitative methods (QA/QM), 568
Quantitative causal models and regression analysis, 150
Quantitative models, 15
Quantity discount models, 202–205, 210–213
Quantity discounts, 189, 202
Queue discipline, 438
Queuing equations, 442–443
Queuing models, 441, 454
Queuing polls, 451
Queuing problem simulation, 484–486
Queuing system, 454
characteristics of, 438–442
configurations, 439
Queuing theory, 436, 447

R

RAND function, 478
Random arrivals, 438, 449
Random (R) component, of time-series, 152
Random numbers, 473–474, 479, 492–493
generating, 474–475
Random variables, 32–33
Range charts, 545–546
Ranking goals with priority levels, 377–378
Raw data, 2
Ray Design, Inc., 337
R-charts, 541, 546, 550
Recovery, 5
Red Top Cab Company c-charts, 549
Redundancy, 264
Regression
calculations in formulas, 147–148
cautions and pitfall, 136–137
computer software, 124–128
least squares, 166
measuring fit of, 117–119
multiple regression model, 128–131
nonlinear, 133–136
as part of improvement initiative at Trane/Ingersoll Rand, 119
relationship among variables, 117
stepwise, 133

with trend and seasonal components, 174–175
variance (ANOVA) table, 123–124
Regression analysis, 114
cautions and pitfalls, 136–137
Regression equations, 493
Regression models, 137
assumptions of, 120–121
binary variables, 131–132
building, 132–133
coefficient of correlation, 118–119
coefficient of determination, 118
dependent variable, 114
dummy variables, 131–132
errors assumptions, 120–121
estimating variance, 125
independent variable, 114
nonlinear regression, 133–136
quantitative causal models, 150
scatter diagrams, 114
significant, 122
simple linear regression, 115–117
statistical hypothesis test, 121–124
statistically significant, 132–133
testing for significance, 121–124
variables, 132–133
Remington Rand, 396
Reneging, 438
Rentall trucks, 532–533
Reorder point (ROP), 197–198, 206, 208
Residual, 124
Resistance to change, 17
Resource leveling, 419
Resources
changes in, 271–272
constraints, 240
most effective use of, 240
slack, 252–253
storing, 189
Response, 5
Response variable, 114
Results, 6, 14
implementing, 6
Revised probability. *See* Posterior probabilities
Revision probability, 31–32, 85–87
Risk avoider utility curve, 91
Risk mathematical model categories, 9–10
Risk seeker utility curve, 91
RiskSim, 494
RSFE. *See* Running sum of the forecast errors (RSFE)
Rules of probability, 24–25
Running sum of the forecast errors (RSFE), 176

S

Safety stock, 206–211
Sales force composite, 151
SAP, 222
Satisfices, 376
Scale models, 4
Scatter diagrams, 114
Scatter plot. *See* Scatter diagrams
Schank Marketing Research, 392
Schematic models, 4
SCO. *See* Supply-chain optimization (SCO)
Seasonal (S) component of time-series, 151

Seasonal indexes, 168
with no trend, 168–169
with trend, 169–170
Seasonal variations, 167–170
Self-tests solutions, 576–577
Sensitivity analysis, 6, 14, 15, 74–75, 196
decision trees, 84–85
input parameters values, 266
linear programming (LP) problems, 266–274
objective function coefficient changes, 268–269
project management, 407–409
resources or right-hand-side values changes, 271–272
technological coefficients changes, 270–271
what-if? questions, 266
Sequential decisions, 81–84
Service costs, 436, 444–445
Service facility, 439
Service level, 207
Service processes, 449
Service quality, 538
Service time distribution, 439
Setup cost, 199
Shadow price, 272
Shewhart, Walter, 539
Shortages, 189
Shortest-route problem, 337–338
Shortest-route technique, 324
Significant regression model, 122
Simkin's Hardware store, 480–484
Simon, Herbert A., 376
Simple linear regression, 115–117
Simple probability, 24
Simplex algorithm, 242, 252
SIMUL8, 494
Simulated demand, 476
Simulating chips, 478
Simulation, 454–455, 470
advantages and disadvantages, 471–472
business system, 470
collecting data, 484
and complex queuing models, 454–455
computer languages, 471
computers role in, 494
controllable inputs, 480
corporate operating system, 493
cost analysis, 490–492
cumulative probability distribution, 480
defining problem, 478
econometric models, 493
economic systems, 493
with Excel spreadsheets, 478–479
Federal Aviation Administration (FAA), 484
flowchart, 480
history of, 471
inventory analysis, 480–484
issues, 492–494
lead time variable, 480
maintenance problems, 487–492
management system, 470
mathematical model, 470
Monte Carlo simulation, 472–479, 480
operational gaming, 492–493
physical models, 470
preventive maintenance, 492

Simulation (*continued*)
  probability distribution, 479, 480
  queuing problem, 484–486
  random numbers, 473–474
  results differing, 476
  systems simulation, 493
  and Tiger Woods, 494
  uncontrollable inputs, 480
  urban government, 493
  validation, 493
  variables, 472–473, 480
  verification, 493
Simulation model maintenance policy,
    487–492
Simulation software tools, 494
Single-channel queuing model, 442–447
Single-channel system, 439
Single-period inventory models, 211–216
Single-phase system, 439
Sink maximal-flow technique, 335
Six Sigma, 539, 543
Ski lift slowing down to get shorter lines, 441
Slack, 252–253
Slack time, 404, 407–409
Smoothing constant, 158–159, 161, 163–165
Software packages and project management,
    419
Solutions
  affect of, 4
  developing, 5–6, 15–16
  hard-to-understand mathematics, 15
  implications of, 6
  integer programming, 366
  only one answer limiting, 15–16
  outdates, 14
  to problems, 572–575
  to self-tests, 576–577
  sensitivity of, 6
  stating problems as, 15–16
  testing, 6, 16
Solver add-in, 11, 254–257
  changing cells, 380
  minimization problems, 262
  objective function, 268–269, 380
  preparing spreadsheet for, 254–256
  solving method, 380
  transportation problems, 326
  transshipment problem, 333
  usage, 256–257
Sources, 325, 326
Southwestern University (SWU)
  food and beverages at, 21
  forecasting attendance at football games,
    184–185
  stadium construction, 329–330
  traffic problems, 359
SPC. *See* Statistical process control (SPC)
SPC charts, 538, 547
Special Projects Office of the U.S. Navy, 396
Sports and probability, 41
Spreadsheets
  decision variables, 254
  entering problem data, 254–256
  left-hand-side (LHS) of constraints
    formula, 254, 255
  preparing for Solver, 254–256
  quantitative analysis role, 10–13
  value of objective function formula,
    251, 254

SSE. *See* Sum of squares error (SSE)
SSR. *See* Sum of squares regression (SSR)
SST. *See* Sum of squares total (SST)
Standard deviation, 42–43, 121, 208, 405
Standard error of the estimate, 125
Standard gamble, 88–89
Standardized normal distribution function,
    44
Standard normal curve, 558–559
Standard normal distribution, 42–43
Standard normal probability table, and
    Haynes Construction Company
    example, 43–46
Standard normal table, 42–43, 45
Starting Right Corporation, 109–110
State-of-nature nodes, 80–81
State-of-nature points, 79
State probabilities, 510–512
  calculating, 513–514
  current period or next period, 515
  equilibrium, 515–518
  vector of, 511–512
States, 510–512
  accounts receivable application,
    518–519
  matrix of transition probabilities,
    519–520
  steady state probability, 517
States of nature, 66
Statewide Development Corporation,
    505–506
Statistical dependence and joint probability,
    30
Statistically dependent events, 30
Statistical process control (SPC), 538,
    539–541
  and safer drinking water, 547
Steady state, 454
Steady state probabilities, 515, 517
Stepwise regression, 133
Stigler, George, 242
Stockout cost, 207
Stockouts, 188, 189, 206
Storing resources, 189
Subjective approach of probability, 25
Subjective probability, 25, 32
Subprojects, 419
Successor activity, 408, 409
Sugar cane, moving in Cuba, 334
Sumco economic order quantity (EOQ),
    194–195
Sum of squares error (SSE), 117, 124
Sum of squares regression (SSR), 117–118
Sum of squares residual, 124
Sum of squares total (SST), 117
SUMPRODUCT function, 255
Sun-Times marginal analysis with normal
    distribution, 215
Super cola example and $\bar{x}$-chart (x-bar chart),
    544–545
Supply-chain disruption problem, 342
Supply-chain optimization (SCO), 369
Supply-chain reliability, 373
Surplus, 252–253
Survey results, problem in, 87–88
Swift & Company, 271
Systems
  simulation, 493
  states, 510

T
Technological coefficients changes, 270–271
Testing solutions, 16
Thermal Neutron Analysis device, 32
Thompson Lumber Company, 66–67
Three grocery stores
  transition probabilities for, 513
  vector of state probabilities, 511–512
Three Hills Power Company simulation,
    487–489
Three Rivers Shipping Company waiting
    lines, 437
Timeline, 419
Time series, 151–153
Time-series forecasting, 151, 167–168
TNT Express, 324
Tolsky, Paul, 514
Tolsky Works, 514
Total cost, 202, 203
Total expected cost, 436–437
Total quality management (TQM), 538
TQM. *See* Total quality management (TQM)
Tracking signals, 175–177
Trane U.S. Inc., 119
Transient state, 454
Transition probabilities, for Three Grocery
    Stores, 513
Transportation applications, 311
Transportation models, 330
Transportation problems, 312, 325–330
  demand constraints, 326
  destinations, 325, 326
  general linear programming (LP),
    343–344
  intermediate points, 332
  linear programming (LP) for, 325
  minimizing costs, 325
  number of variables and constraints,
    326–327
  sources, 325, 326–327
  supply constraints, 327
  transshipment point, 332–334
Transshipment point, 332
Transshipment problems, 312
  linear program for, 332–334
Trend-adjusted exponential smoothing,
    163–165
Trend analysis, 166
Trend (T) component, of time-series, 151
Trend line of deseasonalized data, 170–173
Trend projections, 165–167
Trends, linear, 170
Trial and error method, 5, 266
Truck loading problem, 306–308
Tuberculosis drug allocation in Manila, 378
Tupperware International forecasting, 155
Two decision variables inventory problem,
    480
Two probabilistic components inventory
    problem, 480
Two rules of probability, 24–25

U
ULAM, 26
Unboundedness, 264
Uncontrollable inputs, 480
Unfavorable market (UM), 86

Union of two events, 27
United Network for Organ Sharing (UNOS), 26
University of Maryland, College Park, 441
UNOS. *See* United Network for Organ Sharing (UNOS)
UPS optimization, 305
Urban government simulation, 493
U.S. Defense Department, 396
U.S. Department of Agriculture, 13
U.S. Department of Energy (DOE), 93
U.S. Postal Service (USPS), 368
Utility, 88–93
Utility assessment, 89
Utility curve, 90
Utility theory, 88–93
Utilization factor, 443

V

Validation simulation, 493
Valid models, 9
Variability in processes, 539–541
Variable costs, 8
Variables, 5
  control charts, 541–546
  controllable, 5
  cumulative probability distribution, 472
  investigating relationship between, 114

Monte Carlo simulation, 472–473
  nonnegative, 241
  probability distributions, 472–473
  regression models, 132–133
  relationship among, 117
  simulation, 472–473
Variance of activity completion time, 400
Variances
  of discrete probability distribution, 35–36
  estimation, 121
  Poisson distribution, 51
  testing hypotheses about, 46–48
Variance (ANOVA) table, 123–124
Variations due to assignable causes, 541
Vector of state probabilities, 511–512
Vehicle Routing Problem (VRP), 368
Venn diagram, 26–27
Verification, 493
VLOOKUP function, 478
VOLCANO (Volume, Location, and Aircraft Network Optimizer), 305
Volleyball and Markovian analysis, 522
von Neumann midsquare method, 475

W

Waiting costs, 436, 444–445
Waiting lines, 436–439
Walker, M. R., 396

Water project, California, 410
Weekly budget, 411
Weighted average, 69, 76
Weighted goals and goal programming, 378–379
Weighted moving averages, 156–158
Westover Wire Works, 288
What if? questions, 292, 493
Whole Food Nutrition Center, 308
Winter Park Hotel, 467
Woods, Tiger, 494
Work breakdown structure, 396
Work package, 409
WTVX, 63

X

$\bar{x}$-chart (x-bar chart), 541–545
XLSim, 494

Z

Zara inventory management system, 193
0-1 (binary) variables, 402–404
Zero-one integer programming problems, 364
Z standard random variable, 42–43